# Catalina Summer

*sketches of the past*

## Gil Lefebvre

Library of Congress Cataloging-in-Publication Data
Lefebvre, Gil
ISBN 978-0-9672172-6-0

*To
Benny and
Virginia Lefebvre*

# CONTENTS

PROLOGUE

# Tommy's

O n any given Friday or Saturday, Tommy's becomes a
social center where crowds line up for delicious delights
and conspire about upcoming evening events. Then, in
the late of the night, the crowd returns as a gesture to the final
closure of their escapades.

Tommy Koulax founded Tommy's Burgers in 1946 at the
corner of Beverly and Rampart boulevards in Los Angeles. It
quickly gained neighborhood support as an innovative fast food
outlet. It became prophetic at advancing a culinary product that
reaches the taste buds of the large Mexican population that now
resides in the Rampart District of Southern California.

As Tommy's gained notoriety for its great hamburgers, it
also suffered from the side effects of its locale… snuggled in
the infamous Rampart District that is known for its crossfire
altercations from the local gangster population. It was here, on a
warm Friday night in June, toward the end of my teaching career,
that one of my most memorable evenings began. It was one of
those early summer nights where jackets and coats give way to
short sleeve shirts with island flair.

After engulfing two of Tommy's finest with a friend and colleague of mine, we drove east on Beverly Blvd. As we passed each block, the graffiti script on the walls informed us we were moving farther into Los Angeles' inner city. Here the neighborhood's social structure is defined by names on street signs, from which many local gangs take their names.

The most notorious is 18th Street. Echo Park also suffered from a bad reputation. There were other lesser-known players, like Rockwood Street and Payne Street, but the smaller size of these gangs caused them to receive less attention from the Policia, in this case the Los Angeles Police Department (LAPD).

The Rampart District is the epicenter of gang activity. Each street, in its own way, plays a part in the drama of L.A.'s war on crime. However, the more dangerous conflict in the Rampart barrio was the unheralded war between the LAPD and the gangs.

We drove two miles up the road away from Tommy's. There we came to what looks like a Catholic cathedral mounted on top of Crown Hill, Belmont High.

Founded in 1921, Belmont is one of the oldest of L.A.'s high schools. Its history is legendary. But today it is the bastion of first-generation immigrants from all over the world. The majority are predominately Hispanic.

They cross borders by sea, plane, car and foot. The key to their survival is the family, then friends. But in many cases, for the teens that went to Belmont, the local gang was their primary ticket. With out them, life could be terminal.

Five years earlier, I signed on at Belmont as a teacher. Eager to jump in and fix things, I started a club called the Hill Toppers. We set up social events along with community service activities.

The club incorporated a diversity of opposing gang members working together by appealing to their respective common interests rather than what divided them. So, within the walls of

Belmont, they found a sense of security. But, once they left the safety of the gated campus, old conflicts came back into play.

On this June night, the club held a dance to mark the end of the school year in an area of the Belmont campus called "The Flats." Located on the up-side of the school, it overlooked the football field to the north and to the east it faced the beautiful Los Angeles city skyline.

Students could enter the closed-in area of The Flats from three directions. But the primary passage in and out was a series of spiral stairs. In preparation for the dance, I talked through security arrangements with the campus LAPD personnel, and then evaluated how many volunteers were available to cover other areas of responsibilities.

The LAPD officers are trained specifically for school issues and always wear suits and ties. But it's no secret who they are, for most of the crowd know them well inside and outside of the campus. We have three great officers at Belmont. John Pullman is a Vietnam combat vet. Randy Bartine is a graduate of the University of California-Los Angeles (UCLA), and Ricky Banah is simply very good at his job. They enjoy each other's camaraderie and together share a great sense of humor. I always felt if a problem occurred, and it always did, we had the right people in place to handle it.

As I took my rounds up on The Flats, day began to turn into night and darkness contrasted and illuminated the lights of the city. I stopped and looked out. Here, at Belmont, I felt a real sense of the inner city. It was literally all around. I could hear the sounds of the community itching for something to do. The warm early summer night, cooled just enough by the Santa Ana winds, caused the locals to come out of their houses and begin to mingle in the streets. Down below, local cart vendors strolled about selling their wares, while Latin salsa blasted from boom boxes seemingly in sync with a sporadic siren.

I walked to the gates blocking the spiral entrance and noticed students beginning to queue up at the bottom of the stairs. It was time for last minute checks to make sure the décor was proper to meet the theme of the dance. I went over to the refreshment stand to remind the eager volunteers about the strict school policies on handling receipts. Then, on to the main gate where the LAPD was ready for a series of checks to enforce Los Angeles Unified School District's (LAUSD) zero tolerance policy, as it related to weapons and drugs.

I was in a cheerful mood now, because I knew that we were prepared for the night. At 8 p.m. the crowd began to trickle in and the dancers began to move to the steady beat of the Latin bands. It's always exciting to watch them dazzle their partners with unique steps they choreograph so well with the music.

While chatting with familiar students, it was brought to my attention by Miguel, a student coordinator, that an agitating gang had somehow breached our security at the main gate. I asked if these characters were going to cause a problem. With obvious concern he said this gang, Rockwood Street, had an altercation at Tommy's on Tuesday night with members from the rival 18th Street gang.

I sensed the immediate need to extract the Rockwood members from the dance and asked Miguel to show me who they were. As we walked around the dance area he pointed them out. "There, that group in the corner."

Recognizing the dance is in 18th territory and about 98 percent of the dance was sympathetic to 18th Street, my heart began to panic. I tried to calm myself and think of a solution. I quickly scurried my way to the main gate to find my LAPD friends and was relieved to see John Pullman in the process of frisking a student entering the dance.

I tried to keep my voice low. "John, we've got a problem here." He asked, "What do you mean?"

I motioned him over to the corner and explained the situation. When I mentioned Rockwood Street I quickly got his attention.

John asked in calming fashion, "Okay. How many of them are out there?"

I answered, "About 10."

"Okay, Lefebvre. Bring them right here to the front gate. I'll take care of it!"

As I turned to go back to the dance, it hit me. "Wait," I said as I looked back to John. "You mean you want me to pull the Rockwood guys from the back corner of the dance floor and walk them through the crowd right past 18th Street? You're kidding! Right?"

Now, I've had a lot of experience within my few years of teaching in the inner city and at juvenile hall but physically taking them into custody by myself, in this situation? I hesitated for a moment but then regained my composure.

"Okay, John. I'll do that. But, where are the other officers? Do we have back-up?"

John just laughed. "Don't worry. Randy and Rick said they would be around later." He then reminded me that they were freely volunteering their off- time to help me out here.

"What!"

"Lefebvre, there won't be any problems. Just do as I said. Oh, but make sure you frisk them first."

"What!"

Seeing that I looked like a person who'd just been asked to jump into shark-filled waters without knowing how to swim, John said, "Calm down, Lefebvre. It's not a problem." He went on. "Look, these guys get stopped sometimes three times a day. Just tell them, 'get to the wall.' Then do a light frisk. Look for the big stuff."

"Weapons?"

"You got it! Then tell them to follow you. They're used to this stuff. But, be careful with this "76" guy. He could be dangerous. If he has a weapon, well... just be careful." He went on as he took out his cell. "I'll be right here and, besides, I'm calling for backup."

Now, a bit more reassured that help would soon be on its way, I said, "Okay." Back at the dance, I took hold of Miguel's arm and proceeded to cross the floor. I'm thinking, "I'll just have to fake them out by getting into a Clint Eastwood mode." Carefully shielding ourselves with the dancing crowd, we tried not to be exposed too soon as we moved in. Miguel stopped. "Lefebvre, that's him! That's 76. See the tall gabacho? He's their big shooter... must have a dozen bullet scars on his body." I could see he was now the center of attention.

My tactic was to go straight to the headman, this 76 guy. I'd take him out and pray that the rest would follow. Somehow, the role playing had calmed my emotions, or at least deceived them. I walked up behind 76 and noticed he was dressed in a very loose Caribbean style shirt that probably concealed a deadly arsenal. He stood slowly, and I figured him to be about 6-feet, 3-inches tall. His skin was uncharacteristically white, and his profile made him stand out from the crowd.

As I approached, he was laughing it up with some of his friends. I took over the situation by mustering up an authoritative voice and ordering him to, "Get against the wall!" He gradually turned, looked with displeasure and stepped toward me. But, just like a bullfighter that craftily changed the direction of the bull, I repeated my command. Then he turned and placed his hands on the wall.

His party stunned to a stop, probably not so much at my performance but at the 18th Street crowd that suddenly stepped out of chorus and began to focus on what was going on.

After searching him to find only a comb, a small pocketknife and Chap Stick, I used my deliberate Eastwood tone again to say, "Follow me." To my surprise, he did and the rest of his crew began to do the same. So, ever so slowly, we all began the walk through the valley of death, right down the middle of the dance floor. All the few remaining dancers had stopped by now and began to growl at the spectacle taking place on their turf.

God must have heard my prayer because how we made it across that floor, with the whole crowd following, was in my mind nothing short of a miracle.

Now, with 76 leading the way, we finally approached John. He was patiently waiting at the entrance gate that spirals down to the street below. Little did I know of John's intentions.

As soon as 76 got close enough, John abruptly grabbed him, bringing the crowd to a peak stage of excitement. Then, John began to loudly assail 76 of all his injustices against 18th Street and verbally commend the party who had shot him 12 times. Next, in rather expletive descriptions, he preceded to call him a scum and a disease to the community. Finally, John turned to the crowd and announced, "You can have him. But, I'm going to give this bastard a head start." He pulled 76 to the top of the stairs. And, with a sinister voice, said to him, "You can thank me later."

After turning him around, John gave 76 a high kick to the buttocks that propelled him down the steps. Once he reached the bottom, 76 scrambled up and began to run. John released the crowd yelling, "Go get 'em. He's yours!"

Off into the night, the crowd took to the chase. Then a flicker of light preceded the sound of bullets. We began to hear sirens coming from all directions. John looked over at me and said with a smile, "Good job, Lefebvre."

John served most of his time in Vietnam as a "tunnel rat"...

crawling in dark holes and flushing out the Viet Cong in a war that never had a verdict. Maybe, I thought, John found solace in finding a purpose, a little justice being served up for the community in what he'd just done. And, for a moment, I too believed he was right.

It was around midnight and the evening's excitement began to fade as we closed down and locked up. I jumped into my car in the safety of the enclosed underground parking lot. Then, I raced my Ford Escort off the premises and onto the I-5 freeway. This would begin my 95-minute trip home to San Juan Capistrano.

I usually listened to the radio or just played a CD to digest the day on my ride home. But this night, this particular night, would not let my mind be lulled into comfort. For, as I drove, the many possible scenarios kept probing my mind. What if this or that would have happened? The visions brought on an anxiety attack so strong I had to pull over to the side of the freeway. As more of the night's situations began to resurface, my hands began to quiver.

I grasped the steering wheel to retrieve control, took a long deep breath and reached for something to wipe the perspiration from my forehead. The traffic was scarce at that late hour, so I was able to easily merge back onto the freeway and continue on my journey home. Without thinking, I turned the radio to one of those oldie stations. The melodies served as the perfect antidote.

Finally, after taking the Avery Parkway exit, I maneuvered by instinct to my street in a neatly placed alcove and found my house. I was relieved to be home again, so far away from the troubles and the conditions in L.A. While I was in the act of undressing, my wife woke and asked in a soft sleepy voice, "How did everything go tonight?" Without wanting to replay the evening, I just said, "Let it wait for tomorrow." I quickly slipped into bed and reached over to turn off the light.

# Catalina Summer
## sketches of the past

### Part One

CHAPTER 1

# San Juan Capistrano

S an Juan Capistrano, like other Orange County communities, experienced a recent migration of young families. They hoped to escape the many issues inner city life presented, like overpopulation, crime and congested freeways.

Orange County is really just a generic name for the general area located south of Los Angeles. It begins from Long Beach on the west coast then runs inland for some 20 miles and extends as far south as San Clemente along the coast. After Oceanside, the California coast continues farther south to San Diego and finally stops at the Mexican border.

San Juan Capistrano lies at the apex of South Orange County, just minutes inland from the sparkling clean beaches of Dana Point and to the north of San Clemente – two resort cities legendary for their great surfing culture. Many of the world's finest surfers have been known to traverse the waves that storm onto the beaches here.

This is home and my retreat. Summer had just about arrived. The weather told me so. Anytime the temperature breaches the 70° mark, most Southern Californians think about dashing to the beach.

I woke up that Saturday morning remembering little of last night's transgressions. I entered into my retreat mode and planned to distract myself as much as possible. I attempted to sleep on but was interrupted by the early sun.

I saw no reason to stay in bed any longer so I jumped out and walked into the kitchen. I found the entire family, my wife, Marcia, and our kids eating breakfast and talking about their delightful plans for the day. This included, of course, a trip to the beach. I could see that snacks and beach apparel were being staged at the front door for the excursion. I just needed to say, "yes," and all was smiles.

So, off we went. With such a rash of enthusiasm going around, no one had time to question me about last night's adventures and there was no reason to bring it up. Their lives were involved in other issues this day. And, that was good for me. Because, to find some meaning in this world it's just good to get away for a while, from the other world.... away from work's daily routines, to clear the mind. Find a bit of sanity and it will all make sense, right? Reflection can be a productive process. Well anyway, that's how the theory goes.

We loaded the car with goodies and pressed on to our favorite beach outing, just 15 minutes from home.

Driving south on I-5, we exited on the outskirts of nearby San Clemente. Where the road splits, you can turn left and find one of California's most noted surfing spots, Trestles. Turning right, as we did, leads through a residential district to the T Street beach.

T Street is noted as a family-friendly beach. It's also famous for buggy boarding and body surfing.

Excited at taking in my first day of summer vacation, I was in full anticipation of a warm day of relaxing on the beach, soaking in the sun, reading and watching my kids play. We unloaded our gear at the stairway that leads to the train overpass. Amtrak rushes by multiple times a day, taking vacationers and commuters on a scenic ride between Los Angeles and San Diego.

After unloading my family and goodies at the curb, I jumped back in the car to race around the neighborhood looking for a parking spot. They become quite scarce by 10 a.m. But, as luck would have it on this day, I found one within a half mile. I quickly parked and locked the car doors, pressing the button twice and hearing the horn beep. Knowing now my car was secure, I hustled my way back to the overpass. The kids had already evacuated to the beach with their boards, leaving my wife and myself to channel down the remaining supplies.

We crossed over the bridge to a beautiful sight of blue ocean and large surging swells slowly making their way to the shore. Once we crossed over the tracks we descended down the stairs. With our feet now firmly on sand, we began to search out our favorite spot. We settled down on a plot just south of the main crowd, but close enough to be seen by friends and neighbors and still in range of the hamburger stand. The aroma and smell of cooking hamburgers blend so well with all the other beach attractions.

We placed our towels and beach chairs out on the sand and then, for the first time in a while, sat and soaked in the moment. I turned to my wife and said, "Now, this is what it's all about!"

I scanned the beach, looking for someone, anyone I might know. Not seeing a familiar face, I looked to my right and San Clemente's majestic pier, which stretches some quarter of a mile into the Pacific, greeted me. Fisherman's Restaurant is at the beginning of the pier and at the other end it opens to the Pacific. You can see people fishing. I'm not sure if they are really serious fishermen, but, on such a radiant day, I don't think it really matters.

Feeling comfortable with the surroundings and the kids being entertained in God's playground, I reached into my backpack,

SAN JUAN CAPISTRANO • 13

pulled out a book and began to read. But, my wife looked at me and said, "Wait a minute. Aren't you going to let me in on what happened last night?"

"At the dance?"

"Yes, at the dance! That's where you were last night wasn't it?" She was now a bit annoyed at my cat and mouse ploy. My wife is also a high school teacher and loves to scrub over war stories that go on in school.

"Okay," I said. Here goes. "Well..." I started slowly. "It's Belmont... it's just Belmont. Remember that Times article that said it's a dangerous place, where you better learn to survive? Well, it was one of those moments." After waiting to see if I would continue, she said, "After all your teaching at juvenile hall, what can surprise you now? Haven't you seen it all?"

"Not like last night." I went on to recount the details of the unsettling events.

Since I was not willing to add on any extras, she commented and questioned each event as I told the story. When I got to the frisking episode, she really got upset. "What? You're not trained to arrest people! You should have never been put into that kind of situation!"

"I know, I know," I agreed.

"So, go on," she said.

I took a deep breath and stabbed out the rest. "I was watching this lynch mob, totally out of my hands. It was like a car skidding on ice. No control and not knowing what danger lie ahead. It was a case where the moment just took over the event!"

"Wow," she interrupted. "It really bothered you."

"Yeah. It did." I continued, "On my way home, I had to pull over onto the side of the freeway to stop my hands from shaking. What troubled me was just what you're asking, 'Why this time?' I've seen stuff like this before, but usually I have it under control.

Last night, everything got out of hand. And, the worst part, I kind of agree with what John did."

"You do? Why would you say that?"

"Well, when I interviewed for Belmont, the principal asked, 'Do you know we're in a war zone down here? And, are you willing to fight?'

I said, 'yes' nonchalantly. The principal went on, 'Okay. Remember, the students' constitutional rights end once they come through those school doors.'

I guess this thing last night was where the rubber hit the road. They play by their rules and we play by another set of rules. The gangs' rules protect their kind, but our rules only make us liable."

"Wow. What a depressing thought," she mumbled under her breath.

I continued. "That's the problem. If we play their game, with their rules and invade their space, they get it! They comply. All they understand are their rules. Our campus police do it that way and get results."

"But, who can learn and teach in that kind of environment? And, are you willing to go along?" she asked.

"I don't know. But, that's how it works. Yet, it's still troubling… it's just somehow everything seems out of balance.

Attempting to reconcile my dilemma, my wife interrupted. "Maybe what we do really won't change things in the big picture. So, we do the best we can with each situation. I guess, besides God, we need only answer to ourselves."

I announced, "Okay. Enough of that stuff, let's go for a walk."

"The pier?"

"Yep." I called the kids out of the water and gave my oldest son a $20 bill. I told him to order four hamburgers and said, "Mom and I are going to take a walk out on the pier."

Enhanced by that tempting burger smell, the kids excitedly

raced off to the snack shop while my wife and I began to stroll up the beach to the pier. We stepped up on the pier and passed by Fisherman's Restaurant, where several people were enjoying a panoramic view of the ocean below while eating lunch on the outside patio.

As we walked farther out on the pier, we enjoyed a display put on by the local surfers, who rode the waves that crashed below. A few joggers passed by on the way to finish their runs. We stopped to check out the catch from casual fishermen, who we'd viewed earlier from the beach. Equipped with gearboxes and coolers, they were set to enjoy mingling and conversing with each other while their poles lay unattended, straddling the rails, their lines extended, waiting for a fish to take the bait.

Near the end of the pier, a small snack shop sold popcorn, cold sandwiches and a small selection of beverages. But, it was that popcorn smell that blended so well with the summer sea breeze. We reached the end and made a few short comments as we looked out to sea. There was just too much to take in. We were indulging only in the present now.

There was a signpost next to us. We both looked it over. Arrows pointed to what was out past the horizon. San Clemente Island to the southwest and San Diego due south.

Marcia interjected into the silence. "Know what? Just look at it this way. You have only a couple of years before you retire."

I said, "No, no, no. That sounds too terminal." I laughed. "How about not retired, just financially independent?"

"Yeah, I like the sound of that." Marcia chuckled. "Teaching all these years has been fun and rewarding. But, it's just too distracting." She was obviously trying to make a comical comment. But, there was some truth to her statement.

I turned again to read the sign and followed another arrow. As I looked out northwest, there it was, gleaming in the sun... my moment in time…Catalina Island. Gosh, how many years did I spend there? Whatever, there were just too many to count.

I said, "There it is. It's been a long time."

"When was it?" she asked.

"Oh wow…so way back that I don't really remember. Let's see…maybe in the '50s? It was just after the Korean War. Man, so here we are today, so many years later and where am I?" Nostalgia began to kick in. "Things were different then."

"How?"

"Well, just different."

My wife broke up my retracing and said, "I feel like some popcorn. I'll be right back."

As she walked away, I attempted to clarify my answer to her question. Was it the times, the culture, the dreams or that I was so young then? How did I get from there to here? How did things turn out so different from what I had planned? Did it really matter?

I stood there and continued my gaze, looking for a connection that would take me back, just one more look, to see who I was back then.

CHAPTER 2

# In Conversation With My Computer

At 3 the next morning, I was compelled out of my sleep. I needed to converse with something, somebody. So, not wanting to wake the house at such an early hour, I got up, put on my pants, Bearpaw slippers and sweatshirt, walked into the kitchen, brewed a cup of coffee and reached into the cookie jar. Now, I was ready to tiptoe up the stairs to my office on the third floor.

It was really not an office, just a small room where one window looked out to the Pacific. On the desk sat the computer, and bookshelves lined the walls. They were stacked with all kinds of books that my wife and I had accumulated from our years of education.

I sat the coffee and cookies next to the computer and turned it on. My mind began to tune into what I called my "computer quest." First I read the news of the day, then checked the weather, sneaked a look at the latest political polls and ended with sport scores and analysis.

I laughed to myself, as I watched one of our cats enter the room and slowly stretch out his legs. I thought, "I'm doing the same thing, stretching out the cobwebs in my mind." Little did I know this would become my routine for the next few weeks.

Okay, so what to say? Now, I began a conversation with the only person who was awake and willing to listen. I plucked gingerly on the computer keys and put down my thoughts line by line.

Where do I start? It's been so long ago. Maybe all of what I could recall would be fiction by now. But, even if I had forgotten some of the details, the stories themselves were true never the less. And, hey, why do I care? This is my party and I'll do what I want – not great lyrics, but it worked here.

"Now, how can I put all those years into one book?" I thought. That would take a thousand pages plus. And, what would I talk about?

Attempting to erase all of the morning babble, the save or don't save option came up. I hesitated. Leaving my rambling thoughts still on the screen, I sat back in my chair and took a sip of coffee. Then it happened. As my eyes floated around the room, my mind was taken on a tour. Every inch of my walls was filled with photos. My wife would say it looked like one of those parking lots at the football stadium, congested and over parked, with a hodgepodge of sizes and shapes that lacked a scheme.

Then Marcia called up to me, "Do you want some eggs and sausage?" I couldn't resist the idea so I cautiously saved my thoughts and I went down to eat.

*Two days later:*

It was 3 a.m. and again my mind began to challenge my sleep. It was not that I had a restless night, it's just that sometimes, in the early hours of the morning, I get this compelling urge to write. Between dreams I get these ideas so clear that they wake me up. My mind becomes relentless and prompts me into a dialogue. It's like someone is pressing me to carry on with the story. Once, I thought I even heard my father's voice bantering me with a vague request to get up and write…to tell the story of us.

Now, consumed with guilt in a chilling morning, I pulled myself out of bed. I tried to find some comfort in warm socks, long johns and my old Stanford sweatshirt, even though I'm not a resolute Stanford fan. No, it's just that my room is tossed about with all kinds of sports apparel, which only indicts me as a ranting college football fan.

So, leaving my wife in comfortable sleep with her warm body tempting me to stay and play, I again tiptoed out slowly, trying not to wake her as I went down to the kitchen. After the coffee and cookies were in hand, I proceed with my routine and walked up to my office.

Beginning with my mental stretching program, I flipped on my computer and began looking through my emails. Let's see, advertisements for jockey shorts, cruise discounts and cut-rate mortgages. Wow! Fifty percent off at Borders Books. I hit the delete key and went on to my contacts. In the midst of the crowd of entries I saw a post from Ross. I knew what the message would say. I laughed as I clicked in.

"Hey buddy, have you got the book done yet?"

Amused I replied, "Still working on it! It took how many years to build Rome?" I knew if Ross were actually here he would say, "Rome? Hell, you couldn't build a doghouse. In fact you're always in the doghouse."

Smiling, I sat back and thought about my 25-year adventure in teaching. It was about to end. So, what was next? Maybe travel? No, there's been plenty of that already. My wife reminds me, "We've been there….done that."

I leaned back in the chair and my eyes began to wander the walls again. This time more intently, to possibly find a story there. There's the picture of my father with his baseball campers. Next, my mother, then I strayed to one with my family. That's me in the center, at the beach. Each of us was cleverly arranged, sitting and smiling to the camera. I moved on to the giant photo of my wife, taken from her earlier modeling portfolio. She hated it, but I insisted we mount it. She often complains about it being too "tacky."

I smiled as my eye caught the one of me receiving a punt in a high school football game. Then, as I had done many times before, I stopped and focused on a faded group photo. It looked as if it had come from the Civil War. There we were, a bunch of sunburned kids at camp with my mother and our mongrel dog. I don't recall his name...something like Spot or Stumpy?

Hoping to remember more, I searched the faces in the picture. Surprisingly, I knew most, and their names eventually jumped onto my tongue, causing me to squeak them out loud. Let's see... Ross, Jeff and me. Then a broad smile exploded onto my face. There's Billy Tucker. Now, the rest began to fall in place. We were all co-conspirators to our camp escapades. I reached back in my mind for examples of each mischief or prank. It wasn't hard to do. There were so many. But, it was the details about those close friends that I spent most of my time attempting to recreate.

I stopped for a moment, sensing my emotions had overtaken me. What good does it do to obsess on it? It's been some 50 years ago. The stories and thoughts were there, okay, but what was the point? I attempted to give an answer to the question. "I don't know, maybe to pass some of this stuff on, as a legacy," I thought. "Yeah, but who'll read it?"

I took a second look around the room. The question was partially answered in those photos. Some of them have passed on, but they've all left memories. They still have a place in my life... the life of the island.

Going back, I thought, might help me regain my balance. After years of adjusting to so many things, I needed to see if my core had really changed. Maybe it's a part of healing, but healing for what? Possibly old age and an overused mind? Nah, at the least, I concluded, the effort could be worthwhile. I might just stumble over a clue to help me understand the changing times.

Looking now keenly at those pictures, I started to write…… "Was it that we were so young then? Were we acting on our faith alone? For, we were contemptuous mortals, mavericks in nature. We were above the currents of our time, aloof and impulsive. We played at life, garnished our actions with impunity. Was it that we sensed we could not be blamed for our youth?

"Oh no. It wasn't exactly the day of innocence and clarity, as the poets claim. Could it be that our blind faith had yet to be challenged?"

Caught in the midst of a self-inflicted conundrum, I was relieved to be released from the predicament when my wife called out from down stairs.

"Hey, I thought we were going to San Diego for a few days to celebrate the summer break?"

I pulled myself away from those terribly distracting memories in the photos and yelled back, "I'll be there in just a minute." I smiled and whispered to my computer, "I'll be back."

CHAPTER 3

# Catch Me If You Can

Three days later, I was back for another session on my computer. Now that I had some time to think it out, I plodded on with a new sense of excitement.

I picked up a faded photo. There we were, me and my best friend Ross, all smiles while sitting on a corral fence on Catalina Island with horses in the background, surrounded by at least five girls. Memories flooded my mind. The shot captured the beginning of that remarkable summer of…. I turned the photo over, I'd guessed right, because the date scribbled on the back read, "1959," almost the turn of a decade. The country had just put the Korean War behind it. Dwight Eisenhower, America's five-star General, who led us out of World War II (WWII), was president. The years of McCarthyism and looking under our bed for communists had reached its breaking point. The pressing problem of the day was the atomic bomb. Bomb shelters offered a possibility of survival and testimony to one of man's most tormented creations.

The world was locked in fear of a Cold War with our former ally, the Soviet Union. Vietnam was catapulted to primetime news after the French defeat at the battle of Dien Bein Phu. This remote Southeast Asia country was about to set in motion the most controversial and abrasive period of America's 20th century.

And, just off the tip of Florida, outside of the flourishing casinos of Cuba, another predicament was brewing. In 1957 names like Fidel Castro and Che Guevara became legends in Latin America, by claiming independence from American imperialism. This would shortly create the first major nuclear missile crisis.

All was not bad in America. Just around the corner was a more promising picture that would later be called the "Era of Camelot," when youth and fresh ideas created new hope against the backdrop of a bad dream.

Elvis Presley was still entertaining America, while I Love Lucy, The Perry Como Hour, along with The Ozzie and Harriet show were big hits on television. Love was still formed and charmed by the magical music of Johnny Mathis, Paul Anka, Ritchie Valens and Dion and the Belmonts. Places like the Palladium and the Shrine were front lines for the youth of the day's social interaction in Los Angeles.

Of course, in California, we had the annual football game between cross-town rivals the University of Southern California (USC) and UCLA. In baseball, the Los Angeles Dodgers would soon replace old time favorites, the Hollywood Stars and the Los Angeles Angels.

Hollywood and Vine was a place for tourists, but the intersection was also a place for the locals to parade in their cars, looking for girls. This cruising went on late at night and into the early morning. On the way home you might stop at Pops on the west side of Beverly Boulevard. If the evening had to be cut short, you could drive up to the Ladera Heights district and be served delicious hamburgers right in your car at the Witch Stand. In fact, on Saturday nights, a couple might never have to leave their car for a romantic interlude, for there was always the drive-in movie. But, the best un-kept secret were the Southern California beaches.

They started as far north as Santa Barbara and extend south to places like Malibu, then Redondo Beach and Hermosa Beach.

These beaches, with their perfectly cresting waves, cradled some of the world's greatest surfing giants, like Dewey Weber and Greg Noll. This was Southern California at the height of the late '50s and early '60s. Times would later change, as do the weather and seasons, but for now the turbulence of the '60s was still off in the distance.

The social fabric of L.A. was divided primarily along racial and ethnic grounds. East L.A. was Mexican, south central primarily black. The Fairfax district was Jewish and downtown L.A. had a small but powerful crowd of Italians. The rest of L.A. was white... whatever that meant. This arrangement, so we were told, was less of a legal constraint and more a result of social orientation. Back then, being young in L.A., we were too busy to notice. It really didn't matter to us, because we were white and had no explaining to do.

In 1953, a few years before that photo of Ross and me had been taken, a decision was made that set things in motion for my family's future on Catalina Island.

It all started on a playground at the corner of Rodeo Road and La Brea Avenue. This was our personal piece of Los Angeles, claimed on the back of my father, the director of Rancho Cienega Playground. It's legendary because of the four baseball fields facing each other and a large football stadium. A gate that led to Dorsey High School divided the park. It was Dorsey's home field but also used by many other private and public high schools, most notably Loyola and St. John Vianney.

However, on the weekends, the semi-pro teams took up most of the park's playing time. These Saturday and Sunday games drew formidable crowds, including scouts who motivated the players to strut their wares in the hopes of being picked up by a professional organization. But, some players were simply relics with lost dreams and others were finishing off wonderful and exciting careers.

So it was there that, as a kid short of my teens, I relished in the excitement of life, the fun of the game and the thrill of winning. It was where camaraderie could turn into folly, sometimes resulting in a chilling experience. Everyday presented its own challenge. But, there was always an exhilarating feeling of being alive.

Most every summer day, my father would take us kids with him to Rancho. Once there, he gave each one of us $1. Then, we were on our own. We got together with other boys our age. Often they were the guys my dad had coached in baseball or their older brothers. Sometimes, it was just kids who hung around the park during the summer. We had access to all the equipment we needed: footballs, baseball mitts, bats and bows and arrows. I think we had more equipment than United Sporting Goods, all at the expense of the Los Angeles Recreation and Parks Department.

With everything in hand, we created our schedule for the day. It usually started out with some over-the-line baseball games on Diamond One, close to my dad's office and just in front of the snack shop. The snack shop sold candy, popcorn, hot dogs and beverages. When the temperature went up, a short range of ice cream flavors, vanilla and chocolate only, were offered.

As the day went on, my father would bring out his clubs and begin hitting golf balls to us. We would catch them in flight, put them in a bag and give them back, and he would start right over again. Dad would say it didn't really improve his game much, but he was sure it helped ours.

As the temperature began to climb, we found relief by running through the sprinklers that circulated water to the browning fields. Then, it was off to the stadium. Playing in an official-size football field, with bleachers and all, was really fun. We'd draw sides and play to win. As we crossed the goal line, we'd pretend we were in the Coliseum, scoring in front of 90,000 fans while the USC Trojan band and cheer section carried on.

But, on some days, a few local black boys would walk into the stadium and challenge us to a game. We always took the challenge seriously. Most of the time it got a little rough and out of hand. The game usually would break up and threats would be made. This day was no different from the rest, but we always hoped that the next time we met things would be more cordial.

Next, it was off to the driving range that was sandwiched between the stadium and Ralphs supermarket. That's where our deviant nature took over. We would run onto the driving range, scoop up as many golf balls as possible and cram them into our pockets. When the proprietor took notice and started screaming at us to stop, we would yell back something far more colorful and provocative. Then, the chase was on. This wasn't something new, we knew all the right turns and twists that helped us easily elude him, at least for that day. Tomorrow, well, we'd do it all over again. It was just too much fun. Mind you, we would put the balls in my dad's bag at the end of the day. It wasn't taking the balls that made it fun. It was the chase!

Then, on to lunch, where our lives became even more cavalier, which is a better word then sinister or maybe criminal. There we were, the five of us with $1 each. We entered Thrifty's Drug Store, bought a few things and took a few things more. This pattern would follow us to Ralphs. Once in a while we would get caught, but we were kids with familiar faces, therefore we'd just have to sit and listen to a lecture. Most days, by the time we got to our designated fort, which was on the backside of three billboards located on the opposite corner of Ralphs, we were loaded with all kinds of goodies and most of our allowance was still in our pockets.

In the shade of the billboards, we would talk and joke about the day's antics. A food fight would inevitably break out, and that signaled the end of lunch. Then, it was back to the streets, where we had an intimidating black group looking to dismantle our arrogance, an angry driving range owner brandishing a putter at us and a Thrifty's clerk who looked at us with suspicion. We'd order an ice cream cone, just to taunt him. We knew he'd love to indict us for theft…that would make his day. But, it wasn't going to happen. No way, not this day, we paid…with a smile.

However, the day was only half over. From there, we walked over to Dorsey High School's archery range to dig around for lost arrows. Eventually, a few would be found. What to do with them? No one cared. All that mattered was, we found them. Later, we traced our way back to my dad's office to play ping pong for a while.

Sometimes, we would entertain ourselves by sitting on the bleachers and watching people buy hot dogs. Once in a while they tried to multitask by putting onions, mustard and relish on all at the same time. The wiener would find its way on the ground. Usually, there was no attempt to salvage it, and, to our delight, it found its way into the trash. Once they were out of sight, we would all jump into the barrel and the lucky one, finding the wiener, would give it a good wash, put on fresh condiments, sit down and enjoy the spoils.

It wasn't that we were hungry. It was just the thrill of the chase. My cousin Jeff would point out this same phenomenon when telling stories about courting girls, not that I understood them at the time.

At the end of day, we would slip into the recreation department's dressing room and stop up the drain until the water overflowed and covered the floor. After stripping down to our trunks, we would slide on our bellies like bumper cars. Knocking into each other with great delight always got a good laugh from bystanders.

It was at the end of one of those fine summer days, while relaxing under an awning that shielded us from the late hour sun, that one of my friends announced, "Gil, you left your mitt in the sandpit!"

It was a little over 100 yards away. That wasn't too bad. But, it became a problem, because of who just arrived and stood over the glove. It was the same black characters that exchanged reciprocal threats with us earlier that day on the football field, and they had just picked up my mitt.

Even though I was the youngest of my five buddies, they looked at me with smirks and dared me to go take back my mitt. Knowing I had a hot temper and could run fast, they were amused to see how I would handle this situation.

I couldn't find a reason to back down. Even if the worst happened, it still would be a step forward in the matter of my pride, strictly a guy thing. Not much sense in it, but it had to be done.

With fear pumping in my heart, I knew what I had to do. I got up and stepped into the penetrating sun, which further exacerbated the condition of my trembling body. I walked slowly onward, directly toward the enemy, now feeling much like Gary Cooper in High Noon. As I moved closer, I counted seven adversaries. Once I got into speaking range, I stopped and prepared to make a demand. I was cut short by one of the older kids. Smiling like a cat ready to devour a bird, he broke the silence.

Holding up the mitt, he announced, "Is this what you want? Sorry, found it here, no name, so finders keepers."

I scratched at my throat as I realized the prospect of getting my mitt back without a scuffle would be impossible. In those days, we didn't resort to weapons. Fists were our primary tools of persuasion. This meant I was likely going to take a good beating and probably not get my mitt back either. But, to me, winning never mattered as much as just being willing to fight. That was always an acceptable option for me because my self-esteem would be preserved and by then the cavalry would arrive. I imagined I would suffer a bit, but so what.

I took the chance and said, "That's mine. I never lost it! I just left it here." As I stepped forward and put out my hand, I felt the tension in the air move up a notch. The time for talking had come to an end.

My instinct told me to take control of the moment, be the first, dictate the action. . But…. just then, from the back of the crowd, a deep voice spoke in a demanding tone. "Give the kid back his mitt!"

No one even turned to see where the command had come from…they knew.

As the guy handed over my mitt he said, "This is your lucky day." Then, he proceeded to walk away, leaving only two guys. They were the Pratt brothers and legends in these parts. Both had criminal records and later would spend most of their lives rotating in and out of jail. But, my father looked past their records and did his best to make them welcome at Rancho. And, on this day, they expressed their gratitude.

Matt said as he turned to leave, "Lefebvre, you take care of yourself around here. If you have any more problems, we'll be around."

I strutted back to my friends. I was proud that I had controlled my fear, even if I hadn't overcome the challenge alone.

And that was exactly the kind of day that pressed my mother to get her kids out of Los Angeles, at least for the summers. Her solution? Start a baseball camp, on Catalina Island.

CHAPTER 4

# On Our Way

On the second floor of USC's Taper Hall was a young high school senior, Ross Sarracino. He sat impatiently in an oversized classroom listening to orientation presentations. Ross came from a family of Italian immigrants, who migrated from the small town of Pastena. Along with their great affinity for Italian food, Italian immigrants were noted for their ambitious efforts to secure a part of the American dream.

Like many other European immigrants, they came to America by way of Ellis Island. They were a burly bunch and transitioned much like the Irish before them, wandering into a variety of dubious jobs. Eventually, they would find their stride, in less profitable but respectable occupations and challenge their sons and daughters to do the same. Ross was doing just that when he later chose a career as a certified public accountant (CPA).

However, on this day, he had other plans for his immediate future. He needed to wrap up those orientation lectures as fast as possible, jump into his car, race home and begin packing. Today, he had a date with paradise waiting for him just 19 miles out of San Pedro with his best and disputably only friend, me. I had invited him again to spend the summer at my father's baseball camp on the Isthmus of Catalina.

With the camp opening in a week, we needed to set up beds, whitewash just about anything that didn't object, rake and pull weeds that had accumulated during the winter, carry up food supplies that came in each day by boat, set up the butane tanks and take on our infamous daily trips to the dump. What followed were five different two-week summer camp sessions with 100 kids in each. Along with our full staff of counselors, lifeguards and divers, everyone added up to about 130 people. So, why was such enthusiasm running through our veins to do all this work? That was easy….Catholic girls!

My mother taught at Pious X High School and, for a minimal fee, she would invite the girls' senior class to stay a week on the island before the baseball camps began. There would always be plenty of room because the camp was practically empty while our minimal staff prepared for upcoming regular sessions. So, every year my mother would bring over 50 or 60 high school graduates to spend time basking in the sun, celebrating the past and sharing their last few days together. This summer would be a little different because my older brothers had signed pro baseball contracts and were off playing in rookie leagues. Mother suggested that Ross and I were the only ones she could trust to be around all of those girls and still get the camp ready. That was, of course, a mistaken assumption, which to this day I've never discussed with my mother. Because, when it came to her girls and discipline, she was a stickler beyond Nurse Ratched's standards.

Here we were, presented with this unique and envious opportunity. But there was a predicament: We were not too young but not old enough then in the summer of 1959. Our prurient interest in girls was a given and puberty had passed. Well, that's probably an exaggeration. Not knowing what that meant, we just thought so. But, for sure, we were eager to learn more about the other sex, whom some writers concluded came from another planet.

To make it even more enticing, the Isthmus was 19 miles across the sea from the mainland, and the town of Avalon was hours away from the camp on a bumpy one-lane dirt road. In essence, these girls would be spending an entire week in a remote location with me and Ross, and part of our job was to keep them safe.. We would be the only two males around. Ross didn't need to be a CPA and I didn't need any common sense to realize that a once-in-a-lifetime opportunity was coming our way. It was like putting the fox in with the hens.

Believe me, we had no qualms with that indictment. But, in our defense, we had our moral standards too. It's just that, for the next week, they would be severely tested. We did pray about it. But we also realized they were Catholic girls, so we knew what a rather formidable task this would be.

Now, just getting to camp was more of a disconcerting exercise then one would first suspect. Looking from the bluffs of the Palos Verde Peninsula on a clear day, you would think you could almost touch the island of Catalina. But, the ocean's dramatic currents and erratic conditions can change in minutes. Calm swells grow to large whitecaps that make transportation to and from the island a formidable and, at times, a very dangerous journey.

Catalina Island, as sung by the Four Preps, is, "26 miles across the sea." That's if you left from Long Beach aboard the S.S. Catalina, also known as the Great White Steamer. Sailing roundtrip from Los Angeles to Avalon on a daily basis, the 2,000+ passenger ship carried over 25 million vacationers from 1924 to 1975. The trip took two and a half hours and was filled with entertainment. Dancing to magical sounds played by well-known bands, courted from the finest of the music world, made time fly. Snack shops were open for refreshments, and festive passengers, looking for souvenirs, browsed its gift shops. Once the ship came in sight of the island, speedboats swirled around the Great White Steamer, greeting her with horns and shouts. As she docked, the local divers treaded water below, baiting the visitors aboard to depart with their pocket change. Once the passengers cleared the gangplank, they were welcomed by hula dancers dressed in brilliant costumes. The sound of the mariachis and colorful gauchos on horseback welcomed the tourists down Main Street, where shops, strung with Christmas bulbs all year long lined the busy streets. Buses waited on excited passengers wanting to explore the island. Travelers who longed to stay for more began to file into local hotels, eager to change into their beach attire and flee to the shoreline to relish in its pleasures.

But, for the impatient, there were the Channel Airlines amphibious flights that left from the Long Beach Airport. Bob Hanley started the airline charters in 1959, and they lasted until 1966. Planes departed on the hour for the 19-minute flight from Long Beach to Avalon's Pebbly Beach. Later, flights were extended from Long Beach directly to the Isthmus. Mind you, these amphibious charters did provide a cure for those disposed to seasickness. But, the thrill of the ride in those curious planes made for volumes, I mean volumes, of stories to fill a library, and that made each trip seem more exciting, dramatic and suspenseful than any modern-day thrill ride. At the end of the flight, we joked, that if we made it without incident, we'd get out of the aircraft, politely thank God and then plant a kiss on the spot where we stood.

That was a rare occasion. Because the way we usually traveled to the island was considerably less glamorous. Instead, we made the journey on small boats, affectionately called water taxis, that were shaped like cigars, with a sputtering engine in the middle. This caused a smell of spent fuel and produced a caustic effect on passengers. We'd load all the gear in the middle, over the engine casing. Canvas flaps helped guard against the early morning chill, as everyone huddled in their seats around the warm casing.

After clearing the Los Angeles breakwater, we would set our course to the west end of the island, known by some as the Isthmus and by others as Two Harbors. For two and a half hours our early morning breakfast was digested over and over again, tormented and blended by the rolling Pacific swells.

So, that's what was in store for me and Ross, on this fine morning at the San Pedro Water Taxi dock. We'd taken this same trip several times so we were well prepared for the crossing. But, this time it would be different. Our excitement was never so intense as it was on this day. For, our campers were not scruffy boys under the age of fifteen, but 60 recently graduated Catholic high school girls. Some were simply relishing the idea of getting away for the first time, but others wanted to celebrate their coming of age and independence, and that was better for us.

All they knew was, they were headed toward a romantic secluded stretch of Catalina. That fact kept dancing in our heads, like Christmas sugarplums. For, we would be the only accessible males their age on the entire west end of the island, at least for that week. We knew that, but we didn't think they did.

It was 5:30 in the morning when our car pulled up to the San Pedro pier, from where the water taxi left. The fog still hovered over the harbor, as if to advise us to stay still, for the day had yet to break. My parents began to move about the dock. It was mother who managed to break up my sleep in the backseat of the car when she opened the door and said, "Gilly, it's time to get to work." Reluctantly, I pulled out of the comfort of the warm seat and caught the first scent of local fisheries, whose aroma wandered around the harbor. I began to start unloading the supplies we had packed for the trip. Mother reviewed the campers' names and jotted down, in meticulous fashion, a list of things for us to do. I'd just about finished carrying the heavy boxes onboard when a shinny cardinal-red Chevy Impala pulled up and Ross Sarracino stepped out.

Ross was a year older than me and we'd been close friends for years. We met while in prep school, where we competed against each other on the football team. This competition turned into respect, which developed into a life-long friendship. Ross wore his Italian legacy proudly. He was a little darker in complexion and, combined with his curly hair, it gave him away. Yep, he was Italian all right. His family had adjusted to this country quite well. Ross's father played a significant part in the Los Angeles trucking industry, where his friends, affectionately knew him as "The Bear." Others? Well, that depended on whom you talked to. But, all of us youngsters never brought that up. It was always, respectfully, Mr. Sarracino.

Ross was a tough guy, no question about it. He didn't mind putting himself on the line when us guys needed it. Nuns and priests censored him from the wanton temptations of the outside world. As a graduate, he became interested in another world that he'd learned about from people like me; people who spent time bouncing in and out of Catholic grammar and secondary schools. But, it was because of his parochial schooling and untarnished character that my mother picked him to accompany me on this trip in the first place, and we were both grateful for that

We were so much alike in many ways. Except I was a little short on discipline, which a host of nuns and priests could never remedy. So, off to public school I went. There, the world was opened to me and I gained a new kind of street wisdom, if you can call it that, something my friend lacked. We both hoped that this trip would put us on level ground as I mentored him in all I had learned.

Mother instructed us to start loading the cargo into the water taxi. "Remember, put food goods in the middle over the motor and leave room for the girl's luggage." Moments later, cars began to show up. Girls of all kinds began to scramble about with their luggage. We couldn't get a keen look at their features because they were well wrapped for the cold and looked extremely tired, just coming in from all-night, post-graduation celebrations. So, we went about our task of carrying their luggage down the gangplank with little or no conversation; it was just too early and cold. As some fought off sleep, we got a, "thank you" here and there, but even that was quite an effort under the situation.

Once we loaded the boat, my mother and the few parents acting as chaperons directed the seating arrangement. There was just enough room to stretch out our legs. Fortunately, Ross and I found a comfortable place to rest for the long trip. The flaps still covered the outside of the boat, keeping the warmth in and the fog out.

As the boat pulled away, my father yelled out from the dock to me and Ross, "Make sure to work hard and get the camp ready. No fooling around!"

We maneuvered slowly into the main channel of the harbor. At this early hour, businesses around the freighter docks showed little life and the fisheries, noted for their smell of sea life, had yet to muster. But, through the corners and cracks of the canvas top we could see a wonderful array of multi-colored lights that radiated a bright glare off the fog. We found comfort among the girls, as I sat on one side of the boat and Ross on the other. The girls soon fell asleep, leaning against each other for warmth. I looked across to Ross and flashed a smile. He reciprocated with a smirk when one of the girls snuggled next to him for warmth and rested her head on his shoulder. We knew that the next seven days would be unlike any of the trips we had ever taken before.

As soon as we passed the lighthouse, with its strobes scanning into the fog, and once the bellow of the foghorn was far behind, the boat kicked into gear. We were in open Pacific waters now and our taxi began to gyrate and moan as each swell propelled it from side to side. Inside, everyone was snuggled for comfort from the cold. The noise coming from the motor and the stagnate smell kept out the ocean breeze for the time being.

Nestled in between two of the girls, I let my mind wander a bit and began to think about what was next for me. I knew this would be my last summer on Catalina, but, just as important, it would be the end a major stage of my life. My friends had already started thinking about going off to college, getting into business or meeting the draft head on. They thought maybe if things didn't work out, "Join the Army, before it got you." Some of my more lighthearted friends were even contemplating marriage. What? At 18 or 19? Wow, not for me. Besides, my father trained us to be professional baseball players and this was no time to change track.

"Why even think about plan B?" my father would say. "Plan A will work out." So, this would be my last chance at hitting the 300-foot marker on the Isthmus road. Then, there were things about girls I didn't know. And if I did, I never let on. For me, just asking a girl out with the fear of being refused, was a daunting prospect. What I thought of as a conquest was holding a girl's hand here and there or once in a while stealing a kiss – far from the conquests my cousin Jeff bragged about.

I'd probably happily take more if offered but, at this stage, it was more about looking, thinking and dreaming. I didn't really know what relationships were all about. And, like any kid, I was trying to figure out who I was while trying to figure out the opposite sex too. Every time I'd think about it, my mind would get all numbed up. That's where cousin Jeff came in. He knew all there was to know about that.

Then, there was this thing about who I really was. It's not that I was confused or something by any stretch. But, just in my short 18 years, I had re-invented myself so many times, and I was still working out who I was now. When I first came to the camp I was 13 years old and weighed 190 pounds. I was somewhat of a bully at that weight and never got a second look from a girl. All that changed a few summers later. I lost over 60 pounds and got punched out a lot more, but at least girls started to pursue me, and that created all sorts of additional problems. All this was complicated further by the fact that I had my father's flair with a temper. It reared itself up sometimes at the drop of a hat. It sometimes kept people away from me. Of course, that's what I designed it to do. The bluff seemed to keep me just one knuckle safe, but, at other times, well, let's just say my actions, were less than commendable.

As I continued to rummage through my mind, I remembered when the local Catholic priest would come to the Isthmus and perform Sunday service. Visitors of all faiths would come ashore and participate. Oh, I had an idea coming from a Catholic background what that was all about, but as far as questions about my mortality, I thought I could kick that can up the road for a while. I knew it had a place for me, but not now. I was still thinking of the possibility of living forever. Gosh, by the time I get old, we will have been to the moon and cancer will have gone by the wayside, just like polio. And if I stay out of the Vietnam War, I could live on the island forever. That was a real enticing idea.

But, still I puzzled over this nagging fear that I couldn't easily define but knew it was fear never the less. The kind of fear you get when you stand on a high bridge over a waterway, on the top of a high building several stories up or on Yosemite's Half Dome 9,000-feet high. You feel a compelling impulse to jump or dive, wondering if you could maintain control and survive. It pulls you in, temps you. It challenges you to trespass fate. But, in the last second, the impulse subsides. All that was needed was to just walk away. Find a secure place but survive. It still lingers in your mind, could I have? Audie Murphy said, "Only a fool says he goes into battle without fear. It's not the fear that's troubling, but the pride and how you handle it."

"How would I handle it?" I thought, after this summer, the world out there was waiting for me. Would I let it consume me? Would I be afraid?

Just then, I was brought back from this medley of thoughts by the slashing of the sea as the flaps were thrown up, revealing the sun that was now beating out the fog for another day. A few seagulls flew above, mistaking us for a fishing vessel. Bird Rock was in sight, which meant we were not more than a few miles from shore and our final destination. For me, it was like coming home once again to the Isthmus.

I began to scramble about now, telling our weary seasick passengers that this venture was just about over. For the first time they looked to Ross and me for advice. This was the break we needed. It was a simple concept, but one we made the most of. Now, for the first time, we got our chance to scout out the possibilities. I looked around the boat. Once in a while my eyes made momentary contact with one of the girls and a chill went up my spine. I immediately retreated from the gaze by looking in another direction, hoping to conceal my interest. But, it was there and I laughed to myself.

The dock at the end of the Isthmus pier came into sight as we passed inside of Bird Rock and then cruised by Little Fisherman's Cove beach. The deep blue waters off Catalina began to turn a lighter hue, then green and now crystal clear, signaling we were about to dock. After we tied up, the girls lined up from the bottom of the ramp leading to the top of the pier. The luggage was set out and the girls took what they could carry and proceeded down the pier.

The camp was about a 300-yard walk along a road that wound its way pass the snack shop, later the restaurant and then up a graded dirt road and onto a neatly arranged painted white rock path. That led the girls straight up to the expansive dormitory, which included 12 separate rooms, a kitchen and the main restroom facilities.

Ross and I hadn't really spoken much during the trip. We'd done it many times before and knew the routine well. So, we rushed ahead of the girls to the camp, jumped into the waiting pickup truck, traversed our way back to the pier and began loading the remaining luggage.

Then, it was back to the camp, unload the luggage, set up the butane tanks for the kitchen and slowly assemble the beds that had been so neatly stacked in the main hall at the closing of last year's camp. We really had little time to converse and the girls' shyness was still an obstacle. But, for the first time, a few of the more gregarious types gave us a second glance and even attempted to help us. This was a natural thing to do but still Ross and I kept a low profile.

We pressed on with setting up the camp, seeing some of girls resting while others grabbed their bags to begin the process of getting into their summer attire. My mother jumped in and suggested that we go take care of other things that needed our immediate attention. "Let the girls dress and give them a chance to stretch out and get to know the Isthmus neighborhood."

The sun began to set as they had dinner outside the dormitory on the main eating area's large tables and benches. Ross and I stuck to our chores and, after we cleaned up the kitchen, we got our first chance to go to our cabin. It was about 50 yards north of the main dormitory. I was 13 years old when we started using this cabin and, the stories from then to now, will be our legacy. This little one-room, toilet-free cabin made us chuckle as we entered. Most all the escapades and conspiracies were conjured up and began here. The names, dates, events and remarks carved on all four walls were sacred to us. They documented a record of our history… that we had been there.

Night came as we set up our room and chatted a little, smiling at each other knowing that the next seven days were going to be very interesting, to say the least.

Ross began, "Gosh, it seems like just yesterday we were here."

"Yeah it does," I replied. "Not much changes around here."

We lay back in our bunks and spent the night reminiscing. Ross brought up the time we used firecrackers to raid the Boy Scout camp at Cherry Cove.

"Yeah." I added, "We hit those guys late at night, then ran along the dirt road, slid down the side of the mountain and were back in bed by the time those scout counselors arrived in their Jeep looking for the culprits.

"Wow," Ross sighed. "We've got to do it again."

"Hey, this is our last year, Ross, and this year we're going to top it all."

Full of anticipation and even forgetting about the girls for now, we fell asleep.

# CHAPTER 5

# All About Catholic Girls

O ur first day would begin before the sun and with a soft knock on the door. My mother called out, "Good morning, sleepyheads. We need you in the kitchen." I rolled over to steal a few more minutes of sleep, but Ross, who was much more disciplined and intimidated by my mother than I, jumped out of bed and started to dress. He knew my mother was all about business when the camp was running.

Ross called out, "Come on, Gilly. Let's get going."

"Okay, okay," I responded as I slowly got up and pulled on my faded jeans and-T-shirt. I stepped into my old work tennis shoes and pushed open the creaky cabin door. I yelled up to Ross, "Let's go!" He looked back and smiled as he waited for me to catch up.

We meandered our way over to the main building, and I got to the back door first. When the baseball camp was in full session, this would be our normal entry since the long hallway led to the back of the kitchen. Acting on instinct, I opened the door, but this time it revealed two girls in the act of dressing. Surprised, I muttered, "Oops sorry," and threw my hand quickly over my eyes to shield my view. Obviously it was more for show, letting them think I was a decent guy. But, they didn't seem to care anyway.

I immediately reversed my step, pushing Ross backward. With a smile I loudly proclaimed, "Ross, wrong door!" As we turned to go around front he began the questions, "What did you see?"

Hoping to whet his appetite I raised my hands and said, "Woo, can't tell you."

"What?" he asked after being enticed by my dramatic gesture. "You can't what?"

"It wouldn't be right if I told you." I didn't let on that I really didn't get a chance to see much. But I continued, "Well, Ross, nothing more than what I've seen before hanging on a clothesline, but this time, without the clothesline." I was just putting him on. I loved to do that, to let his imagination drive him crazy. It always worked so well.

I changed the subject. "We've got to be careful, Ross. You know my mother keeps her guard up when it comes to the girls, and those motherly chaperons have eyes on them too." I laughed. "We don't want to become the main suspects!"

"Suspects for what?"

"Anything, just anything, Ross."

"Gilly, that makes no sense."

"No, Ross. That's where you're wrong again. It's just that your sense is different from mine. Okay? Enough, let's go." So, off we went, around the side of the building, up the front ramp and on through to the kitchen.

We'd been so busy the day before there really wasn't a chance to scout out the girls. But now, as we began to serve the food in our usual buffet fashion, we finally got a chance to say, "hi," to a few.

As they came through the line, some of them were half asleep, some still in pajamas but others in full makeup, wearing jeans and sweatshirts, ready for the day. The interesting thing, most of them didn't care about me and Ross seeing them that way. In this short time we had become just the camp helpers. But, that was about to change.

Ross and I begin to inventory our possibilities. We made every attempt to deflect any clues as to our motives by pretending to show little interest in the girls. This was to be our routine for the next few days while we continued sprucing up the camp. This would entail whitewashing, weeding, setting up campsite beds, plus two outside portable tents, laying out the netting and the machines for the batting cages, dragging the baseball diamond twice a day to make it playable, odd patching and painting and finally maintaining the dormitory-style large bathrooms with four stalls and a massive shower. It could hold as many as a dozen people at one time and had a large opaque window that let in the daylight but wasn't clear enough to see in from outside.

Just outside the dormitory, we set up 12 big tables and benches that served as the main eating area. They were nestled under some birch trees, adjacent to the dormitory window, making eating a comfortable outdoor experience.

We walked around, taking care of our duties under an 80° sun. We could see the girls had changed into more casual beach attire and were going off in different directions. Some to the beach, some to the back harbor on hikes and some just sat around the tables already writing letters. Others grouped together to contemplate the future, looking over college brochures while browsing through fashion magazines.

Muddling in whitewash, Ross and I painted the rocks on both sides of the main path leading to our camp. Girls occasionally passed by, but now they paid more attention to us and we began to share smiles.

I said, "Ross, look what we have here. It seems as if a few of the girls have come to their senses. It's us now and all these Catholic girls." He looked over at me as if I had a plan. This time

I did. "Let's go after the most outgoing ones first."

Mind you, our goal wasn't to have a relationship with them. "No way," as my dad would say. "It's good to have them around, but if they stay too long, they have a way of complicating a guy's career."

As we watched the girls stroll around, I said, "Hey Ross, isn't it funny how people hang out with like groups? Some open, some party loving, some a little more quiet. It's those quiet ones that are a bit more challenging. With those you have to dig in to get a conversation going. It's fun that they come in all flavors."

Ross smiled. "Yup."

"And here we are. It's all in our hands, all 31 flavors. We've got to make it happen, Ross." I continued on with my pep talk. "Any guy over there," now pointing to the mainland, "would pay for this chance to be with all of these Catholic girls."

Ross smiled when I said, "Catholic girls." There was something special about them. Ross had spent all his life in one Catholic school after another. As for me, well remember, I started early in a parochial school and then got tossed out. My mother decided I'd probably do better in a public school environment, and I didn't mind. But, there was a big difference between public school and parochial school life. It had to do with the lack of direction of the students you met along the way. You see, in parochial schools, you had your life all planned out, literally, from birth to death. Not so in public school. You just took off in any direction you wanted. Now, that seemed like a good idea at the time, but not too secure for a teenager trying to make his way around.

But what I really missed by going to public school was those Catholic girls. Why? Because they could be irreverent but virtuous. They were spontaneous but not promiscuous. They could be deviant, yet charitable. They even showed compassion to us Catholic guys, who'd gone through puberty a few years after they did. They had the patience and grace to wait for us to catch up. They never left us behind. You see, they lived by a theology of moderation and balance. But delightfully, they also had the tendency to continuously redefine the term, "moderation." They were typically non-scriptural Bible readers, contrary to their Protestant counterparts. They tended to rest their salvation on early visits to their local priest on Saturday mornings, confessing for engaging in acts of passion the night before. The guys, well, we just loved it. It was those sweltering Friday nights that gave us a wealth of information to help in our maturity about such matters.

These saintly girls saw the process of life as part of God's creation, as natural as eating an orange and a sacramental privilege. For non-readers, they still found the appropriate scripture to back that up. This was a good thing, so they plunged in and indulged in worldly passions. The main difference, they demanded commitment, a way of giving it a purpose. "What's the sense," they would say, "without a purpose?" They were rebels with a cause. It would be a few years later, no many years later, before we would know how right they were. For now, we were happy to engage in the pleasure of theses ambiguous creatures. It was well worth the quest, what fun!

Ross was a lot more timid in these situations, coming from a strict Catholic family. His moment hadn't yet arrived. We called him gullible, just because he was a favorite subject for the many pranks we pulled. But, that really wasn't the case. Naïve maybe would be a better description for him. So in earnest, the two us, both really novices, pretended to be more and to know more then we really did.

As we grinded through our daily routine, we would occasionally come in contact with some of the girls and our eyes would meet. We would then, in an awkward fashion, attempt to ease into a conversation. But, some of our lines were just not that good. Like,

"Where are you from?" That was a little obvious of course, so we tried, "How do you like this place?" Not too bad an opening but they never let on what they were really looking for, in this place. So the answers were all too scripted.

Fine, we weren't, at least at this time, willing to pry any more. We just wanted to settle in.

I informed Ross, "At least they're smiling now. Wait until tomorrow. They'll be tempted to start up a real conversation."

Just then, mother called out from the porch. "You guys really have been working hard. Go ahead and take a break for a few hours. But remember, after lunch, I need you to put up the half-tents."

I turned to Ross, "Let's go!"

First, it was back to the cabin to change from our dirty work jeans into our bathing suits and flip-flops. Next, I said, "Let's search out the camp beach."

Ross just stayed in chorus and followed me thinking, always thinking, I had a plan. I knew he was wrong, but any action now was an improvement. And, this just might produce something promising. Hope was always with us.

So, it was off to the beach on this fine summer day. We stopped by the snack shop to get one of their famous malts and by chance happened to run into a group of the girls sitting around looking for something to do. With that in mind, even though we were outnumbered, I courageously jumped in. "So, are you girls having a good time here?" To my great surprise we got an answer, a full sentence. Now, that was progress.

"Yes," the girls called in unison. "We are! What a great place."

I continued on the offense. "Have you been to the island before?"

One answered. "Yes, but not here. I spent spring break in Avalon last year."

Now, Avalon is at the other end of the island and, during school vacations and summer breaks, the teenagers flock to its shores, hustle all day and party all night. That was a good sign. This was turning into a conversation. I started up again. "Kind of more remote at this end, isn't it?"

"Yep, it's different."

"Do you have a name?" I asked.

"Collin."

"Hi, Colon."

She laughed. "No, Collin, with two l's. I'm not named after a body part," she added, with an inviting smile.

"Sorry. Well, nice to meet you. I'm Gil."

"I know who you are. Your mother talks about you guys all the time in school."

"It's got to be good. It's my mother right?"

"Well, she says you do get into a lot of trouble."

"No! Not true. You know mothers. Do you have a mother?"

"Of course," she giggled. "Doesn't everybody?"

"By the way, this is my good friend, Ross. He's one of you guys. He's from St. John's." I paused for a moment and, seeing an opening, said, "When and if we have time, we could show you girls around the Isthmus." I waited for an answer to come from my baiting. But, it didn't. "Okay. Got it. Right. We'll see you all later. We're on our way down to the beach to kick back. So, good talking to you."

As we began to exit the snack bar, surprisingly Collin asked, "Is it okay if we go down to the beach with you?"

"Sure." Seeing my plan of action had some traction, Ross looked over at me and smiled.

While we meandered down to the beach, Ross and I would point out this or that spot, telling one untrue story after another. We got some laughs. It wasn't really so surprising. I mean, Ross and I had a following of sorts. We both were in pretty good shape and, if you asked us, quite accomplished in high school football and baseball. His Italian and my French/Mexican lineage made us very acceptable to a good dark tan. Plus, we were both products of California beaches and in our element, and that made all the difference.

So, as we walked to the end of the beach, where the cliffs met the shore, I pointed about 30 yards out in the water and announced, "This is our camp beach, and that's our float." We staked out a spot on the sand and placed our towels down. Now, for the first time, we took particular notice of what the girls were wearing. They all had on jeans and T-shirts with large handbags and tabbies. They began to pull out beach towels and place them next to ours. Like magicians, they continued reaching in. All kinds of paraphernalia came out, like oils, lip gloss and sunglasses, followed by a few unknown articles that seemed to serve no particular purpose. Then, still standing, the girls began to casually peel off their shirts and jeans. Ross and I were sitting on our towels in a state of complete suspense. We held our breath as each girl took her turn disrobing from their outer garbs, revealing their new summer bathing suits. I thought to myself how erotic this was, especially how these girls were so careful not to just jump out of their street clothes but to somehow slowly, piece by piece, undress. They must have rehearsed this routine over and over in a front of a mirror or something. I thought about what my cousin Jeff used to say and a big smile crossed my face because, at that moment, I knew what he meant. "Girls expose their most prominent features first." And that's the way it was. Of course, he was always right. He also said, "It's the anticipation that makes it all worth it."

Bikinis had just come on the scene in the late '50s, and were still looked at as a bit too risqué for beach attire, especially on a public beach. Respectful girls, well, they still wore one-piece bathing suits, the style that Marilyn Monroe wore in her pin-up pictures. And these were Catholic girls who rarely made risky fashion statements. But again, these were Catholic girls, full of surprises.

Ross and I begin to talk to each other, trying not to give the idea that watching them disrobe was of any interest to us. Ross began, "You know, those tents are going to be hard to put up in this warm weather." I rambled on about how whitewashing was a messy job. We were just stalling, trying not to let the girls feel our anticipation as they continued to undress, one by one.

Again, I had to laugh to myself. Because, I knew that at times like this Jeff would say, "Thank God for clothing." I remember looking at him and asking, "What the heck are you talking about?"

"Gil, it's like Christmas," he would say. "You know, when the presents are all wrapped up nice and seductively? You can't wait to see what's in there. Girls are like that. That's where the fun comes in."

"Fascinating," I whispered to Ross as we snuck our first glance at the girls, now lying on the beach. I turned to tell Collin another story and blushed at what I was thinking as she displayed herself. She was wrapped in a yellow bikini that showed skin from the tips of her feet to the top of her head with the rest interrupted by only a few inches of cloth. I said, "My, Collin, you have a lot of skin available for tanning." God, what a great line, I thought. Ross lost control and burst out a good laugh. Without commenting on what I just said, she turned over to get sun on her back. She added, "I…I just bought it for this trip. I heard the Isthmus was a remote area, so here it is."

Not knowing where to go with that subject, I cooled down my response and asked. "So, how is my mother? I mean as a teacher?"

Collin offered, "She's real nice. I like her. She's strict though. And you sometimes need to work around her."

I laughed. "So what does she say about us boys?"

"Well, she loves you guys. I know, for instance, you've been thrown out of a bunch of schools, but she says they really didn't understand you. And, they always wanted you back because they needed you to play sports."

I laughed. "I don't know about that. So, what about you, were you on her drill team?"

"Yes and no, I guess for a while. I had too much social life going on and spent a lot of my time working, making plans for college and I needed the grades."

As time went on, I noticed Ross beginning to loosen up with one of her friends. To keep their interest, I suggested we all take a swim to the float. While I coaxed them to the edge of the water, the girl next to Ross got up and followed. She wasn't as trim and athletic-looking as Collin, but, wow, I wondered what God had in mind when he created her. I looked over at Ross's blushing face as his stare followed her, while she tiptoed on the jagged rocks. I thought how neatly the suit fit to her body.

I led them into the refreshing water and we all swam out to the float. I arrived first and climbed up the ladder, then held out my hand to help Collin. She stepped up, grabbed it firmly and smiled. The water now ran down, tracing her body as I pulled her up. Her natural beauty took my breath away. I wondered where this meeting would take me. Ross helped the other girls up the ladder. Now we could lie down and take in the hot sun and blue ocean. There were five on the float by now, but my mind was only on one.

Ross was in his element, talking about the past and future. He had plans, boy did he have plans, and he was into a full dialogue now. But soon the conversation became muffled. It was like background music because I consumed myself with Collin and she with me. Not saying much, just watching and observing each other.

Later we swam back to the beach. Our break time was just about to end. I suggested maybe tomorrow we could all take a hike together to Cat Harbor at the back of the Isthmus. We could show them the sharks basking in the shallows. She said, "That might be fun."

"Is that a 'yes' then?"

"Yes, yes! But, how can we get around the chaperons?"

Wow, I thought. She'd now made a big step towards becoming part of the conspiracy. I suggested, "You know, Ross and I have to put up these outside half-tents for you girls. "If they ask you, volunteer to stay in them. We could then find a chance to see a lot more of the Isthmus." She knew what I was saying, but she hesitated for a moment, just to let me know she had character. Then, I jumped in to seal the deal. "Well, otherwise it's going to be a long week," and turned to leave but called back, "Hey, about that walk tomorrow, tell the chaperons and any other girls who would like to come, they are welcomed." I knew this would keep us stealth. And, my mother would be very comfortable and pleased that I would take the time to show her girls around. We left them sunning on the beach and walked back to the camp with a new sense of excitement.

"Ross, what do you think?"

"This is great!"

"So what's with the other girl, Ross?"

"Which one?" he asked.

"The one with the big boobs the bikini could barely hold in!"

"Oh, that one," he responded with a smile.

"Of course that one! And, you knew which one I meant, Ross." He grinned ear to ear as I went on. "Good catch. Now, can you reel her in?" He didn't respond to that. I asked, "Do you even know her name?

"Yeah, she looks good."

I jumped back. "Yeah Ross, I thought you were blind or something, what girl?! By the way it's Kimberly. That's her name."

"How do you know?" Ross asked.

"Cause I asked her, dummy. She's a good friend of Collin, so we've got a match." Ross seemed happy with that.

We hurried on up the path to the camp kitchen and talked with my mother for a while. "Mom, we met a couple of your girls on the beach this morning. I scrambled through some names, and when I hurried past Collin's my mother stood back. "Collin?" She had a funny grin on her face then started in with one of her cautious comments. "She's a little out on the edge, that one."

"What does that mean? With a smile, I asked, "What is out on the edge?"

"Now Gilly, you're starting to play with me. You know what that means."

"No, I don't know," I insisted.

"I always try not to be to judgmental about your girl friends. She's just different then most of my girls."

Mother was a high school gym teacher and, among some of her many extra duties, she was the pep squad advisor and took special pride as the drill team instructor. Under her tutelage, the drill team received plenty of prestigious awards. They were so good, they would be asked to perform at the Rose Parade, and later on at half time for the first Super Bowl in the Los Angeles Coliseum. When she referred to her girls, they were mainly drill team members and cheerleaders, whom she spent literally years training for performances.

"Okay, Mom," I chuckled. "I'll try to stay away from her."

"Now, Gilly, I didn't say that. Look, I've always told you boys, you're going to have to live with them so just don't let them get in the way of your careers."

"Now that's dad talking," I laughed. "Okay, I get it, Mom."

"You do, do you?"

"Yeah, Mom."

On our way out the door she added, "Ross, keep him out of trouble."

"Mrs. Lefebvre, I'm busy just trying to prevent him from killing me with all his antics!"

She laughed then nodded, "I know what you mean."

Ross and I tailed it back to the outside tents and began the arduous task of putting them up. This time, with a new sense of purpose, smiling and laughing and caught up by our new prospects.

It would be 4:30 every afternoon, just as the sun began to settle in the east over the back bay, that my mother would ring a bell. This meant you had a half hour until dinner. Then at 5 p.m. she would ring it again. This time to tell everyone that dinner was being served. Ross and I had to take the 4:30 bell seriously, because we needed to eat before the girls in order to serve the food.

So, Ross and I hurried for our early dinner. We ran to the kitchen, filled our plates with spaghetti, slathered on parmesan cheese, grabbed a slice of garlic bread, walked down to the porch, sat down at a table and began to inhale our dinner. Ross sat on the opposite side of the table from me. I looked at him and noticed he'd stopped eating and his mouth was hanging wide open. I followed his stare. It led me to the hallway window of the dormitory. He finally found his voice and whispered without pointing, "Look at that."

"Interesting," I muttered.

Why hadn't we ever noticed it before? The window glass was textured to let the light in and block any visual intrusion from the outside. But we now noticed one flaw. As the girls leaned against the glass, lined up waiting to shower, you could see parts of the female anatomy! Now, it wasn't like we were looking for this to happen. We weren't peeping Toms or something. And, we certainly couldn't make out their faces or tell who was who. We could see only parts and pieces. There was a special intrigue in this kind of voyeurism but, hey, it wasn't our making or design. It just happened. I thought perhaps it was just a blessing from above. After all, we did have the foresight to volunteer and that seemed enough reason to absolve us from any moral implications. Needless to say, for the next few days, Ross and I ate our meals in precisely that same place. Somehow, it made eating a bit more interesting. Giving it the full respect that it was now due, we referred to it as our "Mona Lisa window."

Later, after we finished doing our nightly dishes, we retired back to our bungalow and began plotting our new ventures. You know, from a male standpoint, we wanted to follow all the right formalities of dating but with only a few days left to work with, the courtship process needed some condensing. Not just a little, but substantial.

I was amused by Ross's comment, "This is going to be like writing a 50-page report using cliff notes."

Full of seductive thoughts, I concluded, "You know, Ross, we've had a very productive day. I think we're on our way."

Ross just kept mumbling, "What a day, what a day. Just think, if we can get the girls in the outside tents…"

"Yeah, then we're in like Flynn."

"Who?" Ross asked.

"Errol Flynn! Gosh, Ross, how 'bout the body on Kimberly? She's yours!" Ross started to reply but I jokingly interrupted. "Calm down dude. You're beginning to hyperventilate!" I looked over at him lying back on his bunk and added, "Me too, buddy." We both laughed. With that in mind, we went to sleep, feeling that, at least for now, things were going our way. We had the situation under control.

CHAPTER 6

# Learning to Navigate

U p before the dawn, Ross rustled out of bed. As usual, Ross was far more punctual than I. He announced, "Gilly, get up or we'll be late!

"Late for what?"

"The kitchen. Your mother said she needs us there by 5:30 and we've only got six minutes."

"Okay. What time did you say it was?"

Ross jumped into his jeans. "Just do the math, dummy."

I thought about that for a couple of seconds then caught on. "Okay, okay. But, you didn't have to call me, 'dummy.' Think about it Ross, who brought you to the dance?"

That made him smile. "Yeah, yeah," he agreed with a slight grin.

Now, let me say something about this idea of punctuality. Not to discredit myself, but you see Ross and I both had professional goals in life. However, on the day-by-day personal side, well, that was another matter. Ross seemed to have a better idea where his was going. Me, well, no such luck. About personal matters, Ross would say, "Gilly, you don't have a direction." And that always created a bone of contention between us. He would explain, "You're always going somewhere, but you don't have a destination. Your personal life is more like the lottery."

You see, it was so easy for Ross. He was always in the process of being successful. So, things like punctuality and making plans kept him on the trail. Needless to say, I gave little reverence to such punctual things, especially when it had to do with work. Besides, there was no need to, I kept telling him, because my parents owned the camp.

Five minutes later we strutted out the cabin door. The sun began to break the horizon and a morning chill, which always stayed around for a while, was felt by both of us. We quickly retreated back to the cabin for a sweatshirt. When we walked around the back of the dormitory we noticed the ever present light on in the kitchen, indicating my mother was fast at work, preparing food for the upcoming day. As we made our way up the steps, my mother sensed our presence and looked up when we entered the kitchen. "Good morning sleepyheads. We've got a lot of work to get done today, especially the weeds in front of the dorm."

Just then, a couple of girls followed by a chaperon came into the kitchen. My mother directed them on the task of preparing for breakfast. Ross and I took a glance at the girls and our eyes met for a short moment. Neither of them belonged to Collin or Kimberly. Mother jumped in, "This is my son Gil and his good friend Ross." Then, she turned to us and said, "You boys can begin your breakfast now, we have enough kitchen help. Right after you eat, get going on the weeds. By the way, I talked to your dad on the phone. He asked if you finished the whitewashing."

"Yep, it's done," I said with pride.

"When the sun comes up I'll look outside," she added sounding a little skeptical.

"I think the rocks look like new, Mother." I assured her.

She smiled. "Remember, I'm checking on you guys." Then,

she introduced us to some other girls who were now fully engaged in cooking pancakes and eggs. They offered up a soft little, "Hi," obviously trying not to make us feel too special. So, Ross and I, feeling a little uneasy and overwhelmed by all those girls, dished up some food and proceeded down the ramp to the tables, making sure to sit in our usual place, just outside of the now infamous Mona Lisa window. I looked at him and he gave me a sinister grin. I whispered, "Can't see anything now, but later, just before dinner." We both laughed at the thought.

There was little conversation as we quickly downed our pancakes, eggs and bacon, because we knew that if we got to work early and finished the job quickly, we would have a lot of time left in the day for our venture, or should I say quest. Especially now that Kimberly and Collin showed some interest in us, it made things much more promising and our juvenile minds began to lay out a plan. We needed to quickly get to work on the weeds and then finish setting up the outside tents. Because it was those tents that were the essential component to our plan. We needed them, to set the bait. I reminded Ross that we told the girls to volunteer for the outside tents. If they did, we'd know they were definitely persons of interest.

While we worked on the weeds, the sun turned the warm day into a hot one. As we worked beside the path, Ross and I had a clear view of the blue Pacific as far as the eye could see. But we could also view every girl, dressed in flip-flops and some kind of outerwear with towels draped over their shoulders, heading out for the beach. They began to pass us, one by one. But, our eyes were looking for just two girls.

"Bingo," I said to Ross. "There they are."

He looked up immediately and saw Collin and Kimberly walking together, down the path toward us.

"Okay, Ross, let's see if we can get this thing going."

We both noticed one of the chaperons bristling in conversation with my mother up at the table at the top of the ramp. Still trying to stay under the radar and look cool and calm, we looked down, pretending to be hard at work weeding. Without looking straight into their faces, I said, "Hey, did you girls volunteer for the outside tents?"

Collin answered, "Yeah, they asked us this morning."

Looking for clues, Ross remarked, "Really?"

"Yeah. And, guess what?" Collins went on with a sensual tone. "Only Kimberly and I volunteered."

My heart seemed to drop down to my feet. It began to pound loudly. I felt it was about to burst. I started to sweat and pellets began to form on my forehead. Wow. They were not only interested but had taken the bait completely! I attempted to rebound back into the conversation. "What are you girls going to do besides the beach today?" We attempted to calm down a bit and show them we were cool hombres, but again, another surprise.

Kimberly led this time. "Do you guys have anything planned for us?"

"Well, yeah, after we get done here we could take some of the girls around. Maybe show them the horses and then take a hike to the back bay."

"That sounds like fun!" Kimberly exclaimed.

"Yeah!" I added. This was great, actually way beyond our expectations. They had no trouble in acquiescing to our suggestion. I became bold now. "But first, encourage some of the other girls to come along with us. We don't care how many."

"Okay," they both called out.

Kimberly added, "Then after lunch, we could take off. If all goes well."

I thought mother might be happy with getting the girls off of the beach and keeping them busy doing other things. It seemed every summer the light complexioned girls would overexpose their bodies and look like red lobsters. The rest of the week they would struggle from the burns. Plus, I knew mother wasn't too happy about her girls lying about the beach in those itsy bitsy bikinis. She thought, and rightly so, it invites trouble.

Ross and I now had a purpose and, with a growing sense of anticipation, we raced through our morning tasks. "Okay," I said. "First, we'll take them up to the girls' camp stables." They were on the upslope of the mountain above the Isthmus valley. All the camps used those corrals and, when winter came, everyone pooled their horses there. The horses were allowed to wonder and feed through the off-season months. We had our own harness and would go up to the stables, bridle up and ride the island. Through the years we became quite proficient at riding bareback. Not only was it a lot of fun, but it also gave us a chance to show off to these girls, who we assumed were beginning to starve for male companionship.

It was apparent that some of the girls were rather shy to us guys, while others seemed lukewarm to the idea of romance. But, the few, more progressive and gregarious types, like Collin and Kimberly, were all for it. Women's liberation movements would be a few years off, but I think these two girls pioneered the cause. They threw caution to the wind.

Interestingly enough, with these new developments, Ross and I felt a little discomfort about their brash complicity to conspire with their conquest. In a funny way we kind of felt a little left out. They had plans that skirted way beyond even our most optimistic fantasies. We needed time to breathe. They had turned the table too fast, faster than either of us would have liked to admit. There was also this feeling of being smothered. We needed more time at romancing, maybe more courting or whatever comes before the serious stuff. But, we couldn't back down, not now! What would we tell our friends later? No way, to save face we had to just go on.

As I got older I began to realize the obvious. Boys are different from girls. This, I was informed by my cousin Jeff again, was the result of, "boys and girls coming from different planets." But, he also gave a counter explanation that had a genetic contextual twist. "Men are primarily mechanics by nature and women, being the emotional type, are romantics." I'm not really sure which one makes better sense, but I do know for sure, we both come from opposite sides of the same coin. That's what makes the struggle so interesting, isn't it?

For some reason, I felt it was my responsibility to pass on these important insights to Ross. I began to preach at Ross about these good antidotes for life's central issues. "So just be happy, feel blessed, at least for the moment, with these wonderful creatures that God has given us to share these summer days." I laughed and continued. "You know, Ross, think about it, these girls are not really wild. They're just advanced visionaries." Of course there wasn't any truth in that statement either, but it served as a good moral rationale for our conspiracy.

So, after finishing our daily chores in record time and engulfing our lunch while being entertained by the illusions presented to us on the shower window, a.k.a., the Mona Lisa window, Ross naturally looked to me for advice. He did this only if it had to do with girls. Of course, he was entirely wrong and again rather naïve, to think I knew anything more than he did. What I knew, I got from my cousin Jeff. Guys are that way, we get a little from a girl, then parade ourselves way out of proportion, passing on our highly exaggerated episodes with girls freely. This is kind of like earning achievement badges as a Boy Scout. While some girls, on the other hand, say they do little. They profess their virtue, when in reality, many times, it's quite the opposite. They know more and do more than they let on. And, because of this, Jeff said, "It leaves nice guys, like us, at a complete disadvantage, especially at a young age and living in these times."

While finishing lunch Ross piped in, "So, what's the plan again?"

"Well," I said, "Let's go ahead and take the girls and chaperons up to the horses. Get to know them better, then take a long walk to the back harbor and see if we can make a break with Kimberly and Collin. And, we'll go from there." I noticed that now a titillating chill had pleasantly taken over our mood, knowing, of course, that courting the opposite sex is a process that can only go one way, forward. In a progressive fashion, you get to know her, ask her out and possibly hold her hand. It's a small but important commitment. You may get nothing out of it, but, on the other hand, if while holding a girl's hand you get sweaty palms… Now there's something to tell your buddies about. Then, maybe you get a kiss, maybe a hug, then a feel, whatever that means. Because, at that point, when you're with a girl, things get a little fuzzy, if not confusing.

Something to look forward to, but, for now, we felt a little uneasy. Because, there are times in life when it seems events are pushing you forward, faster than you ever wanted to go. This was one of those times. It was as if we were trying to cross a stream at the wrong point, but we had to keep going anyway. 'Cause the chance might never come again.

Even with the awkward feeling about going forward with our plan, it didn't matter. We'd take that risk. There was no going back, now that the girls egged us on. We were compelled to take the leap. We knew we were getting into uncharted waters. But, for sure, we weren't going to let each other know how we felt.

So, there we were, Ross and I, moving up the courtship chain. But, there was a caveat. We had only four days left to make it happen.

CHAPTER 7

# The Splendid Day

After lunch we stepped up the camp's front ramp and walked back into the kitchen. Mother was just finishing up some dishes and starting a few preparations for tonight's dinner.

"So, Mom, what else do you have planned for us this afternoon?"

She looked up at Ross. "You guys got a lot done this morning, and by the look of things outside, something's up."

"No, no Mom, just wanting to get these projects done so we can get out and about for a while." I looked at her thinking, "Oh no, she's about to put a wrench into our plans."

She turned to me. "Tomorrow, you and Ross need to start dragging the infield at the back bay and setting up the batting cages."

Even though I knew that was always a dusty and dirty detail, especially with this warm weather, I obliged. "No problem, Mom."

She continued. "Your dad called again today and guess what?"

"What?"

"All of your friends are coming back this summer as counselors. And, Billy Tucker's dad called to let us know he's sailing in next week to drop off Billy. So, it looks like we'll have him with us all summer again." This brought on a big smile, because Billy Tuck, outside of Ross, was my closest friend.

Tuck had been with us from the beginning, when his dad enrolled him as a camper. His father was a larger-than–life, robust businessman, adventurer and who knows what else. He lived and did business on the mainland but, in the summer months, most of his time was spent at sea, skippering his well-known yacht, the Geronimo. In between he spent time moored at the Isthmus near Little Fisherman's Cove. This was good news, to know Tuck and I would be summer stable mates once again.

I brushed that news aside and got a little impatient. "Great!" Now thinking entirely about getting on with our plan with the girls, I said, "Let's go, Ross." I hoped to get out of there before mother had a chance to give us another project.

"Hold on, guys. Don't go anywhere yet."

Darn, I knew our schemes were about to be crushed.

"Gilly, I've got a favor to ask you boys."

Oops. That's it. The plan was shot.

"Now, Gilly, don't look so disappointed. I need a favor. Some of the girls and Mary Ellen, the chaperon, would like to get a tour around the Isthmus. I told them you might be willing to do that … show them the sights?"

I smiled and Ross shot me a slight grin, for mother had just given us the opportunity we wanted. Wow, it left the door wide open for our plan. "Okay, no problem, Mom. Just get them together. Ross and I will spend about a half hour at the beach and take a dive to cool off. Tell them to meet us in about 30 minutes at the bottom of the ramp."

"Great. Thanks, boys, but you'd better be here."

"We will!" I called back as we started to run off. If only she knew.

Out of motherly intuition, she added, "Now, Gilly, remember, watch out for Collin and her friend Kimberly. Don't get yourself in any trouble."

"Of course not, Mom. You know I won't."

"Oh, I'm not too sure about that," she smiled back.

I didn't want to elaborate any more and give away our hand, as Shakespeare would say, by protesting too much. So, I quickly dropped the subject but still wondered if, just maybe, we weren't really pulling the wool over mother's eyes after all. Her many years of teaching high school gave her insight about these things.

Ross and I turned, ran out the door and down the ramp. Almost at our cabin, I said to Ross, "This is great, but we need to get down to the beach and tell Kimberly and Collin to get up to the camp and ask to be included on the tour." We threw on our bathing suits and hurried down to the beach.

Sure enough, there they were, Collin's brown body lying face down on the towel, gloriously soaking in the sun. And Kimberly, just coming out of the water, showing off that body, such a gracious gesture. As the water began to trickle down from the top of her head and stream over every crevice and curve, Ross stopped. He couldn't hide his trance-like state caused by this display. Seeing Ross, Kimberly rushed up to meet him. Collin was now turning over and looking into the sun for a brief moment, giving me an opportunity to admire her sunbaked anatomy. The scent from her tanning lotion made the moment even more tantalizing. She shaded her eyes with a hand, just enough to recognize me. She refused to move, allowing me to indulge on as she lay posed on the towel. "So what's the plan?"

"If you can get up to the camp in about 20 minutes, we've been asked to be tour guides for all the girls who want to take a hike around the Isthmus." It didn't take long for a reply. Kimberly jumped in and said, "Sure, sounds like fun. Let's go Collin!" They quickly packed their things and began to race back to camp.

After our quick dip in the ocean, we grabbed a few things from the cabin and re-entered the scene at the bottom of the ramp. It was just in time to hear my mother, as she stood and talked over the banister to about 15 of the girls who had gathered for the tour. Seeing us now, standing behind the girls, she said, "You all know my son Gil and his friend Ross by now. They have volunteered to show you girls around the Isthmus. So listen to them, and be careful. Oh and Miss Ellen, your chaperon, will be going along with you too. Have fun!"

Off we went. I told the girls some brief history of the island and talked more about our camp. The Catalina Baseball Camp accommodated 500 boys ages 12 to 15 in five, two-week sessions every summer. We also carried a staff of 15 counselors, two lifeguards and two ex-military divers. They supplied our food on fish night. I went on to describe the prize commodity brought in by these divers, the delicious pink abalone that could be found everywhere around the cove, even in shallow waters. We'd get 50 to 100 and pound them down to a tender state. Finally, we would chicken fry them until perfect. What a treat.

It had been five days since their graduation and almost three days on the island so the girls began to show a keen interest toward the idea of 15 counselors. One of the girls asked, "When will they be coming?" I answered, "Unfortunately, the boat that comes to pick you up will be the same one that brings them in. Sorry, girls."

Now, with 15 girls and only one trusting chaperon, Ross and I felt at liberty to lead on with the dialogue in any fashion we liked. The girls kept asking questions about guys. One of them bluntly asked, "Okay, where are all the guys on this island?" Another spoke up, "I heard there's a Boy Scout camp somewhere around here." And, "What goes on around here in the middle of summer? I mean, what's the social life like?" We chatted on with all kinds of general answers. The girls responded as if we really knew a lot, more than we actually did.

I led the girls up the mountain path to the back of the Banning House and told them about its Civil War history. It had been remodeled to serve the summer needs of a prestigious girls' school. Next, we took them behind the main house to the stables, where we found several horses grazing. I explained that they were allowed to run free during the winter and Jack White's cowboys, from the Black Jack Ranch, maintained the horses. Those few seasoned cowboys lived back in the hills year round. As I explained how we rode them every chance we got, I reached into my backpack and pulled out two bridles. "There's only one catch, if you want to ride here, you must ride it with just a bridle, no saddle, bareback."

Ross and I corralled a couple of nice slow horses. After bridling them, we jumped on and showed them how it was done. A few girls took the chance and, with our help, climbed up. But, most of the girls wanted to be spectators and cheer the others on. After a while, Ross and I mounted two of the most spirited horses and raced then in short bursts. This gave us a chance to show off a bit of our macho. It was still in vogue back then. Finally, I said, "Okay, the horse thing is over. It's time for the back bay."

From the Banning House, we had a clear view of the back bay, known on the map as Cat Harbor. It's a majestic site from up there. Not only does it pick up the blue of the water with its whitecaps that contour the cove, but also it's most impressive for the panoramic presentation that extends to the farthest Pacific horizon. There, the mind is able to envision wherever your imagination will take you. Way out, many miles to sea, maybe to Tahiti or other exotic places and beyond.

We strolled along the ridge for a while and then traversed the mountainside down toward the main road of the Isthmus that would eventually lead us to Cat Harbor. After passing our dirt infield and walking through the gate, we were finally on the edge of the back bay. Here the girls got a rare view of the sharks meandering in the shallows. Their fins flashed around as they basked in the sun.

Then, I heard it, pop, pop, pop and sputter, sputter, sputter. It was the familiar sound of a plane seemingly dying for lack of gas. I told the girls to look back to the front of the Isthmus, just above the tree line. Seeing, nothing, they looked quizzically back to me. I said, "Just wait, you'll see." Then, like something out of a WWII movie, an amphibious airplane appeared and passed above the eucalyptus trees silhouetted by the horizon. It took a branch hostage on its wing and swiftly advanced toward us, abruptly losing altitude and looking as if it were about to land on the dirt road. But, just then, it accelerated, helping it stay the course, subsequently skipping like a thrown rock across the bay, until it came to a swishing stop. It pepped up its propellers and trolled to a strip of asphalt that extended out into the water. Then with a roar, it jettisoned itself out of the water, where a few cars were patiently waiting to receive its passengers. Once unloaded, it hastily returned into the water, revved up its engines and again skipped across the water, this time to find an uplift of wind. It disappeared, just for a moment and then turned back into view, crossing over the Isthmus one last time to become lost again in the horizon, as it ventured back to its Long Beach terminal.

The girls stood in stunned silence. I announced, "That was Channel Airlines, legendary for infamous escapades." As seasoned veterans of the amphibious plane, Ross and I began to tell stories of its questionable reputation and how we jokingly kissed the ground every time we landed safely.

Continuing on the path and caught up by the interest of our captivated audience, Ross and I enticed the girls with more myth than truth. After all, we felt it was our responsibility to make the hike interesting. We talked about our exploits with the sharks, snorkeling and diving in the blue waters around Catalina. One of the girls questioned our integrity. "We'll see who's telling the truth," I said. "By the way, did you see that dirt spot we passed? That's the infield for our baseball diamond. Many a famous ball player has trained there."

One girl asked, "Who?"

I quickly replied, "Me!"

She laughed. "Right."

I went on. "And, remember that gate we went through? That's there to keep out the Brahma bulls."

"Bulls? What bulls?" Collin asked. "What are they here for?"

This time Ross jumped in. "Well, a long time ago they made this movie here, brought over some bulls for the scene and then left them. The fence is to keep them out of the Isthmus."

"Are they dangerous?" Kimberly asked.

"You bet!" I replied dramatically. "They run trucks off the road in the interior."

"What other kind of animals live here?" Collin asked. By now the two girls were leading the conversation.

"Well, goats by the hundreds, and boars…"

"Really?"

"Yeah, really. And even some rattlesnakes. No telling how they got here in the first place, but they're here nevertheless. Let's see, fox, the four-legged type…"

"You've got two-legged types too," one girl interjected and the girls giggled.

"And there's buffalo."

"You're kidding. Will we be able to see them?"

"Maybe. And, believe it or not, legend has it there are also black panthers that roam the island, but only a few people have ever seen them."

"Have you seen one?" Collin asked.

"Nope, never, but I know they're here cause I talked to some hunters. They swear they have seen them, even though they've never gotten close enough to know for sure. Some say they were left over from the early settlers of the island."

"Right," Kimberly said sarcastically.

"Hey, just telling what was told to me."

We hiked on and followed the dirt road to the back of Cat Harbor. Looking up at the towering mountain ridge on one side and down to the bay on the other, I was reminded of how breathtaking it could be. As we continued to walk, the girls began to string out in small groups, leaving Kimberly walking with Ross and Collin staying close at my side. I think they felt privileged having the attention of probably the only two available guys on the west end of the island. At least we hoped they did. When we first entertained a conversation with the girls, it was like cursory observations, kind of like persons of interest, but, as we became more familiar, we began to observe each other's interests, sense of timing and personalities. While we continued walking and talking, conversations began to take form. With each minute I felt as if these girls were giving us clues, helping us get to the next step.

It was just like when you install a computer program nowadays. After completing the basic ID address and such, the computer tells you to push "continue" and so we did, looking for clues, looking for signals it was time to push "continue." It was a great game.

When we finally arrived on the bluff at the farthest point of the Isthmus, we found something to sit on and gazed out into the Pacific. I was sure they all felt the sense of adventure, watching as the waves bounced around giving us quite a show. We could see ships, visible as black dots on the horizon, flushed out by the sun as its rays sprayed across the water.

"Hey, Collin, where do you think they're going out there, so free?"

"What a great line," I thought.

She looked at me and upped mine. "Well, Gil, where would you like it to go?"

For the first time, I was too flustered to answer. I just looked into her eyes, hoping to find out what she meant. Her eyes began to talk back and, for a few moments, we sat there in silence, so timeless and free as ideas began to form beyond our mortal thoughts. We would have loved to stay longer, in this silence. But, as the sun slowly became engulfed by the horizon, clouds began to drift in, as they did on most days, cluttering the view and signaling the show was about to end.

I announced, "It's time to get back to camp."

We headed back toward the infield just in time. Fog was about to cover the entrance of the harbor in a tsunami-like gust. Just then, I looked ahead and noticed an out-of–place, weathered fishing vessel creeping into the harbor, staying just ahead of the thickening fog. It looked foreign, much like you'd see in some old Russian fishing village. There was something sinister about its presence. Two men were standing on the front deck. One looked older with a long unkempt beard, and some kind of sea captain's cap sat crooked on his head. One thing for sure, as it came closer, they both appeared to be looking intently at us. This suspicious context sent chills up my back. It was almost ghostly.

With that in mind, Ross and I both picked up the pace and hurriedly retreated from the back bay. We must have been in tune with each other's uncomfortable feelings, because neither of us mentioned anything to the girls. I caught up to Ross. "Did you see them?"

"Yea, spooky," he replied.

"Look over there at that old Chinese junket that looks like a barge. You know, the one that's sitting on the sand bar just inside the cove?" He looked to where I was pointing. "It's always been a mystery to me. Maybe there's a connection here, between those spooky guys and that weird-looking barge thingy. They seem to be heading in its direction." The fog moved in, now engulfing the boat and most of the bay. Little did I know we would have a rendezvous with these characters before the summer ended.

Ross and I refocused on our conquest. Looking to the situation at hand, I whispered, "When we get back let's see if they want to get together tonight, outside the tents."

We looked up to see a group of guys coming toward us. "What? Oh no, Boy Scouts."

"Yeah, for sure," Ross said. "Look at that, uniforms and all. Oh, oh, it's Randall Cunningham III in the lead!"

Over the past few years Randall and I had had our run-ins. His ego and mine never seemed to get along very well. Most of our raids on the scout camp at Cherry Cove had targeted his tent. We'd never see much of them, except on weekends, when girls were around. It was understood that there just wasn't enough room around the Isthmus for the both of us.

Randall was a strong kid. He knew it and liked to bully his way around. So far, we'd been able to keep some sense of civility between us. But, I knew that wouldn't last much longer. My temper and his abrasive attitude were about to clash. As he approached, he said to his troops, "Look who it is, the baseball guys."

"Now's not the time," I whispered to Ross. But, the troops had already started in on conversations with some of the girls walking ahead, so, as I passed, I had to throw out something, just to keep up my macho. "Look, Ross." This time loud enough for Randall to hear, "It's the scout guys. I think they're lost or something." I couldn't stop myself now. I was on a roll. "This is the Isthmus, not Cherry Cove. Oh, I guess they must smell skirt."

Randall just smiled and mumbled as he passed. "Hey, Lefebvre, anytime."

I kept walking, then turned back and used my best authoritative tone to say, "Break it up. We've got to be back at camp." Luckily, Miss Ellen, the chaperon, caught up with us and helped herd the girls along.

As we approached the campsite, I closed in on Collin and proposed a breakout that night. Of course this was a big step in the courtship process. I guess most girls really don't understand how big a step this is to a guy. This is where we have to take a risk. One of the greatest threats to our esteem is being denied, turned down.

Sometimes, I would sit for hours rehearsing a call just to ask a girl out. If she said, "no," I would be crushed and it could take several months to regain my confidence to pick up the phone and try again. Back then, if a girl called a guy, well that indicated the girl wanted to forget the courtship thing, forget the appetizers and just get down to the main meal. So, it was really up to the guy to start things off on a proper footing. Here I was, suggesting we should get together that night, knowing if she said, "yes," Ross and I could maintain the dream. But if she said, "no," it meant all bets were off. The stage was set. Would they allow us to continue with the drama?

Ross and I sat in our regular eating spot for dinner and passed the time enjoying the evening's entertainment. Just as we stood up to clear our plates, Collin came over and slid alongside of me, thrusting a neatly folded paper into my hand. It was obvious she wanted to be secretive, letting no one see what she was up to. She swished by, never even glancing in my direction. I clinched my fist in a tentative manner, holding the note just tight enough not to lose it, yet not too tight to make it unreadable.

We walked into the kitchen and Ross started to wash off his plate. I stood next to him and said, "Drop it. Come with me!" Sensing my urgency, Ross plunged the plate into the hot dishwater and followed me, his hands dripping soap bubbles across the kitchen floor. We moved to the backroom, where the freezers were. I whispered, "Look what Collin just gave me."

He knew what it was about. "Well, hurry up and read it!" I just stood there looking at my hand.

"Come on Gilly, open it up!"

I laughed. "It's either all over or..." Slowly I unfolded the note and began to read it out loud.

"Sorry guys, but meeting you somewhere out at night is just too risky." I think Ross and I were about to cry or commit cooperative Harry Carry, but then the tone changed as I read on. "But, past 9, after lights are out, we would love to go out with you guys." It was signed, "Looking forward, Collin and Kimberly," followed by a P.S., "Destroy this paper after you read it!"

Ross and I looked at each other and just about jumped through the ceiling. It was really happening. We went back in to finish off the dishes. It was one happy washing.

Later, mother came in, as she always did, to inspect the kitchen. There was no telling when the health inspector would show up. "Good job, boys." She looked over at me to say good night. I recognized that look. It was as if she knew I had something going on but really didn't want to know about it.

"Good night. Remember, stay out of trouble."

I protested. "Why me? What about Ross?"

"I don't worry about Ross. His mother does that for me. But it's you, and what your dad brings up. You're like two peas in a pod. That's what worries me."

"But, Mom, you married him."

Mother ended with a smile on her face. "Don't remind of that. Good night, boys. See you in the morning."

Ross and I walked across the road and entered our cabin. "So, what shall we do?"

I answered, "Let's see. How about we take the girls out for a walk on the pier then wander down the beach a bit. Next, we'll tell them we want to take them on a snipe hunt. That'll get us alone. And, maybe then, back to the tent."

Ross added, "We've got to stay away from anyone seeing us."

"Yeah, that's the idea. But I hear some of the girls like to stay up to drink and kind of party when the chaperons go to sleep. So, we need to be careful because some of them might still be awake."

We lay down in our bunks listening to the radio, marking time. After finishing his Forbes magazine, Ross reached under his mattress and found a Playboy that Ret Taylor hid last summer. In those days, Playboy was more of a pin-up publication and hadn't turned into the prevailing show-all yet.

At nine o'clock, Ross said, "Let's go!" We found two flashlights, jammed some snacks we'd squandered from the kitchen into our backpacks, turned out the lights and slowly opened the cabin door. Except for the flickering of a few flashlights coming from inside the dormitory, the campsite was almost totally dark.

After walking some 100 yards to the outside of their tent and seeing no movement, I whispered, "Collin?...Kimberly?" The front flap of the tent was quickly pulled back and, one after another, the two girls stepped out, dressed for a date. Silently they followed our unspoken prompting, until we got far enough away from the campsite to whisper. Ross and I coupled up with the girls and proceeded on to the pier, where only a few safety lights were on.

We started up the pier in semi-darkness, lit mostly by the stars and a full moon. The romantic affect was perfect. Once we stopped at the end of the pier, our effort became less of a collective endeavor. Ross walked to one corner of the pier with Kimberly, and I pulled softly on Collin's hand, guiding her over to the other. These were intimate moments gathering steam. To feel her hand in mine signified trust, warmth and togetherness. It whet my imagination of things to come.

We stayed there for a while, talking in hushed tones to each other, grasping the moment while listening to the sounds of the ocean pelting its music against the pillars. We began to walk back down the pier, Ross in front, holding Kimberly's hand, signaling that we both were on the same page and moving with assurance of other things to come. Ross stepped off the pier and passed out of view, holding Kimberly as they faded into the dark night. Collin and I began to roam over to a separate part of the beach while carrying on a conversation about the travails of life, waiting for the right movement, an unintentional passing that might lead the way. It happened when Collin asked me to help with her coat. As I placed it on her shoulders, it gave her a chance, so close now, to turn and kiss me. It was prolonged as I responded in kind, and our souls became one just for a minute; the seal was broken. We fell to the sand and reached out to each other. I now took the liberty she gave me to press on, enough to sustain and gain momentum, warming our bodies until it was necessary to take control.

We backed off with a blush of excitement, giving us time, a respite, to regain a quality of our relationship, to avoid looking too wanting on our first date. I knew Catholic girls, more than others, needed a rational to give them the courage to love, to make a relationship a moral affair, even though it might end up as just an affair. So, we backed off, hoping to cultivate this imperative. She spoke first, "We better get back to the tent before someone discovers we're gone."

So, we stood up and found Ross entangled with Kimberly, but the darkness still hid them from full view. I whispered into the dark, "Ross, we better get these girls back now. It's getting late." Out of the shadows came Kimberly and Ross, smiling without a blemish of guilt. Ross cleared his throat and asked, "So what were you guys up to?"

We all laughed. "You guys should know," Collin chimed in.

We knew we were all reading from the same script now, as we hurriedly backtracked to the tent. Without a goodnight kiss, the girls quickly opened the flap and disappeared inside. Ross and I quietly walked back to our cabin. Once inside, Ross said, "What do you think the girls are saying about us now?"

"Not much. I just kissed her, but, dang, Ross. I thought I was going to teach you something, but you and Kimberly were way ahead of our program."

Ross laughed. "You didn't see us, did you?"

"No. It was too dark out there. Man, you were working fast."

Ross stood back and, with a broad smile, asked, "What's next?"

"First off, Ross, did you get anything beside a kiss?"

"Like what?"

"You know what I mean. Maybe a little fondling?"

"Well, I wouldn't call it that. But, she's so top heavy that, when I kissed her, she rubbed them around."

"Wow. I told you this was going to be fun, didn't I, Ross?"

"Yeah but I didn't think it would be this good, this easy."

"Ross, remember we're the only guys around for miles. Did you think we were that bad?"

It was getting late and, for the first time, I had to tell Ross to get to sleep. He climbed into the top bunk and said, "This is really getting interesting. What a great day."

"No. How do they say it in that refined university you're going to?" I got it, a 'splendid' day. Think about it, Ross." Now flaunting, I held up my hand to count off with my fingers. "We got to show off with the horses and demonstrate a little grit, thanks to our boy Randall and the scouts. Oh, and how about that Channel Airlines landing? What a sideshow. And, those fishermen in the back bay, some suspense there, hey? Hah, then at the end, we get the girls. Splendid day. Yes, Ross, I call it a splendid day!" I looked up at him. "And, Mr. Future Accountant, it didn't cost us a dime! I repeat, not a dime. We're number one buddy. Yes we are, at least for this day. The Isthmus is coming to life. I can feel it. It's coming to life." Now dropping my notes and finishing my song, I settled back down on my bunk, letting the excitement dwindle out of me for a few moments before I finally pulled the switch on the cabin lights.

From the corner of the darkened room, I closed with, "Get some sleep, Ross. Looks like we're going to need it." I pretended to drift away on my pillow. I needed time to think. Then, in the dark, I realized, for the first time, the more I got to the know Collin, the more I began to be torn between wanting her and liking her. This could eventually complicate a good relationship. And, it was about to do just that.

CHAPTER 8

# The Hanging

F our o'clock came early this morning. I think it had less to do with the Earth's rotation and more to do with last night's capers. Since our cabin had no restroom facilities, we needed to walk about 50 yards through a dark wooden grove on chilly nights. This became a rather uncomfortable endeavor, so, over the years, we secretly cut a hole in the cabin wall to be able to relieve ourselves. This seemed to be a clever idea and very convenient for young men growing up who had no time to waste on mundane bodily functions. After going through this ceremonial rite, we dressed then rushed over to the kitchen. Seeing the light already on got our attention, especially this morning. I was afraid that mother was a step ahead of us.

We ran up the ramp with an overly cheerful, "Good morning."

"Boys, come over here. We have to talk." Mother's stern voice was evident.

I whispered to Ross, "Dang, I think she knows." As we walked over, a sense of guilt overwhelmed me. Somehow, mother had caught on to our act. We stood speechless for a moment while she continued to work on her breakfast concoction and waited nervously for her to explain.

Mother took a deep breath, looked directly at us and said, "We've got a problem."

My heart picked up the concerned tone. I replayed it in my mind. "We've got a problem?" What the heck did that mean?

As usual, Ross was about to start in with some kind of an apology. But, this time he thought it better to try and leave my mother's complaint squarely in my hands.

"Last night," mother continued, "after the lights were out, some of the girls snuck out."

I was about to throw out an alibi. Thankfully, my response was too slow. Because, as my mouth opened to speak, she raised her hand and continued. "They went down to Cat Harbor and partied all night with some of their friends from high school. The boys sailed over yesterday on a private boat. They slept on the beach at Little Fisherman's Cove last night. Then to make matters worse, Miss Ellen caught two of the girls coming in inebriated!"

Wow! Attempting to conceal any knowledge of last night, I asked, "Really?" With a slight pause, I went on. "What are you planning to do about it, Mom?"

"First, we need to search the camp and confiscate the alcoholic beverages. Hopefully we can find them when the girls take their trips to the beach today. We need to check out their baggage, of course with Miss Ellen's supervision. Next, about the guys, I talked to the Harbor Master, Doug Bombard, about them being at the Isthmus. He said there's nothing he can do, as long as there's no evidence they broke any laws. But, he promised to notify the sheriff and see if they would look into the matter. With luck, we'll take care of the alcohol problem today, but we'll need you and Ross to patrol the beaches at night, after lights are out. I'm going to let the girls know about the patrols, hoping it will deter them from getting into any more trouble."

Interestingly enough, once the news got back to the mainland that 60 girls were basking on the isolated Isthmus beach, the gold rush was on.

Ross and I remained silent. There was no reason to speculate on the issue. Relieved that our own escapade went undetected, we went along with mother's ideas. As we walked out of the kitchen to set up our committee of two, I said, "We're just plain lucky that those guys went to Cat Harbor and we went to the front side of the Isthmus." For now, our quest was placed on hold, but not totally impeded. However, some good tweaking in our strategy was needed.

Ross and I continued with our morning chores and picked up some of the scuttlebutt going around. We overheard a few of the girls were meeting the guys up at the stables in the afternoon while others were planning to stay clear, obviously deterred by my mother's threats. Also, the chaperons were viewing everyone with suspicious eyes. So, Kimberly and Collin just melted into the background, hoping, as we did, to deflect any suspicion.

After most of the girls left to the beach and some of the others ventured out to rendezvous with their young visitors, Ross, mother and I, along with Miss Ellen, began the task of confiscating the booze snuck in by the girls. It was an enormous cache, enough for a whole army reunion. Even mother was surprised at the amount of alcohol we found. She put us all on notice.

"Get your sleeping bags and flashlights. Until we can get this thing under control, it's going to be the beach for you two. I'm hoping the girls will hear about it. Maybe just knowing you're out there, looking for them, will keep them from trying to sneak out."

Mother called all the girls together to let them know she was aware of their shenanigans. If any of the girls continued to violate the rules, and that meant the curfew, she would personally call their parents to notify them their daughter was being sent home on the first flight out. She stressed, "We have four more days, so let's have fun and please try not to cause any more problems, and you girls know what I mean!"

Some of the girls gave mother their support, while others had their own ideas. Those girls were looking for romance and saw the unique situation slowly slipping away, as we did. They were about to do anything to make it happen. Mother had always been cautious of mixing guys and girls together in a camp setting. The attraction between them was just too much to handle in situations like this. "All we need is to come up with a few pregnant cheerleaders, and that will be the end," she would say.

However, Ross and I had only two things on our mind. One, our territory, our paradise, our exclusive domain, had just been breached by these outside, opportunistic intruders. Two, if that wasn't bad enough, now the whole staff, mother, the chaperons and even the girls were all alerted to the problem. Okay, I guess rightly so. But, this put a tremendous crimp on our own covert activities. Ross reminded me that we had only four more days with these girls to pull it off. Time was our enemy, as well as this situation.

Just before lunch, Ross and I abandoned our work and ran down to the beach, hoping to talk to Collin and Kimberly. We started to brainstorm ways of getting out after curfew, which my mother had just set at 8 p.m. How could we do this without being noticed while the rest of the camp was under these new night restrictions? The good thing was, a major part of the surveillance was left to me and Ross.

A while later, we found Collin and Kimberly in the snack shop, sipping on a malt. I got an idea. "Hey Ross, walk in and ask Linda to make me a chocolate malt." I reminded him to ask her politely, because nobody tells Linda or any of the other soda girls what to do. They didn't work that way. "Say, 'please, mix a banana in with Gil's malt.' She'll ask, 'where is he?' And that's when you tell her, loud enough for all to hear, 'he's on the beach.'"

"A banana?" Ross asked.

"Just do it, man! Why do you keep asking me these stupid questions? The important thing is to ask her loud enough to let the girls know where we are. If they catch on, they'll find us." Ross finally got on with my instructions and caught their attention as he walked over to the snack shop counter. He tried not to make eye contact with the other girls sitting around while he ordered the malt. Collin discreetly signaled by scratching her chin intently while looking at him.

Ross came out, "I think she got it!"

Twenty minutes later, the two girls walked causally down the beach looking for us. We were sitting on the sand, leaning up against the sea wall under a palm tree, facing the water. This way, we could only be seen by some boaters bouncing about in the outer bay.

"Look at that, Ross. Here come our girls."

He laughed. "Not yet, but soon."

As they drew closer their presence was felt. These two fine girls were interested in us. I had to pinch myself and take in a deep breath of air, anticipating our next step. We told the girls about our nighttime patrol duties on the beach. "So here it is, after we're sure the coast is clear, we'll come up, throw some rocks at your tent and get you."

"That's going to be tricky," Collin explained. "We were lucky we didn't get caught last night."

"I know, I know," I added.

Kimberly appeared more willing to take a chance when she said with a smile, "The riskier it gets, the more intriguing."

Collin put up a concerned defense. She didn't want to be caught for a variety of reasons. But, after Kimberly joked that flying home in one of those Channel Air planes could be exciting,

Collin reluctantly conceded to our plan. "And remember," I added. "If everything doesn't shape up or we have a major problem, we'll let it pass tonight."

As we continued talking and planning with the girls, I picked up Collin's fragrance. My mind rolled instantly back to last night's kiss. The perfume, or whatever, was beginning to cloud my thinking. You just don't think clearly when things like this happen. Especially when you're young, excited and your mind alludes to all kinds of possibilities.

We needed to get back. So, the girls got up first and walked away. I said, without losing focus on their fading images, "You know what the problem is, Ross?" Now underscoring our fortunes, I added "It won't get any better than this."

"Is that your idea or your cousin Jeff's?" Ross asked sarcastically.

"No, Ross. I picked that line up from a movie. Of course it's my idea!"

"No, it wasn't."

"Oh, what's the use talking to you? Okay, whatever you say, Ross. Does that make you feel good?"

"Yes it does. Real good."

"Okay!"

We got back to the task at hand. These new intruders or "trespassing scuttlebutts" as we started calling them by now were to meet some of the girls up at the Banning House corral in the afternoon. Ross and I decided it was a good time to make our presence felt. We'd show those intruders who was in charge here and, at the same time, let the other girls know we were aware of their goings-on. It could be counterproductive for us. But, if we could scare these guys off, send them packing back to the mainland, Ross and I would be back in business once again.

So around two o'clock in the afternoon, Ross and I made

our way up to the corral. Just as rumored, there were five guys. They were attempting to bridle a horse with just an old rope. We weren't about to offer any bridles, letting them expose their city boy ineptness. After watching them struggle to rope a horse, I interrupted with a slight arrogance in my voice. "Gentleman!" Why "gentleman?" I felt it would give me a flavor of authority. And really, after spending all these summers here, it gave me something didn't it? Not to mention the fact that my family owned the camp, again that must be worth something.

"Gentleman!" Now speaking with the authority of a camp owner, I said, "These horses are privately owned and belong to the local camps. So I strongly suggest you leave them alone and go on your way. There's a lot more of the island to see."

"Oh really, like what?"

"Well, if you don't get out there you won't know, will you?"

One of the boys, with a bulging Pious X athletic T-shirt, stepped forward and asked, "What are you going to do if we don't?"

Gulp, I wasn't ready to escalate the situation that fast. Maybe this was the wrong group to scare off, especially in front of their local girls. It just wasn't going to happen. These nice Catholic boys were anything but. Rather than fight a battle here and probably lose, I thought better and said, "Now, you guys got this thing all wrong. I'm just letting you know, that's all." Ross gave me a look of relief. He knew, most often, my temper got the best of me. Now, I wasn't this gigantic specimen or anything. But, I was always willing to try and vet out my rage in situations where I felt I was right and something should be done about it. But, even though we were in the right, this wasn't the right time. Hoping not to appear as though we were backing down, especially in front of the girls, I kind of gave them a feeling that leaving the scene was my idea. Somehow, if you believe that whatever happens to you is your idea, it really helps. It goes a long way in saving face. I don't know why, but it does. So off we went, saving ourselves some broken bones, with our esteem still intact, letting wisdom be the better part of valor, or something like that.

We dove around for a while in the refreshing ocean water and went back to camp around 4:30 p.m. Bingo. Right on time. Ross and I sat down for our early dinner and glanced up at the Mona Lisa window, which by now was becoming addictive. We were abruptly distracted by the familiar sound of airplane props and pops from its engine. The plane maneuvered over the Isthmus, but this time so low that we gave up the food and shower window to run to the other side of the tennis courts. This gave us a clear view of Cat Harbor just in time to see the old Channel Airlines plane barely miss another disaster and skip across the water to safety. "Man, I thought this was it." Again, they continued to surprise. Those Channel Air pilots prided themselves with their exploits of daring flights over dangerous, high-altitude lakes and waterways. With a little touch of the firewater, I think their courage sometimes outmatched common sense.

With the show over, Ross and I retreated back to the dinner table. For whatever reason, I looked back over my shoulder to where we'd just been. Something caught my eye. I'll never forget the sight. Looking back at Cat Harbor, silhouetted between the setting sun and the old army barracks, a horrific spectacle unfolded. Between two of the trees that lined the barracks building, some 100 yards out, I saw what looked like a person hanging from the tree. I turned and yelled to Ross, "Damn!" It took two damns to get his attention away from the Mona Lisa window. He finally turned to see what I was dramatically pointing to. "Look, over there!" Ross followed my extended finger. "What the heck is that?"

We couldn't believe what we were seeing. The vision was right out of a movie scene. So captivating as death can be, yet chilling. We both stood up and slowly leaned forward trying to wrap our minds around what we were looking at. We began to walk tentatively back up to the tennis courts to get a better view, willing to take only enough steps to make out what was hanging, listless between the trees. Whatever it was, it showed no sign of life. As we closed in, it hit us. It was a horse, hanging by its neck.

The fact that we realized it wasn't a person didn't help much, it was just too big, too real or unreal, to comprehend. Upset at the thought of getting any closer, Ross and I ran back into the kitchen and excitedly told my mother what we'd seen. Mom's first words were, "Oh my God, those horses belong to the girls' camp!" Predictably, her first concern was the liability of the baseball camp.

As we led her closer, she could see for herself the awful site, which was now clearly contrasted against the backdrop of the closing day. She quickly turned to me, "Gilly, take a kitchen knife, at least go cut it down."

Now, I'd never cut down anything hanging that was dead, let alone that big. It was the most bizarre and eerie thing I would ever have to do. With nervous trepidation, Ross and I walked over to the grizzly scene. I took out a knife and cut the horse down. Its lifeless body fell limp to the ground. I did my part, now the rest was up to mother.

The horse, we found out later, was ridden by the same guys we'd met up at the corral. They'd tied it up to a high branch and then took off to frolic with the girls. The frolicking must have been good, for they forgot all about the horse. The horse apparently tried to free itself, eventually got tangled up, tripped, lost air, stumbled and hung from the tree until dead.

This was definitely a major incident so the sheriff was called in. Mrs. Cruikshank, the owner of the girls' camp, also needed to be informed, and that would be a difficult conversation. After their parents were notified, the boys had to pay for the horse. They were also instructed to leave the Isthmus or be prosecuted for trespassing along with destroying personal property. Further, the sheriff called back assuring mother they would be more responsive to boys wondering around the Isthmus, especially while the girls were still there.

So, the downside for Ross and I was our newly acquired friendships with the girls were still up in the air. The upside? Our invaders had been sent home and we hadn't lost any prestige over the matter. Quite the contrary, our deed of cutting down the horse only embellished us as compassionate individuals and, at the very least, deserving of some kind of respect. We became champions of humanity, and all the girls began to address us by our first names, and why not?

We were back in the saddle again, a pun of course, no jest intended. However, we needed to salvage our nights out on the beach. Mother didn't let up on her demand that we supervise the clandestine late-night beach activity. "Enough of that kind of excitement," she said. "We certainly don't need anymore." But, this plea from my mother was more like a silent prayer, for intuitively she knew possibly the worst and the best were yet to come.

CHAPTER 9

# When Things Go Wrong

As the day went on, our fortunes were looking good. The prospects with Kimberly and Collin were coming along. The invaders were vanquished from our Isthmus, and our pre-camp setup was progressing well. In fact, so well that, when we sat down with mother in the kitchen, she said just that. "You guys have done a really good job. Everything is looking great. Your dad called and said the camp sessions are filling up rapidly and it looks like most of our senior and junior counselors are committed, along with our divers Pat and Lee.

"What about the lifeguards?" I asked.

"That's in the works. The City of Los Angeles Recreation and Parks superintendent called dad about a certified lifeguard named Johnny Cuevas. He's on a visa from Mexico and wants to attempt swimming the channel by the end of summer. They referred him, and a deal is in the works for me to train him in return for his lifeguard services. We'll see what happens."

For many years, mom and dad supervised the Los Angeles Olympic pool, the one adjacent to the Coliseum. She was a terrific swimmer and instructor.

"And, Gilly, you know what that means?"

I knew what that meant. I'd be spending hours in the bay pacing this Johnny Cuevas guy. That, plus baseball and all the other stuff added up to…it was going to be a busy summer.

"Okay, Mom. Who are the counselors this year?"

"Let's see." She started counting off on her fingers. "There's Shane, cousin Jeff, Dennis, Bilko…"

"Bilko? He's not a camper anymore?"

"No. He'll be staying in the cabin with you boys this year as a counselor."

"How about Tauso, the wrestler?"

"Yes, he'll be here too. Your dad promoted him to head counselor."

"No way!"

"Yes." Mother smiled. "We need somebody to keep you guys in line. And along with Tay Taylor's cousin Ret, we hope that will take the place of your brothers. And then, of course we'll have Billy Tucker. I know with those guys around you'll find a way to create enough interest. Let's make this summer fun, not havoc, this year.

"Havoc? Geez, that's a pretty strong word, Mom."

Looking over at Ross she appealed, "Please keep Gilly from causing us anymore headaches than we already have."

"Me?"

"Yes. You know Gilly sometimes comes up short in the commonsense category."

Betraying me, Ross nodded in agreement.

"Hey Mom, I can tell some stories about Ross. But I'm too good a friend. So, I won't go there."

Ross began to blush.

"Okay, enough about your wild bunch. They'll be here in just three days. So, first and foremost, we need to make sure we have no more incidents like yesterday. It's going to cost those guys

$400. Fortunately, they were nice enough to admit their mistake and go home."

"But, Mom." I laughed. "They had no choice, did they? It was pay up or go to jail."

"Okay, tonight it's back to beach supervision for you boys. Oh, I almost forgot. Guess who's coming in today on Channel Air?"

"Who?"

"Father James."

That was just fine. Father James was well liked, even though he was a little hard to understand with his broken English. I knew him because he worked with my mother at Pious X High School.

"He's going to stay in the cabin below and will hold Sunday mass in camp while he's here."

Sunday mornings a priest would always come to our camp and hold services for all the other camps and boaters who wanted to attend.

"I want you boys to make him feel at home, if he survives the flight," mother added with a laugh. "Gilly, we need to get those cages completed and the backstop raised today, dad's orders. So, get the truck and get over to the ball diamond. Look for Channel Air to arrive around 11 a.m."

"Can't miss that, can we?" I said.

Mom went on. "Then pick up Father James. Okay?"

"Okey dokey, Mom," I replied.

Our 50-percent dirt and 50-percent sand baseball diamond was located about a quarter-mile back at the mouth of Cat Harbor. A hard-packed dirt road, previously used as an airplane landing strip, led from the front of the Isthmus to the back bay. That road had a slight curve at its beginning, however past that it was straight going to the rustic gate.

The old gate seemed out of place and unnecessary, but it really did protect the Isthmus from those ferocious attacks of the movie star Brahma bulls. At least that was its original purpose. We sort of exaggerated the story for the girls because now it was there mainly to slow down trucks. Drivers quite often used this road as a racetrack while on their way to the Isthmus dump or to pick up passengers from Channel Air.

Only the few cautious and more timid drivers could claim their innocence while driving this stretch of road, especially behind the wheel of the Catalina Baseball Camp's pickup. Many fond memories were made and tragedies prevented on that road. Stories about the dangers imposed by the gateposts at the end of its run were awe-inspiring, all of course depending on who was relaying the adventure.

"Boys, after lunch, take the rest of the day off because you're on duty tonight."

Now, full of excitement and forgetting about girls, I jumped up, grabbed the keys and yelled, "I'll drive!"

"No, I will!" Ross argued but eventually gave in as I slid into the driver's seat first. Now, don't get the idea that Ross was any less determined than I or somehow less ambitious. Again, it might just have been the fact that my parents owned the camp. I'm sure if it were otherwise, he would have prevailed.

Jamming the keys into the ignition, then hearing it roar, off we went. When we turned the corner and the road straightened out, I accelerated with the pedal pushed to the floor. Adrenalin raced through my mind, my heart started beating to the rhythm of the racing pistons that easily kept pace with the startled combusting engine. I am, for these pleasure-filled minutes, Mario Andretti. Oh yeah! Ross saw me more as a madman and, I suppose, at this moment, I'm a little of both. I pressed on and saw the old wooden gate. It was open. Nothing left to obstruct my blazing dash except two large posts, well-placed, tree-sized timbers, giving us just enough room to pass through. That wouldn't stop me now. It just intensified the seductive task. This was the thrill of it, hypnotizing and begging me on. I held my breath, not out of hope but out of faith. This act now has become a proclamation to my creditability, a pretense of my arrogance, a testimony to my skill to deliver us once more from a pending peril. So, we pass through, now without even attempting to look at the speedometer; it served no purpose at this moment. Once we passed safely, I grasped the reality of my performance. I slammed on the brakes, to stop the truck from hurling into the back bay. A cloud of dirt covered the truck and its passengers.

Ross looked at me with terminal disgust and, without giving him a chance to comment on my artful driving, I shouted, "We've made it again, Ross! We made it again! It's still there! I still have it!"

Attempting to quickly eject himself from the truck, he looked over at me while opening the door and shouted, "You're crazy! You're crazy!" The second time so loud that anyone from the mainland could hear.

After his unwarranted outburst, we began to transform the back bay wash into a workable baseball field. While erecting the backstop, like we'd done so many times before, nostalgia took over. I sat down for a rest and began to reminisce. There'd been thousands of kids who had played and left memories on that dusty old field. I thought about how many went on to be successful, not only in baseball but in all kinds of professional endeavors. I was abruptly interrupted from my melancholy journey by a cloud of dirt.

Seeing a chance to possibly pay me back a little, Ross dragged the field against the wind. This caused a mini dust storm and covered me from head to foot. He was having fun now.

I yelled as I stood up to fight off the dust. "What the heck are you doing?"

He continued, laughing it up all the while. Then, as it usually does, the sounds of the aircraft proceed itself. Pop, pop, pop. We both saw it now, Channel Air coming over the crest.

"Bet on it!" I yelled. "It's not going to clear the trees!"

"Yeah it will," Ross countered. "I'll bet it hits the sand before it hits the water!"

We were both wrong. This time the plane made it over the trees without grabbing branches along the way. The propellers sputtered, as normal, as the plane glided over the sandy beach, reaching the bay and splashing into the shallows. It just missed a sailboat claiming the right away and causing the pilot to rev-up his twin engines to avoid a collision. He stuck his hand out of the cockpit window to express his dismay. Ross and I broke into applause.

As the plane jettisoned up the ramp, we jumped into the truck, rushed through the gate and drove over to the back bay to pick up Father James. He was the first to climb out of the cramped seven-seat amphibious plane and seemed about to lose his balance as he stretched out his legs to reach the first step to safety.

"Looks like Father James has just been born again."

Ross laughed at my joke.

Instead of kneeling down to kiss the ground, he looked up and made the sign of the cross. It seemed, as a confirmation of faith, that only God could have played a part in this breathtaking flying adventure. The plane simply slid empty back into the bay and, as fast as it came, disappeared into the sky.

Using his broken English Father James greeted us with, Giiillleee! Gooood to seeee you!"

"Father James, good to see you too." I introduced Ross as my good friend.

While walking to the truck he asked, "What school do you go to Ross?"

"I just graduated from St. John Vianney."

Father replied, "Good school, good school." Now Father James showed a little humor and sense of timing with, "Giiillleee, wasn't that the school you were expelled from?"

"That's the one, Father." I laughed. "How did you know?"

With a warm smile he answered, "Oooooh Giiillleee, your mother shares all the things her boys have done."

"Okaaaay, let's get back to camp. It's almost time to eat."

This time I tossed the keys to Ross and allowed him to drive. Now in the care of one of God's disciples, Ross, of course, was compelled to display his conservative driving skills. He took it slow, pausing at every tree as if it were a stop sign. Mother was clearly relieved to see him at the wheel when we drove up to the camp. She greeted Father with a wave, and he called out, "Virginia, gooood to see you!"

After we stopped and he stepped out of the truck, Mother asked with concern, "Father, did you have a pleasant flight?"

"Yes, Virginia, with God's help." This time we all laughed.

"Let Gilly and Ross take you to the lower cabin and get you set up. Then, when you're ready, come on up and have lunch with us."

After setting up Father James, we rushed back to camp. The hectic morning almost made us forget about the girls.

"Whoops, where are they?"

Ross stuck out three fingers and exclaimed, "Only three more days left! We need to get things going. But, first let's have lunch."

We sat down at our usual table to watch our Mona Lisa art show, offered by a few girls taking midday showers. Suddenly, Father James stepped in between the view, and, with lunch tray in hand, he asked, "Since there are just us few boys here, is it okay to sit and eat with you guys?"

Ross looked bewildered, not wanting to let on to our mealtime entertainment just a few feet away. I recovered first by suggesting, "Sure Father, sit here," placing him with his back to the window. As the meal progressed, Father continued on, inquiring about this and that while the scene just over his shoulder continued on. Ross and I sweated out the lunch and kept Father James from turning around by bombarding him with all kinds of facts and questions. This resulted in Father finding us very congenial and attentive, feeling quite comfortable and appreciated. He stood to leave and, just as we were about to congratulate ourselves on our performance, the good Father leaned back in and said, "This is fun. Do you mind if I sit here for all of the meals while I'm here?"

What could we say? We resigned to come up with a whole lot of stuff to talk about during mealtimes, in order to keep him from discovering our furtive treat.

After lunch, I helped Ross quickly clean the restrooms then bolted to the cabin and changed for the beach. Next, we ran down to the snack bar and ordered malts from Linda. After surveying the room and not seeing our girls inside, we pushed on to the beach. There they were, sunning on the float. We resisted the urge to wave at them for fear of letting on to the other girls on shore.

After greeting the girls on the beach, we dove in and swam over to the float. As usual, I reached it first and hopped up the ladder. I pretended to be looking down into the clear blue Isthmus water as Ross finally climbed up the ladder. Without looking directly at the girls, I said a casual, "Hi there." There was an awkward pause, so I added, "Sorry, we've been really busy lately. But, we missed you girls. What's been going on?"

Kimberly answered, "We thought you guys lost interest."

Ross attempted to explain our neglect. "No, no. It's just Gil's mother and dad have us doing all kinds of things to get ready for the summer baseball camp. And, I'm sure you know about what happened with the horse and the boys from your school. We've been busy helping keep everything under control. But, tonight, after lights out?"

"I'm game!" Kimberly jumped in.

"Me too!" Collin added.

As we started to sit down, Kimberly then Collin found refuge from the searing sun by diving into the water. We stayed alone on the float for a few minutes then dove back in and swam to shore. Our popularity was growing with the other girls on the beach, so we stayed and talked well after Kimberly and Collin had left. Later, walking back up to the kitchen, we felt good knowing we had our ducks all lined up for tonight.

We were told by mom to go over and pick up the camp food supplies from Taylor's restaurant. That's where the deliveries were dropped off and, because the regular sessions were just a few days away, they'd started coming in at a greater pace now. Our main crew, along with my father, would arrive in three days on the water taxi. It was all working out and the final touches were almost done, allowing the camp to start without a hitch. Sometime, within those three precious days, Ross and I wanted to have a few good tales to flaunt to the guys.

Dinner with Father James, sitting in his now official seat with his back to the window, was full of our ramblings. After eating, Father spent some time with mother in the kitchen and then retreated to his lower cabin to rest. On our way back to our cabin, I asked, "So Ross, when we go to confession, do we need to tell Father about the window? How we purposely placed his back to it?"

"What do you think God thinks about it, Gilly?"

"Well, I think," now trying to rationalize our misdeeds, "God, made woman for man and He liked them, right?"

"What?" Ross asked while squinting at me.

"It says so, in the Bible."

"Where?"

"Somewhere in Genesis and then in the Song of Solomon."

"Solomon?" What are you talking about, Gilly?"

"Well read it, dummy! Solomon had this thing for girls' breasts, like cherries and grapes."

"Gilly, you don't know what you're talking about."

"Yeah? Don't you remember all those catechism classes we sat together at St. John's? I bet you slept through them."

"No I didn't!"

"Yeah, you did, or you would have known about Solomon."

Ross shot back, now laughing, "At least I wasn't kicked out of St. John's. So, you must have gotten something wrong."

"Well, that's another story."

"I bet you can find some Bible verse to back you up there too, right?"

"Ross, you missed the point!"

"No I didn't. I got the point, but I don't agree with your point, and, as usual, you don't know what you're talking about!"

"Look, Ross. All I said was God created these girls for our pleasure."

"No, He said...." Ross paused trying to figure out exactly what God really said about the issue.

"I'm right. See?"

"No way, that's nonsense!"

"Okay, Ross. Then you're right. So, when you get into confession, you tell Father what you did and then you ask him what God said about that."

"Yeah, sure I will," Ross said with a smile. Getting nowhere, we just moved on.

We stepped into the hot cabin and sat down on our bunks. The conservation led to the girls and sketching out our next move. "How far do you think we'll get with these girls?" Ross asked.

"Scary question," I thought.

"We did make out for a brief moment. So what's next?"

"Which one do you want me to answer first, Ross? I have to admit you've gotten just a little more up the road with Kimberly then I have with Collin."

"How do you know that?"

"Cause I haven't gotten very far. That's why." After an awkward pause, I continued, "So, how far have you gotten, Ross?"

"You don't know how far I've gotten, and I'm not going to tell you. Gilly, let your BB brain fill in the dots."

Just then Carla, my mother's favorite helper, pounded on the cabin door. This surprised us because she was the first girl to wander out to our cabin. It was on the no-no list. Ross opened the door. "What are you doing? You know, it gets pretty dangerous out here."

"Why?" she asked tersely.

"Well, see that old restroom up there?" Now pointing to an old dilapidated bathroom about 50 yards back in the trees, "That's where they found the body and now they say that restroom is haunted."

"No way."

"Yes way!" Ross continued. "And, if you want, before lights out tonight, I'll take some of you girls out there and we can look for the ghost."

"What?"

"You do believe in ghosts, don't you?" Ross asked with a serious tone.

"No, of courses not."

"Okay, then you have nothing to fear. Meet us up here just after dark."

"All right," she agreed. "But you better get in the kitchen right away. Mrs. Lefebvre wants to see you guys."

"What about?" I called from my bunk.

Carla turned to leave, "She didn't say. She just told me to go get you guys."

We quickly ran back to the kitchen. "Gilly, I know you boys have been busy, but I still feel uncomfortable about some of these girls. Are you okay with spending the night on the beach in your sleeping bags?"

"Yes, Mom, we are and don't worry; we'll handle it."

Mother went on. "Rumors are, the girls want to have a party on the beach tonight and that spells trouble."

"But, Mom, didn't we just confiscate all the booze from the girls?"

"I know, but it's a party, whatever that means. So, let's not let this one get away from us tonight."

"Ooooookay." Ross and I looked at each other knowingly. This wasn't bad news and wouldn't complicate our social life that much; in fact it gave us a very good reason to be out and about the Isthmus late at night. Trying not to sound too happy about it, I said, "Mom, don't worry. We'll take care of the beach tonight."

Off we went. But, I got to thinking about Carla and the ghost thing. "Hey Ross, let's go down to the boat shop and see Ty."

"Why?"

"Because, I got an idea, and you're going to like it."

I can't remember the Isthmus without Ty Ewing or his family. He started to work for Birt in the boat shop and, from then on, they went hand in hand. Any boater who ever came to the Isthmus would sooner or later run into Ty and, when they did, they were blessed to have known him. Ty became a mainstay and one of the few who took up residence in the Isthmus year round.

Sure enough, Ty was at the shop and, as usual, hard at work. "Can we borrow the cannon? Just for tonight?" He thought for a moment and, since there were only a few boats moored in the harbor, replied, "I don't have it, never did. It belongs to that crazy Dave Wells. I think he left it somewhere in the back storage room. If you want to look, go ahead. But, I don't know anything about this, right?"

"Right, thanks Ty! It's just a prank we're playing on the girls up at camp," I said to reassure him.

Dave Wells, one of the Isthmus summer workers, was an erratic character. He acquired a small cannon that was used the previous summer. Late at night, when the boaters were fast asleep, he would shoot it off into the air. The noise was so loud that it echoed throughout the coves and sounded like one of the boats had exploded. Lights went on and people woke up; it was a great joke to us. But, awoken late at night and fearing for the worst, the boat people went crazy looking for the pranksters. The cannon was hidden away, and they never caught the culprits.

Sure enough, we found the cannon and set it up in the old vacant bathroom. We added some dead fish guts we found in the garbage behind the snack bar. After throwing the guts and stuff on the bathroom walls for effect, we hid the cannon in one of the toilet stalls. Just as the girls would go in and get all squeamish, we would shoot off the cannon, hopefully scaring them to death.

So, just after dark, the girls came knocking on our cabin door. We played it out to a tee. Just when the girls started to gasp from seeing and smelling dead fish, I slipped into the back stall. While they listened to Ross telling the story, I pulled the cord to the cannon. The sound caromed off the walls and echoed, bringing it up to another level. The girls got what they came for. They were scared out of their shorts and away they ran. If it had been in the middle of summer, all hell would have broken loose. But now, with barely anyone around the Isthmus, hardly anyone else even noticed. With ears still ringing, Ross and I quickly gathered up the cannon, hid it away and found our way down to the beach. "Good timing!" Ross said, as he slapped me on the back.

We laid out our sleeping bags and nestled between two palm trees on the beach. They acted as centurions, protecting us from the late offshore breeze that came through the Isthmus almost every night. On the sand, with the ocean splashing just a few yards away, it was a cozy place, but we didn't want to fall asleep. We had to keep our late night date.

The silence was broken as a group of girls passed by on their way to an isolated stretch of beach. We slid out of our sleeping bags and began to follow, undetected. We found a bluff just above them as they laid out their towels. The moon reflected across the water and gave us ample lighting to see what they were doing below. They seemed to be in a jovial mood as they played around and laughed.

Ross leaned over and whispered, "I think they're smashed."

"Ya think?" I whispered back.

Just then, one girl must have suggested a night swim because, in unison, the girls began to slip out of their clothes. I stood up and said, "Uh-oh, they're going to try and swim out to the float... drunk. Let's go, show time!" We raced down the bluff yelling, "No, no, no!" By this time the girls were in all stages of undress, some in bras and panties, some further along than that. Some had already peeled down to their birthday suits and began their plunge into the night's black waters. It was out of control! Ross and I waded in and started pulling slippery, squealing girls out of the water one by one. Once we had them safely onshore and dressed, our task was made easy by the fact that now they were afraid they might be sent home for this drunken rampage. They quickly began to sober up at that prospect. Hoping to rectify the problem and get on with our night's plan, I thought it might be a good idea to negotiate. "Girls, if you get back to camp unnoticed, right now...not a word, from me and Ross. Otherwise, you'll have a problem. Deal?"

Seeing the wisdom of our proposition, they choose the deal. One of the girls took charge and encouraged them to get all of their things together. That done, they stumbled quietly back to camp.

We found our place on the beach and sat down on top of our sleeping bags while we waited for lights out. Ross and I had just about caught our breath when again we were disrupted...this time, in a more dramatic fashion. Out from the dark sky burst a Coast Guard helicopter. Its loud engine roared overhead as white searchlights scanned the area and red lights sparkled. It was heading in the direction of the camp!

We jumped up and ran over just in time to catch the helicopter's descent. The swirling noise of its blades created such a loud sound that Ross and I found it hard to talk to each other. As it continued down, whatever was beneath was swept away. Then, as it landed, all kinds of things were flung about. Landing skids came to rest in the field adjacent to the camp. The whirling continued while two paramedics climbed out and sprinted by, staying low, just under the rotor blades for safety. They carried a stretcher as they quickly advanced up and across the road, over another mound in front of the camp and then proceeded up the camp's ramp and into the dormitory. Waiting for a brief time outside, we'd now become simply spectators to this awesome spectacle. In seconds, the stretcher was pulled out of the camp, down the ramp, across the road, loaded into the copter and, as quickly as it came, it departed.

We stood in dazed stillness for a few moments, then rushed up the steps to find mother. Fortunately, she'd been a paramedic instructor for the City of Los Angeles, so she calmly filled us in. "The girls had been drinking. One of them, under stress by the recent graduation, her future in question and an estranged relationship, had succumbed to a nervous breakdown. She needed immediate medical attention." Mother had already spoken to her parents. They weren't surprised because their daughter had a similar episode just before leaving on this trip. The parents were sorry for the trouble and thankful that mother recognized the symptoms and took care of the issue so quickly. That was my mother, I thought, always in control.

Her calmness reminded me of the time when she was at home making a dress or something on the sewing machine and somehow ran a needle all the way through her finger. She merely stopped the machine, cut the string to free her finger, came into my room, pliers in hand, and said, "Gilly, here, pull it out for me." I immediately fainted and hit a table edge on the way down, bruising my head. When revived, mother first gave a good laugh, then calmly took the pliers and attended to herself by yanking the needle out of her finger. Mom liked telling that story, and, yeah I just about fainted every time she told it.

After all the unexpected excitement, Ross and I once again found our way back to the beach, still hoping to revive our blooming romances. Again, we lay still under the stars, now struggling to avoid falling asleep. Again, a noise came from the bushes. It sounded like something or someone had stumbled on a rock or run into a tree. We looked at each other and said, "The girls?" We jumped out of our sleeping bags for the third time now. Out popped Father James. "Hi, boys," he said, clearly a little disorientated. "I must have hit a tree back there somewhere. I thought you might like to have some company tonight, out here alone on the beach." Well, what can you say to a priest, except, "Of course, Father."

"Good. Okay. I'll go back and get my sleeping bag." And, off he went. I flopped down in the sand and said, "What the hell? He's going to sleep here all night! Our night's gone." I grabbed a rock and threw it into the night. "Wait, let's think about this

WHEN THINGS GO WRONG • 105

for minute." Then it came to me. "Let's gather a bunch of rocks and put them in the sand and, when Father James finds out it's too uncomfortable, he'll return to his soft bed, back in the cabin. So, we did just that. After searching around the dark we found and planted some big rocks and camouflaged our deed. This night was getting out of hand. An amusing thought came across my mind. I razed Ross, "When you go to confession, you've got even more things to explain to the good Father." We both couldn't stop laughing at that thought.

Father James returned shortly with sleeping bag in hand. And, we directed him to lay it down on the very spot we'd just sabotaged. With all of us now on the ground looking up at the stars, I attempted to quiet my guilt by asking, "Father, what does God have planned for me?" Father began to talk in noticeable English, distracted by his native language. "Geeeelly, it's all in God's hands."

"But, what about me, Father? What do I do? Nothing, if it's all in His hands? What's the purpose?" I garbled on. "Do I have any control here then? I mean, if He's in charge, what am I here for?"

"What do you mean, Geeellly?"

"Why am I here and why am I different than someone else?"

"Geeellly, that's a question that eeeach of us must work out with God, by himself. I cannot answer that for you. I just know He's there and He cares. I wouldn't be here if He didn't. The Bible says that God so loved the world. That means you and me. Geeellly, that's' enough to make me know how important I am to Him. St. John Vianney said," and this got Ross's attention, "We have nothing of our own but our will. It is the only thing that God has so placed in our power that we can make an offering of it to Him."

That went way over my head, at least for this night. However, I would come back to those important words time and time again, later in life. Feeling the conversation had run its course and had lost steam, my thoughts turned back to the situation at hand. "Father, you've had a long day. Get some rest."

"Yes, Geeellly, I have." And with that, we all said, "goodnight." I turned over, pulled my sleeping bag up over my head and lay still, pretending to fall asleep.

Time passed. Then Ross pulled at my sleeping bag, looked at me and cocked his head over toward Father James. He was finally sound asleep. While slowly slipping away in complete silence, we were halted by a soft crunch in the sand. "Oops. We must have woken him up. We'll just tell him we need to patrol the beach for a little while," I said. But, just then Collin and Kimberly came out of the bushes. They'd gotten tired of waiting for us. We went over the circumstances of the night with them but it really didn't matter now, so away we went, walking hand in hand down the beach.

At the water's edge Ross snuggled with Kimberly then headed off into the dark. Collin and I did the same, but in the opposite direction. We talked for a short time, but our anticipation turned into an embrace. A sense of immediacy took over, as we plundered into each other. I had no idea what Ross was doing. It'd been awhile since I'd heard a word from over there. The warmth of Collin, along with the balmy summer night Isthmus air, was working on us, adding to the problem and was about to take over the situation. Any sense of reason began to vanish. As we began to explore beyond the kiss and find our way, Collin, like the times before, became distressed by the fast moving progression of our courtship. Not wanting it to get out of hand, she suggested, "Let's cool off."

"Okay. But, how do we that?"

"The float."

"The float?"

"Yes, let's swim to the float." And with that she got up, peeled down to her bra and panties and dove in. I did the same and we both swam out to the float. After helping each other up, we kissed again and began to talk. Looking out to the lights that outline the mainland, I said, "Hey, this gives us the best of both worlds." We talked on through the night as the moon flashed across the water and the stars displayed their splendor. The noise of each passing swell surrounding the bobbing float was a constant reminder of where we were. We laid back in the dark, taken in by the scene from the heavens and talked on about our future dreams. When we'd run out of conversation and night was cutting us short by the impending sunrise, we swam to shore, dressed and then went to find Ross. When we finally found them, they acted very cordial and appeared quite satisfied with each other's performance that night.

We walked them up and departed from the front of the snack shop. The girls left for the camp, and we had to slip back down and into our sleeping bags, hoping not to wake Father James. Ross and I had little time to compare stories, but, what the heck, I thought. This story's not over yet. Anyway, we'll have a lot of time, the rest of the summer to talk about this night.

CHAPTER 10

# What's a Bra Strap For?

M other let us sleep in the next morning. But only after I complained, "With all the goings-on, Ross and I didn't have a chance to rest. It was pleasant having Father James on the beach. But, he talked throughout the night, discussing our spiritual health." Now, that was a great white lie and something that needed confessing. And, I told Ross so.

It was around eight o'clock when my mother's trusting errand girl, Carla, who seemed a little too eager to bang on our cabin door, did just that. I opened the door in a sleepy haze and said, "What now Carla?"

"Your mother…"

"Okay," I interrupted, not waiting for her to continue with the message.

"Tell her we'll get to the kitchen in a few minutes." I added, "Carla, you don't have to bang on the door like that. Do it again and we'll sic that ghost on you like last night." We laughed.

She started in, but I cut her off again as I shut the door. "See you later, Carla."

"Not if I can help it," she sang on her way back to the kitchen. When she was far enough away I mumbled, "Kiss ass."

"So, this is a first," I suggested to Ross, whose eyes were just beginning to find the daylight. I continued staring at him.

"What? What are you looking at?"

"You."

"Why?"

"Why, you ask me!" I shot back. Then a sly smile came across my face. He knew what I was about to say. "So, Ross, tell me about last night."

"What about it?"

"Well, for one, you disappeared on the beach with Kimberly and we had to go looking for you!"

"So, what's that supposed to mean? Besides, what were you and Collin doing…academics?"

"Ross, for your information we just swam to the float and talked for a while. But you… cough it up! What happened? I've got to know."

"No you don't!"

"Come on, man. I always share with you. Don't I?"

"Okay. So we kissed for a while."

I deserved more details than that, so I prompted him on. "Did you get a feel?"

"What do you mean, 'get a feel?'"

I laughed. "You damn well know what I mean! That girl's so front loaded. They must have gotten in your way." Ross started to smile, the way he always does when I'm really getting to him. I went on, "Well, you know what my cousin Jeff says about this."

"I don't care what your cousin Jeff says!"

"Good, so then let me tell you what he says. 'All girls have different attributes,'" now literally keeping this conversation above the belt, "'And, whatever's their best attribute, that's what they like to show first.'"

"Yeah, so you've said. So what's your point, Gilly?"

"Well, Kimberly is well endowed, right?"

"Okay, got it."

"So what happened Ross?" Now, we both were laughing. "How are they?"

"They were nice. But…" Ross gave a thoughtful pause and continued. "It's those stupid bra straps."

"What are you talking about bra straps for?"

"Well, I couldn't, um, unhook it."

He was sincere now. I couldn't help but give him a pep talk. I stood up with my finger in the air. "See? There you are. Women think we guys understand all that stuff because we're supposed to be the mechanics, and they're the romantics. But, we really know very little about those…bra straps! Look, even the good girls go to the store and buy those sexy bras. Some hook in the front, some in the back, some just pull down, and for what? They say… to protect their breasts. But, what are they really for? Now, us guys, when we play sports we wear jock straps. We know what they're for, right? The girls say they have a reason too. They need support, just like us. But, what's with the foam rubber to raise them up? Besides that, bras come in all kinds of colors and some are transparent to help us see what they're hiding. What's the deal? Also, there's another problem. If a guy walks down the street or sits on the beach and looks at those shoved-up, protruding girls… if she likes him, great. But, if he stares at her and she doesn't like him, well, he's a pervert!"

I sat back down on the bunk. "It's really a tough call for us guys. I have no idea what the rules really are. I guess you just have to take your chances. But, there are two things I do know. One, getting past the bra issue is a remarkable milestone. The other, it's rather peculiar how a guy's amorous admiration for a girl's cleavage can so quickly turn into a case of sexual harassment, which ironically depends entirely on who's doing the looking."

Ross nodded in agreement, like I was really on to something. When I got older, I still found this troubling. But when I was young, it was almost impossible to get the signals right.

I wasn't through. "This bra thing, girls have no idea how much esteem we lose, when we try to look cool while nonchalantly fumbling about with that stupid hook. Until the girl gives up, reaches back and does it herself. Maybe that's the plan all along. Because now, she knows she's in control. Now she's got the clicker to the remote." I chuckled a little as I finished. "I've been there a few times, but never made it past that milestone." He looked at me genuinely surprised, that in the past few days he'd made more headway then I ever had. I think this helped his ego a lot.

As we walked over to the kitchen, Ross had a new flair about him, a new strut. It was this newfound confidence that somehow, I knew, I would have to deal with.

Mother told us to hurry up and get our breakfast. We were to drive into Avalon and pick up bread, milk and other supplies. "You can take a few girls with you. A couple of them want to see Little Harbor, and you can drop them off on the way. I don't think they can get into any kind of trouble way out there. Make sure you remember to pick them up on the way back."

"Sure, Mom." And we began to walk out the door.

She wasn't through. "By the way, Gilly, did you hear a loud noise early last night?"

"No, not really."

"Well, it sounded like an explosion. You wouldn't know anything about that, would you?" I couldn't keep the smile down. She knew. Raising her hands over her head while she walked back to the freezer, she added, "I don't even want to hear about it."

We grabbed a plate and filled it with leftover pancakes, scrambled eggs and sausage, then walked down to our eating table. In route, I continued my inquisition about last night. When

Ross started to open his mouth, we heard, "Goooood morning." We looked over to see the omnipresent Father James, standing at the table. After sitting down in our designated seats, with the window to his back, his first comment was, "I don't think I'll be able to keep you company on the beach tonight."

"Why Father?" I asked?.

"I'm much too stiff and sore. I guess there are way toooo many rooocks out there." We choked on our food, caused by a good mix of guilt and humor. Ross recovered and asked Father if he was going to give confession before Sunday service. Father said he was and stood to leave. "Well, Virginia's got me calling the parents of last night's unfortunate girl. So, I'll talk to you later, boys." After he picked up his plate and moved on, I said in jest, "Ross, you Italian Catholic... you need to confess, don't you."

"Who me?"

"You're hiding something from me, Ross. You got more from Kimberly than just learning how to unhook a bra didn't you?"

He laughed. "Maybe." Now parading his secret like an arrogant peacock, he added, "You'll never know."

"What do you mean, 'I'll never know?' Yes I will." You'll tell me."

"Why?"

"Because you owe it to me."

"For what?"

"For getting you here, that's for what!"

He smiled, picked up his empty plate and chucked it into the trash. "Okay, let's go check out the truck."

We got lucky. The girls picked up rumors from the snack bar that Boy Scout camp leaders and their pre-camp crew were due in the Isthmus this morning. These felines were hungry, practically starving, for some kind of male companionship. One of the girls had a brother in the mix so they knew when the boat arrived, around 11 a.m. Something was in the works because, when Mother announced a trip to Little Harbor was on the agenda, only a few girls signed on for the excursion. The rest would rather stay in the Isthmus to check out the boys. Of course, our girls were in, so we didn't care.

Ross and I flipped coins to see who would drive with three girls squeezed in the cab and the others in the back, then we took off with Ross at the wheel. Little Harbor is really two coves broken up by a stretch of land facing the open sea and located on the backside or windward side of the island. One of the two coves is called Shark Bay. This is where Pacific swells channel toward the shore, forming waves big enough to crest and break onto the beach. Few people know about its great body surfing. The next cove over is actually Little Harbor. Its calm waters make for good swimming, snorkeling and mooring of boats. But most boaters rarely stray to the backside of the island, due to radically changing sea conditions. The remote location and secluded beaches make it one of the most seductive paradises for sunbathers on the west coast. Located seven miles away, almost at midpoint between the Isthmus and Avalon, it creates a perfect place to cook the daily catch or sit for hours roasting marshmallows over a campfire.

The dusty road to get there leads out of the Isthmus and up to a summit. It's a great location to pause and take in the panoramic view across the miles of ocean to the mainland. The girls, dressed in halter tops, shorts and tennis shoes, poured out of the truck to soak in the scene. Ross and I, in our shorts, flip-flops and T-shirts with "Catalina Baseball Camp" printed on the back, gladly joined them and stayed long enough for them to snap a few pictures. We drove down through the central part of the island. It's quite a dissolute area except for a few cactus patches and frequent clues of animals here and there. The drive is a bouncing, arduous trip along the ruddy, winding one-lane road. But we hardly noticed because we're always in high spirits on our way to Little Harbor.

After coming around a corner, Ross jumped on the brakes and switched off the truck. Everyone gasped. Some 40 yards up the road stood three Brahma bulls. After a minute, Ross turned the engine back on and slowly inched toward them. One by one they raised their heads and looked straight at us. Then, as if they knew the routine, they casually walked off the road and let us pass. We moved on until I could see a wisp of fog just beyond the mountain. I knew we were almost there because, as the Pacific breeze comes in contact with the island's inland heat, it always creates a fog bank. The good thing is, the sun usually burns it off by late morning.

Arriving at Little Harbor is always a treat. The closer you get, the more you feel its presence. I'm not sure if it's the sea air or the smell of the beach that tickles your senses, but you know it's there even before you hear the waves breaking on the shore. Shark Bay is revealed first from the bluff above. After stopping a safe distance from the edge, we all climbed out of the truck with anticipation. The vision was concealed until we inched closer and then all the wonders of paradise revealed themselves.

There the ocean races up and becomes wedged in on both sides by the bluff that leads to the beach. Large crescent waves come crashing onto the waiting hot sand. With over 300 yards of shoreline, it's really one of Catalina's best kept secrets.

We left the girls with swimming apparel in hand and those big bags. Two of the girls carried the basket mother loaded full of drinks and sandwiches for the duration of the trip. Waving goodbye, we continued on, crossing up about halfway between Little Harbor and Avalon to El Rancho Escondido. The road improved as we reached Catalina's popular Airport in the Sky. Appropriately named because it's located on the very highest island mountain, making landing and taking off quite an exhilarating, if not a frightening, experience. It's like landing and taking off on an aircraft carrier, but with a 1,000-foot drop on both sides.

After the airport, we drove down through a valley, where fruit trees lined the sides of the road. As usual, Ross stopped the truck. I jumped out and grabbed a few apples and plums. This would be our arsenal for the upcoming roadside mirrors that help guide travelers downhill on the winding single-lane, narrow road into Avalon. The mirrors were placed at hairpin curves, allowing the driver just enough time to see anything coming from the opposite direction. But, our intention while moving along was to unleash our arsenal of fruit on those poor defenseless mirrors. Mind you, they rarely broke. They were far too rugged. But, it was just the possibility that kept us trying each time we traveled this way. It was like a carnival feat, knock down bottles or hit a target and you get a prize. Obviously, no prizes would be given, just a new story to embellish back at the Isthmus.

In Avalon, we picked up our supplies, fuelled up at Pebbly Beach and then began to retrace our way back to Little Harbor. While we drove on, plans for tonight's strategy took shape. Boy Scout counselors already took notice of the girls' presence, so we knew the snack bar would be hopping. But, that didn't matter to us. We already had our girls staked out. With all this going on, it would give us our best chance to break from the pack and finally get quality time with the girls. "I tell you, Ross, it's going to happen tonight."

"It has to; it's the girls' last night on the island."

Once we returned to Little Harbor, we dashed over the bluff with towels in hand and spotted the girls. They were adorned only in their skimpy bathing suits while lying on the sand and reading books.

Seeing us now, Collin stood up, exposing her well-trimmed, sun-baked body to me. Kimberly was lying on her back, her head pillowed with that big bag she always carried, shaded only by sunglasses and a few inches of cloth. Need I say more?

As the day wore on, we challenged them to body surf with us. Then, we strolled hand in hand along the beach, not worrying about tomorrow. We talked of little things that really didn't matter as we treasured the moment, grabbing every minute, as if it were all we had. Later, the other girls returned to the truck from their hiking adventures to the outer points of the bluff surrounding the bay.

Most of these girls were preparing to work the summer and then take off in all directions for college. You had a feeling that, unlike Ross and me, they were now looking forward to getting back home and getting on with life.

We arrived back at the Isthmus just before the dinner bell. After a quick thank you, the girls rushed to change and shower for the evening. Ross and I unloaded the truck, put the milk in the giant kitchen refrigerator, stacked all of the bread in the storage room and then raced to pick up a plate of food. As we sat down to enjoy a good meal, we paid no attention to what was going on around us. There were more important things to worry about tonight.

After dinner, as expected, the girls dressed for the party. Covert conversations with the scout crew became an epidemic in camp. Even mother picked up on it and gave in to the girls. After all, it was their last night. The girls did their best to present themselves and applied more war paint than normal. They gathered together and swished down to the snack bar.

About the time, Ross and I finished with dinner dishes, mother came over. "Okay, boys. I'm sure you're probably going to the party. You should know I've talked to Howard Mays, the scout coordinator, along with Sherriff Riley and our chaperons. They said they would all be out and about to handle any problems that might come up. Let's keep our fingers crossed. I'm just hoping everyone can enjoy themselves. I set a 10 p.m. curfew. But, you know how that goes when gals and guys get together."

"It'll be okay, Mom. Don't worry."

"Well, I hope you're right. We don't need any more incidents like last night."

"Good night. Mom."

Ross and I cleaned up in rapid fashion, now jubilant and toying with all kinds of fantasies. By the time we arrived and found our girls, the party was in full swing. The night moved on with the jukebox playing out one rock 'n' roll song after another. I just stood around feeling a little inadequate because dancing was something that didn't come easy for me. So, I marked time with Collin, just hoping to slip out the back and get into the dark with her. However, I remembered what my mother said and thought I'd better stick around until this thing broke up. Then, I could get on with the night. But, when the music slowed to Johnny Mathis, I felt comfortable and danced, snuggling up to Collin and swaying to the music. Then the snack bar staff turned off the jukebox and began to shut the doors.

After curfew came and went, leaders attempted to put a stop on the evening by shooing everyone home as quickly as possible, hoping to shut down the chemistry brought on by the night. This became more of a formidable task than they expected. For, this was the girls' last chance to tie up loose ends, quickly make promises and exchange names, addresses and phone numbers. Eventually, most of the crowd disappeared back into the dark, flashlights in hand attempting to find their camps. While a few of the scouts, wanting to prolong the night, meandered to the end of the pier, finding only… the end. Then, looking for something to do, they began to peel out of their clothes and dare each other to jump from the pier into the water below. The height of the pier and the distance to the poorly lit black water made the challenge even more intriguing. A few of them, like the girls the night before, had consumed a fair amount of alcohol, too much for their own good. This would only serve to make matters more complicated.

As Ross and I strolled down the pier with our girls in hand, still under the auspices that we were on patrol, rounding up girls who were attempting to stay out past curfew, we heard the ruckus at the end of the pier. Concerned it might involve some of the girls, we moved closer, only to find ourselves confronted by a few flamboyant, inebriated scouts challenging us to make the jump. Now, Ross and I had no problem here. For, we had dove off this pier many times before. This was our home turf. Except, this wasn't the time. We had other things on our minds. But, the scouts wouldn't allow us to back off. It just wasn't going to happen. One scout stepped out of the dark and said, "Hey, you pussy baseball guys, what's the matter? Height scares you?" From there it all started to go downhill. A few more insults were thrown our way. That didn't matter. We knew they were intoxicated, just harmless fools. But one grabbed Collin's arm and said, "She's mine or she's going in the water!"

My good friend Ross always said, "You can see it in Gil's eyes, just before his temper explodes." And he was right. Enough was enough. I lunged into the scout and shoved the fool backward, off the pier. He went flying into the water below. When he surfaced he began screaming profanities at me. While scrambling up on the float he also worked in some more verbal threats. I recognized him now. It was Randall. He continued to yell while bursting up the ramp, "You shithead! Let's see how good you really are! You pussy!"

I raised my hand to protest. "Randall this is not the time!" This was not my play for this night. I attempted to back off. Hoping the cool water, combined with a little levity, would change things,

I said, "How's the water? See any fish down there?" But, he wouldn't quit. When he drew closer, I reached out my hand. Not as an apology. No way. Just as an offering to shake hands, attempting to find some Boy Scout virtue left in him. But, to no avail, the threats continued. Then, he was in my face, and he pressed on.

I said, "No man, not tonight. You don't want this, Randall!" Feeling boxed into a corner by his advance, my pride had been brought into question. When he began to poke a finger into my chest, I said, "What the hell… it's your ass." This had gone too far. Now, I had to deal with it. So, I did. My temper offered me a quick response. I stunned the drunken scout with a few appropriate punches and we were on. Ross and I were left with the envious task of taking on the remaining scouts. Ross caught one in an awkward position and pushed over him over the side, while I came to terms with Randall. It didn't last but a few minutes, though it seemed like an eternity. Traces of blood began to appear along with scraped knuckles and torn shirts on both sides of the struggle. Finally, out of nowhere a fellow scout jumped in and said, "Quit this!"

He was obviously someone of authority because everyone stopped when he spoke. "Randall, you've had your fun. It's time to go." Then, reacting to Randall's reluctance to heed his command, he grabbed him by the back of his shirt and said, "We don't need this kind of trouble. Move on back to the camp, and I mean right now!" It wasn't God's voice out there that night, but it was surely one Randall believed was sent by Him, because he scurried off the pier in a hurry. The leader turned to me and Ross and said, "I hope this will be the end of this." I nodded in agreement, that neither one of us wanted it to go any further. "Okay then." He turned and walked off the pier.

I thought the night was going to be a wash. Putting our tempers on display and exposing our violent side could cause romance to be the real casualty tonight. My hand was bruised and bleeding and Ross's nose was pelting out blood. I turned to Ross and smiled as we walked off the pier, feeling rather grand now, regardless of the cost. "That was a good fight." He returned the smile.

You see, Ross and I had done this together many times before. In fact, on Friday nights, under the lights with a grandstand full of people to cheer us on. Then, it was about defending the pride of our school. This night was about defending our girls. It was all about principles, wasn't it? Except, we really didn't know which ones. It's interesting when the fighting begins how things get messy. What you're fighting for sometimes gets lost and the only thing that matters is who wins. After the carnage and the point is settled, we still needed more. A belief that helped us make it seem alright. That's all that we needed in those days.

As we slowly walked to camp, to my surprise, all the excitement only helped push Collin and our relationship forward. Her nurturing instinct, which I was pleased to be the recipient of, kicked in. She carefully nursed me along the way. When we arrived at camp, the lights were off and all was quiet. Collin suggested that we wait about an hour and then return to their tent. Wow. What a turn of events! Ross and I stepped back into our cabin and began to summarize the events. Filled with expectation, I said, "Ross, our motto tonight is the bra strap! Remember how to unhook it!" We laughed uncontrollably and the thrill of pending romance emanated from the tips of our noses to the bottoms of our feet.

After waiting out the hour, we turned off the light and radio. We opened the door to the pitch-black night then proceeded to make the 100-yard journey to the girls' tent. In this late hour, there were no lights on across the entire Isthmus, except for a few stars attempting to evade the summer night's fog. We didn't bring a flashlight and refused to breathe in, for fear of waking anyone.

This added to the suspense of it all. Without warning, a hand came out of the dark, grabbed my shirt and pulled me into the tent. A soft voice whispered my name. Ross followed and was found by Kimberly. The mattresses were arranged on the floor and placed in opposite sides of the large tent, giving us privacy. Conforming to their arrangement, we both quickly separated into our dark corners with our girls. There was little noise. Then, Collin began to kiss me, giving me a rush.

I was lost now, not only to the night, but also in her arms, smelling her and feeling her. She whispered some words of passion, but conversation was really meaningless. The sensual wave was taking us away and through the cover of night I could only feel a shadow of her body. While my hands advanced on, her kisses became more and more demanding. Then, she placed her hand on my chest. When I attempted to reach and find her, she pushed me back, abruptly stopping me from going on.

I was just far enough away from her for the trickle of starlight coming through the tent to expose her to me. She sat up now, letting me see all of her, saying nothing, just holding me back. She was dressed in only her panties and bra. She looked at me, until she knew I saw her. Then, she reached around her back and unhooked her bra, releasing her breasts from restraint but leaving it just dangling on her arms by the straps. This was a moment of truth, but for what? My heart beat out of control and my mind became lost on her. The test of my manhood was in her hands now, no talking, no giving reasons.

Collin had made all this too easy for me. She had made up her mind. My hands attempted at the art, to do its work, as the mechanic does, by feeling and reaching out for the parts that she offered me. But again, she stopped me and abruptly broke the silence. "You can have all of this tonight," she said softly. I reached out for her. She grabbed my probing hands and looked directly into my eyes. But this time I sensed tension in her voice. "I don't need the words now, but you must promise me, that if I become pregnant, you will marry me."

I stopped, as if I were about to do something wrong. My head needed time to register what she said. As I did, a sudden chill came over my body. I fumbled in my mind, trying not to let on what I was thinking. I was ready for passion, but commitment at 18? Taken aback by the fantasy and question that both stood in front of me...what do you do, after you've had it? For me this was a problem, for her... this was love. The romance was there and she was willing to substitute that fleeting feeling for love. Did we really even know what this thing was? It was nothing more than an illusion we had created with our senses over these past few days...wasn't it? It was the songs on the patio, the scent of her perfume, the sensual visions of her on the beach and the intimate touch of her hand. But when it was all tested against the real thing, it was so trivial, too cosmetic. It meant very little. I was just this mechanic, learning only how to unhook bras! Nothing more. The whole thing was just good fun to me. I was just playing the part. But commitment... here? Now? No way. Was she really ready for that too? Maybe it was her way out. To help her get the assurance she needed to somehow make it right.

My mind raced on. I needed something to come back to her with. But, what was there to say? The truth? Did I mislead her? There had been no talk of this in our little conspiracy. I began to evade her plea, hoping to carry on with this, but she wouldn't let it happen.

Sometimes it's the words left unspoken that make going back impossible. Trying to hide my fear, I backed off. I began to get up in the dark. Collin just sat there looking at me, piercing me with her eyes. She knew what I was thinking now and began to weep, ever so slowly, trying not to let me know how much it hurt.

I just wanted her. That was enough for me. But, this Catholic girl needed more, something of value for the exchange. At this moment I knew the relationship we'd brewed in the past few days was lost to romance. Romance ruined it all. Cupid played his part too well. I was in that place he took us, where reason was easily overrun, but I stopped and looked around.

All of a sudden, this perfect night turned into a goodbye. Clearly, the terms were simply too great. I couldn't press on with Collin. She was going somewhere with this, and me? I had no direction.

Leaving Collin in tears, I thought maybe I could come up with the right words, but they would be without meaning. As I moved out of the tent, knowing I had turned down her offering, guilt began to plague my mind. How could I leave her this way?

As I think back now, I hope Collin is still around somewhere. We could talk. She probably never knew the impact she had on me, for those few brief days. I learned more about what I didn't know about girls, romance, intimacy and such things…from her.

And for Ross? Well, as Collin was replacing her bra, she picked one up in the dark and discovered it wasn't hers. She smiled while wiping away a tear. Somewhere, Kimberly and Ross were lost in the darkness. I left, trying to think I'd done something noble. Maybe I did.

But, looking back, it wasn't the nobility of the thing that saved the night. It was knowing we were just two young people getting our first chance at playing with life. She had offered me all she had, hoping it was enough. That our time together, the time we had shared and those brief magic moments on the outside, would make me feel it on the inside. But there was something missing in the recipe to make it right. For me there had to be something more than the whistles, bells and shiny buttons that she relied on so much as trump cards. It wasn't enough. It never is. I needed something more too, something to make it what I had imagined it to be. Not just a memory to look back at or a good story to tell my friends, but something to look forward to, something to cherish.

As for Collin? I couldn't go back. It doesn't work that way. Oh no, that wasn't in the offering. I had to get away from it... turn back, think it all over and start again. We just ran out of time. I know that now.

But, what was the lesson in all of this for me? Well, let's see. The usual, it wasn't just her. It was both of us. We both dreamt all of this up together... didn't we? Or maybe it was that we're all alike in some ways, regardless of our age...aren't we? For, there are times when we knowingly disguise our intentions in virtuous terms. Intuitively, I think we needed to find acceptable reasons for giving into our sensual impulses. It just makes it more palatable and simple than merely calling it something it's not.

In the end, we both knew that life would give us another chance to do it right. We still had the time. But, out of all this, I still feared that, given the same chance, I just might be tempted to play it out differently, to say the words...risk it all. But, come up short again.

# Catalina Summer
## *sketches of the past*

## Part Two

CHAPTER 11

# High Noon At Eleven

For the first time the girls were up earlier than Ross and me. As we stepped out of our cabin, the lights were already on and laughter was coming from their dormitory. Later, we heard their stories about playing pranks on each other. This would be their last day, actually half-day in camp. Then, they would be on their way home on the 11 a.m. water taxi.

Ross and I had some unfinished business to take care of. He had to seal this relationship with Kimberly. Me, I had to deal with the issues involving Collin. Ross was in a happy mood. It appeared as if all had come out good for him. I really didn't know why he was so cheery. However, I did know that, once the girls left, he would tell me each and every detail. That's just what guys do, brag about your achievements, like getting merit badges when you were in the Boy Scouts. We needed to confess our quest to our friends to somehow gain a little stature. And, besides, what else was there to talk about in a boys' baseball camp anyway?

Here's how it went. On "turnaround days," the water taxis would arrive from San Pedro. They would be full of a new group of campers and the old group would use that same taxi to depart for the mainland. My father and mother would shuffle back and forth from the island to San Pedro to meet and greet the new campers. A few designated counselors would ride with each group. It all worked out smoothly. But today the boat carried only our advanced team of counselors and foodstuff in preparation for opening day of the baseball camp on Monday.

I told Ross I would write Collin a message, and he asked, "Why? You really don't care that much… right?"

"No. You don't understand. Collin's a nice kid."

"So what?"

"So, what are you going to do, Ross?"

"I'll get her phone number. Then, call her after summer."

We walked over to the kitchen with Ross looking forward to a few last words with Kimberly and me looking to avoid Collin, even though I knew I should somehow give her an easy landing to remember this past week by.

Mother was in the kitchen preparing breakfast. After a few good mornings, we grabbed some food and rushed out to our table. To our surprise there sat Father James, maybe not really a surprise because Father was showing up just about everywhere. But this time, he was already sitting at the table and facing the Mona Lisa window. Ross and I sat down keeping our eyes focused anyplace except on the window. When Father said, "Good morning boys. How did you sleep last night?" it was like God had caught us with our hand in the cookie jar. But, had he really? No…Father was just carrying on like usual. So, we kept our eyes low while rushing through our breakfast, hoping and praying that the good Father would not look up at the window. We continued talking to him about things, trying to distract him, like usual. Miraculously, to our great relief, he grabbed his plate and said, "Well, looks like a big day boys. See you on the pier." A little later, as I stood to leave, I turned to take a last look at the steamy window. Adding on to its obituary, I shook my head and mumbled, "It will never be the same around here." Ross mimicked my affection by putting his hand to his heart. Now, looking as if we'd just lost a good friend, we moved on.

Clearly our charmed days at the Isthmus were just about over. With the arrival of the scouts, counselors and our crew, we'd be just like any other guy. I said to Ross, "Now, it's back to the real world. No easy scores." We laughed.

Mother called us over to let us know it was time to get the truck, load the girls' bags, drive up to the end of the pier and place them to one side. When the water taxi comes in, unload and line up the incoming stuff first. Then, pass the girls' luggage down into the taxi.

"Remember to be there early and get it done, your father might be coming in and you know what happens if it's not done right! If your father comes on the taxi, I plan to go back to the mainland with the girls and be there to greet our new campers on Monday." She turned to go but then swiveled around. She wasn't finished with me yet. That would be too easy. "By the way, I heard from the grapevine that a son of mine got into some kind of fisticuffs with the Boy Scouts last night on the pier." She purposely avoided looking at me, keeping her eyes on Ross. I don't know why mother always had to do it that way. Why not just look at me? She was talking about me, and I was right there. I think this was some kind of interrogation technique. She probably thought Ross would blurt out the answer she was looking for.

Obviously, since her other two sons were halfway across the country, I became the prime suspect. I started to laugh but stopped when I saw mother wasn't quite that amused. The grilling continued. Attempting to break her concentration, I interrupted, "Who told you, Mom?"

"I'm not talking to you, Gilly."

Finally, Ross muttered in my defense, "Mrs. Lefebvre, it really wasn't Gil's fault this time."

"I see you have a few bruises here and there too, Ross. Does that mean you were with him last night?"

"Mom, it wasn't our fault!"

She finally turned to look directly at me. "Gilly, it's never your fault. That's the problem. Never turns into always." Before she could get rolling into her predictable response, I said, "Mom, look at it this way. If I'm right and the other guy's wrong, well, what am I to do? Right?"

"No. Two wrongs don't make a right."

"Correct me if I'm wrong here. But, Mom, there weren't two wrongs, just one right and one wrong. If that's not the way it is, then why fight at all? What's the purpose?"

I couldn't keep my face straight now, hoping to have baffled mother into a laugh. She just shook her head and looked back at Ross, sensing her talk with me was fruitless. "I hope the next time you have better sense than him."

"I will, Mrs. Lefebvre."

I tried to change the conversation but mistakenly opened another can of worms. "Can't wait until Billy Tucker gets here!"

"Oh no, not Billy Tucker," mother said with a grin. "Now, that's trouble. Neither one of you have enough sense to lick a stamp. He'd follow you off the end of the Earth, if either one of you could find it."

Back to the fight, now jesting with her, I said, "I just do what dad always tells me. You got to stand up for yourself or they'll keep coming after you. You don't have to beat the other guy up to win. Just bite the guy's ankle… make him bleed a little. He'll think you're crazy and stay away. Show them you're willing. That's all."

"Okay, alright. You and your father rarely see eye to eye, but he's always making excuses for you." Mother shook her head as she headed out the door. "Ross, just keep Gilly out of trouble. I can't get rid of him. God gave me that burden. But you, I can send packing back to your mother." With that she was gone down the hall.

I just laughed to myself. Ross, keep me out of trouble? Ross? If she only knew...

We backed the truck up to the open doors of the camp as each girl, one by one, began handing us their luggage. Ross and I packed it in tight. I hoped to avoid seeing Collin, to just let it pass away. And, the moment I thought it would, here came Kimberly carrying both hers and Collin's bags. She handed them to Ross, ignoring me. She didn't have to say it. That's what friends do when they think you have harmed the other. Ross smiled like some choirboy and took the bags.

We continued on until they'd finished then rushed to the pier to begin unloading and stacking. The sun had just broken through the early morning fog and shined on the water, announcing a better day. Finished with that, we raced back to our cabin. There was time now to just sit around and wait for the arrival of the water taxi. Ross was busy writing a letter, settling his claim on Kimberly. I asked jokingly, "So what happened with you two?"

"No way, Gilly. If I told you, it would only take a few days and everybody would be hacking on me around here." He finally looked up at me, laughed and continued. "You have a big mouth that comes out with pointy little words."

Not getting anywhere again, I leaned over and took out a piece of paper and began to write a few words myself. Ross finished his letter, folded it neatly, placed it in an envelope and sealed it up.

"Hey, Ross, give me one of those things."

"Envelope?"

"Yeah, an envelope. Come on. Give me one."

He threw one across the room, and it landed on the end of my bed. I put my note in the envelope and sealed it. "Look, do me a favor. When you give Kimberly your letter, give this to her. Tell her to give it to Collin."

"Why don't you give it to her yourself?"

"Come on, man. Just do it. It's easier that way."

Today, when you really don't want to talk to someone face to face, you just text them. That way you're not invading their space, but you get the idea across. That's what I was doing with the letter. This was how it was done back then.

Ross said, "Alright, but you owe me."

"What?" I asked with shock in my voice. "Who got you set up this last week? Huh? Me, that's who, remember Mr. Italian Stallion. Me, the French-Mexican from nowhere...that's who!" We laughed as we walked down to the pier. All the girls were there now, hanging over the rails, just looking at the water, taking their last pictures of the surrounding beaches and of each other, for memory's sake. Kimberly came down to where Ross and I were standing on the beach, just under the pier, pitching rocks. She held out her hand with a letter and photo. Ross walked over and they made the exchange, his letter for hers. Then he attempted to give her my letter for Collin. She looked down at me, like I was dirt or something you step on in a park. Reluctantly, she took it, looked quickly away, walked back on the pier and disappeared somewhere in the pack of waiting girls. Ross immediately turned the photo over and read the inscription. He looked up at me and smirked, "Did you get one?"

Just then Carla, mom's messenger girl, walked by and I called out, "See you later, Carla."

She looked over and replied, "You guys are going to miss me, right?"

"Every chance we get, Carla," I answered as she passed on.

Just then, coming onto the horizon, to the right of Bird Rock, we could see it. We kept our eyes on the water taxi until it breached the harbor, struggling along at a snail's pace. As it came closer, the girls began to wave, not really to anybody but to everybody on the incoming taxi. Girls just do that, especially when the boat was loaded with our male crew.

Finally, it pulled alongside the dock and I could see some somber faces, sickened by the voyage. However, I couldn't recognize any of them yet. It had been a long time since I saw most of them, at least a year or so. I locked onto each face as it appeared and, when they climbed out of the boat, I tried quizzing myself on their names. With each one, I remembered a story from past years. My pulse quickened as I acknowledged most of them. There were some new faces, but I knew, in just a few short weeks, they too, like the rest, would become countless memories. The island, living so close together, same routine, the food, the games, it all worked on you here. Then, with a blink, the present and the future turned into the past. It happened that way ever since I first arrived on the Isthmus.

So who were they? Each person my parents hired had to be trained and certified for their designated job. Ross and I looked over the rail and down on the lower dock as they unloaded. There was my philosopher cousin Jeff, one of my closest allies against the world on the mainland. He had taught me just about all I knew about girls, until this past week. I knew he'd clear this recent stuff up for me. I admired him and was happy he'd made it. Golf was his game, and he played it well.

Next was Michael Mullen, better known as Bilko. His stanch frame and amazing bristle of a smile seemed to fit the name. Dennis Titchener, a good friend, was probably one of our most consistent warriors. He'd been with us from the beginning of the baseball camp. Dennis came from San Pedro's Mary Star of the Sea High

School and his cousin Tom was with him again. Tom was a junior college pitcher who threw nothing but fastballs. My father hired him every year to throw batting practice to my brothers and me. Then came Shane Bachman. He was one of those rascals from Rancho Cienega playground. Way too many stories there. His big demeanor, jovial mood and refrained disposition overcame any preconceptions. He was just a friendly, comfortable and good-feeling guy. But, take that too far, and look out.

My good friend Dickey Kozlowski stepped out next. Dickey came from Venice Beach, and we'd played baseball with him at St. John Vianney High. He was always a fun-loving guy; I mean that was his life. Then, there was Jimmy Brown. He kind of reminded me of Mickey Mantle but had the mouth of Billy Martin. If you'd been around baseball back then, you would've known what I meant. His mouth got him much further than his talent supported. Browny taught me how to use the vernacular, "your ass," in the most appropriate of situations. But, like all of my friends, he had an extremely competitive inclination. I think they all were provoked to be like that. It was the natural infection of being influenced by my father. All of them had backgrounds in one competitive sport or another. It was a rather entertaining and volatile group that, at the drop of a hat, could unleash a lot of excitement.

Stepping out behind those guys were some of the new members my mother talked about. A very Latin-looking older gentleman, I presumed to call him a gentleman until I was proven wrong. It had to be Johnny Cuevas, the channel swimmer and lifeguard. Then two rather out-of-place husky, shaved-headed individuals stepped out carrying their own bags that bulged with scuba gear. One was a muscular looking guy with a tattoo on his arm. In those days, it usually meant former military. So, I assumed he would be Pat Quinn, the ex-Seal diver my dad had hired for the summer. Beside him was Lee Goulding from Palos Verdes, just across the channel, a surfer by trade, actually then it wasn't a trade but a way of life. He and Pat would be our camp divers and backup lifeguards. They would provide the camp with abalone and whatever other food product they gathered from the sea.

Out poured the older guys. Tauso, a regular at camp, was a former champion high school wrestler and now a college student. John Radcliff was next. He was my dad's camp manager. So that was our camp crew. The only one missing out of the expected arrivals was my dad. John explained that dad had some business in the morning and might arrive in the afternoon on Channel Air. Then again, knowing Channel Air, maybe not.

We began to help with the supplies when out stepped a beautiful collegian dressed in a summer outfit and a wonderful smile. Lyan Adler was to be our nurse for the summer. We'd all get to know and love her. She was just that way. Chatting with her as she walked up the gangplank was my older sister, Yvonne, as always giving advice. She'd arrived in our family before any of us boys, therefore she knew the playing field better than we did, and that was quite an advantage. Whether she was in her late teens, 20s or 30s – it really didn't matter – my father needed a flyswatter to keep the counselors at bay because she was always older and very attractive

The guys unloaded to the preying eyes of the departing girls and filed past returning their looks with interest. With everything now unloaded off the boat, they packed their bags into the truck and went off to the campsite. Slowly, the girls began to carry their stuff down the plank and into the boat. I kept busy loading, not wanting to run into Collin. My letter said it all and any more remarks by me would just spoil it.

After the girls and gear were finally all aboard, Ross and I moved to the top of the pier. We waved to the nebulous group, our gesture of goodbye. As the boat turned toward the mainland, to my surprise, Collin raced to the back, raising her arm. Smiling now with my letter in hand, she waved until the boat was out of sight. When it passed Bird Rock, Ross looked over to me and asked, "What did you say in the letter?"

I smiled. "You'll never know. So there!"

Now it was time for Ross and me to gloat to the guys about our past week. Time to make up all kinds of good stories. Then again, we really didn't have to. This time. They were good enough on their own.

CHAPTER 12

# The Program

Feeling a sudden compulsion to be left alone, I got up before sunrise that first day of camp and carefully slipped out, not wanting to wake any of my cabin mates. I found myself, like so many other times before, pulled toward the end of the Isthmus pier. Standing there, looking out to the mainland, a sense of anticipation overcame me. This wasn't that unique. I'd felt similar feelings before. I would stand there and entertain my mind with the possibilities the summer would bring. Except, this would be unlike all the others.

I began to lament over those things I'd thought about on the boat trip over, to ponder where I was and where I was going. I was worried about my career. There was the question of whether I'd live up to my dad's expectations, let alone mine. And, what about that girl I let go on Friday? Would she come back into my life? Would there be others? The future was weighing heavily on me. I could only see bits and pieces of my life's puzzle. The missing parts were still out there, and I'd just have to wait and see how they would all come together.

In the quiet of morning, I stood alone at the end of the pier, just listening to the barking seagulls and the crushing of the ocean as it leaned on the shore for rest. With each surge, I could hear the rocks crumbling against the wooden pillars, making the pier creak in time to the ocean's rhythmic swells. The sun hadn't broken yet, as I looked toward the mainland that still partially hid behind Bird Rock. Then, as if the world had turned off, the mainland dimmed along with the lights of the pier, all together as if choreographed, just in time to meet the morning sun. I thought less now about what tomorrow would bring and more about what this day would offer.

My eye caught the early arrival of an old ship that had just rounded the corner. It was still so early. Who could that be? It gave a ghostly appearance as it came into view, much like the vessel in the back bay we saw a few days earlier. It couldn't be the water taxi. It was way too early. Eventually, it became clear that it was the tugboat owned by Birt Groves. It always seemed to wander the island aimlessly, positioning the moorings in every island enclave. They would be for ships to rest at night, finding comfort from the North Easterly winds that thrashed the Catalina shores. "What a splendid vessel," I thought while it came in closer to find its own mooring. As the day began to come and play, she took her rest.

There were many days that started this way. Just me standing alone at the end of the pier, talking to myself and hoping that someone was listening, looking for some kind of revelation. Maybe God would actually talk to me. It would certainly make all this much easier.

≈

After working our heads off over the weekend and getting caught up on stories, with old and new friends, opening day was finally here. Back in camp the bustling of activity had begun, and the great smell of my mother's cooking reached out to anyone passing about.

I walked into the kitchen to see her working hard at getting ready to feed the new crew. I picked at the batch of freshly cooked sausages in the pan and ambled about the kitchen putting away this pan and another. Mother intuitively seemed to pick up on my somber mood and broke the silence. "You know, Gilly, you didn't say 'good morning.'"

"Sorry, Mom. Good morning."

"So, what's on your mind?" Somehow knowing what I was thinking and without allowing me time to wallow in it, she continued. "Gilly, we've had good times here, haven't we?"

I nodded in agreement. "What a great analyst," I thought.

She proceeded to give me a remedy for my lingering malaise. "Well, your brothers are gone now and I must admit something special is already missing around here, all those antics you and your brothers pulled off together. That kept us all so young for so long. I know this will probably be your last full summer here. Time is pulling you away. You know this place, this business, was for you guys."

The conversation began to echo with emotion. Mother kept bouncing ideas to me, and I tried to reply in kind. As always, mother was ahead of me, leading me out from confusion. That's what moms do so well. At least mine did. She pulled me back from dribbling about the past. "So, Gilly, make this summer one of your best, one to look back on and remember. Just have fun."

Mother was never the driver. That was my father's job. She was the great navigator who kept things going in one direction, forward. She helped me connect the dots, showing me day by day how they would come together. And, if they didn't, she explained why. Her Catholic faith was deeply rooted in tradition. Her core beliefs were hard to define. But, she was what I called an efficacious believer in divine providence… that was simply a fact of life. Also, the unknown equation between fate and chance was not necessarily contradiction. She felt there was no reason to dwell on the subject, for somehow God worked all that out. This gave her plenty of reasons to always be the optimist. After reviving me from my low dose of despair, mother would always conclude with a little lighthearted pampering. "Gilly, remember, it's just the way the ball bounces." I was hoping that it would continue to bounce in my favor.

I left the kitchen revived and ready to take on the day. I just needed someone who knew me as she did to kick me on down the road.

We all knew our respective roles on this day. Meet the boat, unload the campers and make them feel comfortable. The next two weeks for many of them would be their first time away from home. Looking from the Isthmus to the mainland might as well have been like looking off to New Zealand, they could feel so far away from home here. Keeping them busy and secure was an important antidote to prevent them from thinking too much of home.

Many of the campers came from celebrity homes. But, there were also kids whose parents came from all kinds of professions. Plus, we had an ongoing relationship with the Los Angeles Times newspaper that allowed some underprivileged boys to come free of charge. Therefore, it was the first time for some of them to mix with kids of diverse ethnic and economic backgrounds. They would meet, challenge and compete with each other on a level playing field for the first time. That was the genius of sports, my dad would say.

Our staff waited patiently on the pier at 11 a.m. Some of us passed the time by showing off, diving into the refreshing water. "Oh no," I said as I looked up to see our only true adversaries, the scouts, walking down the pier toward us. As always, they came in a pack led by, guess who? Yep, Randall Cunningham the Third.

Somewhere in his childhood, I suspect he quit reading the Hardy Boys way too soon and was introduced to Col. Chesty Puller and General Patton at far too young an age. Randall had this presence about him. Even when sober, he was arrogant and defiant and lacked any form of common civility. We'd already had an altercation a couple of nights before, which I brought to the attention of our crew. It was becoming obvious that this summer would be a defining one.

Randall and his troops, in tactical formation, met us at the end of the pier. He walked directly up to me and went on about being pushed off the pier. I replied sarcastically, "Is that so, my friend? I thought you'd be over that by now. Hey, it's just water and, besides, you gave the girls a good laugh."

The other counselors stood behind me, laughing it up. As we faced off, their senior counselor, Mr. Mayhem, (yeah, that really was his name) stepped in and ordered the troops back down the pier to wait for the water taxi to arrive. You see, all the camps shared space on the incoming boats for economical reasons. The scouts were there to pick up supplies once we got our campers and luggage off.

After they retreated to the other end of the pier, we continued to laugh and dive. In those days, there were no posted signs to say, "no diving." They would come later, but unfortunately they only made the dive more appealing. Why was it always that way? I was too young to know and too young to care.

Then, to the right side of Bird Rock, some two miles out, a boat suddenly appeared. One of my comrades shouted out, "There it is!" Our attention was on the boat coming directly toward us now. As it came closer, we could see some of the weary campers sitting in the front, hoping the sea breeze would give them relief from the nauseating smell of burnt fuel that accumulates inside the taxi over the two and a half hour trip from San Pedro to the

Isthmus. Standing there in front was my dad, cheering on the new campers with news that their trip was coming to an end. He was waving, and we all waved back, not really knowing any of these new campers but simply waving to the occasion, a greeting that made them feel special.

As the crew began to tie the boat up to the dock, my father stepped out first, giving orders. Immediately, we fell in place because we always knew in advance what he wanted and, besides, most of us had done this many times before. Dad was a doer and what he did, he wanted done right. Meaning, the right way was his way, and that was good enough for us. My father was slight in stature, some 5-feet, 8-inches but a muscular guy with an extremely credible demeanor. An impatient man, he had dreams and was willing to throw in the lot to achieve them. My father never saw limits in people. He believed in the old adage, "luck is the residue of design." Therefore, if you worked hard at your skill, success would naturally follow. What made my dad different from the rest was he really believed that stuff. At least, he made us believe that he believed. Anyway, that's all that mattered. But, the most admirable part was all his ideas were a reality in progress. Some say he was a great con man. Yes, he was. He conned me, my brothers and many other athletes to strive beyond our expectations, to believe in ourselves and make our own opportunities. This mindset had a major influence in the lives of so many who were fortunate to have come under his spell.

Now, as he stepped off the boat, the mood switched from jovial to serious in light of the business of running a responsible, safe and secure camp. My mother would always spout out our camp mantra before each session: "We've never lost a camper, and we don't intend to." And, that's the way it was.

After getting the bags unloaded we walked the campers up to the camp. They were given their assigned rooms and beds, then introduced to their respective counselors. My mother and Lyan had the health office in order and immediately tended to the campers who were suffering from the boat trip over. Lyan begin to set up the files that included medical data, medication and medical release forms required from their parents. The bank was opened, my dad's idea when he first started the camp. Each camper would put their cash in the bank, and then, when they needed it, they would make a withdrawal. This way, parents could call and get an idea of their sons' spending habits. Once all this was taken care of, my father would ring a bell. Then lunch, like all the meals, was served in buffet style. After lunch, the bell rang again. This time all the campers filed out to the eating tables with the full staff in attendance. My father, along with John Radcliff, would give the campers a complete orientation, going over what they would be doing for the next two weeks.

First, the introductions of all the counselors, the nurse and of course, my mother, then our lifeguard and our fishing crew. Next, they went through the daily itinerary.

Dad would start by saying, "This is a baseball camp, but by the end of two weeks you won't be a professional ballplayer. That's going to take more than two weeks. However, you will learn some valuable knowledge about the skills you'll need to be one. And, after two weeks here, you'll find out that's not all this camp is about. I hope when you leave you can say you had fun, met new friends and want to come back next year. So, this is what we have planned for you. As far as baseball is concerned, well, to play baseball is easy. All you have to do is hit, catch, throw and run.

"Starting tomorrow, we'll begin to test each one of you in these areas to see where you are. Then, we'll start training positions. Once that's done, you'll break up into teams and play live games, under the supervision of our counselors. They all have been selected because of their achievements in the sport on either the

THE PROGRAM • 143

high school or college level. And, for you more advanced players, I brought along a couple of good left- and right-handers to throw batting practice.

"Of course, we also have pitching machines set up next to the tennis courts. They are ready and waiting for you to use anytime during your free schedule. Toward the end of the session, we pick our best players and travel by way of the Blanche W. to play the city of Avalon's all-star team. It's a big game for the camp, but even bigger for Avalon. It's something to work toward.

"Each day after workout, you'll be given free time to go to our designated camp beach. First, you'll be given a swimming test by our lifeguard, Johnny Cuevas, and you must pass this test before you'll be allowed to swim out to the float. Once you do this, then you're on your own. The lifeguard will give you the beach rules. But, number one... no one, and I mean no one, is ever to skip rocks, period. We've lost a lot of teeth by campers not following that rule. We have early morning fishing trips twice a week. As far as boating, we have sailboats we call, "flatys." There are four of them, two rowboats and five canoes. But, you must always be accompanied by a counselor to use them. There are snorkeling tours to Little Fisherman's Cove, and you'll all get a chance to go to Avalon to see the town and buy souvenirs to take home.

"Also, we have an overnight campout planned for you at Little Harbor, seven miles away on the backside of the island. There's a great body surfing beach. You'll hike there and then return by truck the next morning."

I looked over at Ross now and whispered, "Boring." He added on, "Especially after the girls."

My father continued, "We have campfires for roasting marshmallows and, every night, each team will put on a skit. You'll find them a lot of fun. After that, lights out, and we mean lights out. Until the breakfast bell is rung, all campers must stay in their rooms! Most of you will need the rest anyway. A couple more things… we'll have the craft room open all day and there will be non-denominational services every Sunday morning, right here. They're not mandatory. It's up to you if you want to attend. Oh, and by the way, yes, we do have mail every day." Now, looking directly at me he said, "Some of you guys, in the next few days, will be dying to get letters from somebody back home. We have postcards for each of you to write home, and you will start tonight by writing to your parents. Please invite them to the island a week from Wednesday for our fish and abalone night. If they can make it, it will be fun. We know most of your parents are working hard every day just to get you here. You need to send them the postcard with the camp's address. About phone calls, if your parents call the island, they'll get a switchboard operator asking for the number. Then she'll dial through to us. In other words, phone calls are hard to get through." My dad always made this point because many of the kids would get homesick right away. But, given time, they would, almost to the last one, overcome it.

After saying all that, he let John Radcliff stand in and answer all of the kid's questions. He said a few words of greeting. "Okay, the rest of the day we'll be showing you guys around our beach area. After that, we'll go to the back bay area, named Cat Harbor, and show you where the baseball field and batting cages are. By then, it will be time for dinner. The counselors will now pass out the postcards. Take them with you to your rooms and, after dinner, write something. We'll take the cards and send them home. Questions?"

One camper raised his hand. "What do we say on the cards?"

"Anything you like."

Another kid asked, "Where are the horses?"

I leaned over to Ross and whispered, "In the tree." Ross's laugh became so noticeable that, in order to conceal it, he got up and walked away. John looked at me and said, "Gil, something I need to know about?"

"No, sir. Sorry, Mr. Radcliff, nothing."

John then replied to the kid, "I didn't see horses in our brochure. Did anybody else?" That drew laughter from everyone. One kid, sounding a little too mature for our camp, asked, "Are there a lot of girls here?"

"Yes and no," John said with a smile. "But, I don't think you'll be spending much time with them anyway."

Another question. "What famous players have come from this camp?"

John quickly answered. "You of course," and he turned the table on the kid by asking, "You're going to be famous someday, aren't you?" Left to no other alternative, the kid nodded an approval.

"Is it okay to gamble in camp?"

Now, this was one of those oddball questions that really grabbed our attention, and we all took down a mental note of the kid asking it. He was from Chicago. I never remembered his real name because, from then on, we just called him "Chicago." That fit him quite well, and he felt comfortable with it. Finally, as in every session, there's the one kid who asks, "When are we going home?" Everybody laughs, but, again, we take note because unfortunately homesickness was an immediate issue we always needed to deal with.

The first day was all about business, but the fun was just about to begin. My mother introduced me to a boy named Clyde. "Here he is, Gilly. This is Clyde. You remember his father, Mitch Clayton, the friend of your dad's?"

"Yeah, the car dealer."

"That's him. Well, Clyde is going to spend the summer with us."

"The whole summer?" I leaned in to whisper, "Gee, Mom, why me?"

"Never mind, Gilly. You just watch over him. He'll need it."

Now, this kid was just old enough to be proclaimed a true nut but still young enough to do what I told him. But, hang out with him all summer? No way. Later, I informed Ross, "He'll be gone in a month."

CHAPTER 13

# When Summer Began At the Isthmus

I remember watching Lawrence of Arabia and seeing Bedouins traveling across an endless sea of sand, shifting from the pressure of the wind and vibrant sun, looking intuitively for an oasis, which nature so poignantly had provided. The desert oasis served the purpose of providing the basic necessities for survival for those weary travelers. It was also a place where one could find a respite from the surrounding desperate conditions. Over time, the oasis became even more prominent as a destination for social discourse. Here one could come into contact with other foreign wayfarers, venturing off in different directions, all hoping to find something they were looking for. In a few days, they could retreat, rest and leisurely spin tales about their sorties to any inquisitive ear. At the oasis, they celebrated their existence together, insulated from the past and the future.

The Isthmus's combination snack shop and restaurant bar was not a quirk of divine providence like the oasis but the product of visionary Preston Taylor, known as "Press." As the sole proprietor of the infamous Chi Chi Club in Avalon, Preston saw an opportunity in 1953 to expand his business to the island's remote west end location of the Isthmus. Like Avalon, after WWII, the Isthmus/

Two Harbors area had transitioned from high and low periods of popularity. But, unlike Avalon, the reclusive Isthmus location and exotic surroundings, with soft sandy beaches rimmed by palm trees flittering through the back bay, appealed more to another type of visitor. They were more like adventurers than tourists.

Lured to this parched land of paradise, they came and played during the summer months. The Isthmus topography lent protection and shelter against the Pacific's North Easterlies that occasionally passed through. The boaters' homeports were as far south as San Diego and as far north as Seattle. But, the Isthmus was easily accessed on a fair, calm day from the coast of Southern California, just 19 miles out.

Preston's idea was to provide them with the basic comforts of dining as they pursued the backdrop of the island's mystic. But, he also envisioned something grander and created a destination where celebrities of all kinds, not just of the Hollywood genre, could find an experience quite unlike any they had on the mainland. Anyone set for adventure, blown into the Isthmus by the Pacific winds, was welcome.

Preston set up the restaurant to serve fine wines and dressed his menu with the fresh catch of the day, which usually included a variety of fish, lobster, crab and abalone. All this was presented with fresh vegetables and sides of rice or crispy fries.

His creation was located at the mouth of the Isthmus pier, and the aroma of the food in preparation for the night's feast enchanted the hardy sailors into its doors. Once inside, they were greeted by the Wild Goose Girls, named for their living arrangements in the round house adjacent to the Wild Goose Lodge, leftover from a previous movie production. From the flair of their presence, the name stuck with the locals. Over the years, these girls became a close-knit group and were brought together each summer by Preston's daughter.

Linda, like her father, had a keen interest in business and the ability to make customers feel welcomed. She was willing to direct lingering teenagers casing the snack bar and looking to fraternize with the opposite sex, "It's time to move on." But, if you asked for a malt, a midday sandwich or just a quick hamburger, she and her well-trained crew went beyond the call of duty.

As night pursued the day, the restaurant took over and Wild Goose Girls served delicious dinners on the patio. Afterward, those who desired a bit of adult spirits entered the enclave of the bar, while the young at heart stayed to dance and romance on the patio. The spell of current love songs harmonized through the jukebox that played late into the night.

"What went on in the back bar…stayed in the back bar." Or so the saying went. Celebrities and local boaters knew they could kick back, drink and be merry. Preston entrusted their privacy to Ernie, the well-liked bartender who migrated from the Mexican town of Chihuahua and, for many years, also served as bartender at Avalon's Chi Chi Club.

Well-known Hollywood figures spent many late nights there perpetuating its glamour. But, the celebrity list went way beyond cinematic talents. Among the patrons were moguls of industry, artists, writers and even vagabonds who found their way to the Isthmus, some driven by the wind of their sails and others in luxury cruisers.

Over time, the Taylor establishment became the epicenter of social life for the island's west end while Avalon remained the island's bustling downtown. The Isthmus, in contrast to Avalon, was a timeless experience, a place where history was not in the past but made daily by wandering flights of mavericks treading out their own paths.

Another dominant and constant presence on the Isthmus was Doug Bombard. His job was to temper the civility, or lack of it.

Administrator and facilitator of all the daily Isthmus issues, he also reconciled the diverse interests of the many different groups, which was a challenge. Some met for the first time after they'd found themselves in conflict with the other. Without Harbor Masters' Doug and the McElroys, the Isthmus would have been void of structure. They were unlike us half-breeds that met every summer and disconnected at its end by returning to the mainland. Doug, his wife, Audrey, children Randy, Greg, Tim (aka Bumper) and Windy, along with the Ewings and the Groves, held the entire west end, from the Isthmus to Parson's Landing, in check, all year.

On this Saturday night, all was in place. The snack bar opened its doors for business. Boaters began coming, first as a trickle, then turning into a flood. They searched aggressively for an open mooring, tied on, then came ashore for snacks and drinks.

The Blanche W. was now on a daily schedule, and the snack bar jukebox began to play out memories while some of us sat around on the patio knowing that, in a few days, this quiet tempo would pick up considerably. We met old friends and greeted new faces as they came into our lives.

"So, when does summer really start here at the Isthmus?" a young lady asked me one boat ride over.

"Let me answer that with a story my dad told me. You see, he asked that very same question to Ernie the bartender. Ernie answered, 'Well Benny, legend has it, John Wayne and Ward Bond, whose visits were perennial occasions, sat in the bar drinking late one early summer night. At their table was Jack White, the island's very own genuine rootin' tootin' cowboy. Their entourage gathered round as they boasted about a recent fishing expedition to Mexico. All of a sudden, a large robust-looking sailor climbed on top of the bar. It was apparent he was hard put for a good fight and brandishing a pistol. He stood tall and bellowed, "I'm the biggest, meanest, baldest sailor around! Anybody have any problem with that?"

'John Wayne calmly gave a big grin, looked into the man's eyes and said, "Not me, sailor." It was Cliff Tucker, who gave in to his disguise with a welcoming smile of his own. And, while still trained on John Wayne's smile, he fired the pistol into the ceiling, jumped off the bar and shouted, "All drinks on me, Ernie!" The roar of laughter was heard all the way to the end of the pier.' Ernie always finished his story with a dramatic flair, 'Now, that's when you know the Isthmus summer has begun.'"

CHAPTER 14

# Play Ball!

My dad was my dad. I never considered him a friend. He was an intriguing, compelling and brash celebrity of a man. Dad, along with my mother, had this co-conspiracy on how to direct and guide my life. Mother gave just enough comfort to keep me going when things appeared to be not going so well. However, it was never too much to undermine my father's grand plan.

His eccentric ways simplified my life. He prescribed goals even before I could talk. This gave me little chance to disagree. I was born left-handed but, so the story goes, that wasn't to last but for a few days. After delivery, he managed to make me right-handed before I left the hospital. That was part of his master plan. How else could I become a switch-hitter and have the options to play more positions on the diamond when I signed my major league contract?

Every day had its purpose... to get closer to that final destination. "To be a professional baseball player, you have to believe in yourself," dad would say. "As far as the skills, I could teach a monkey to run, throw and hit, that's easy." (And, believe me, anyone who trained under him would say he could) "But to get up in front of 40,000 fans in the bottom of the 9th, with two outs and a three-and-two count and you're happy to be there – now, that's something I can't put inside of you. It's that precise moment, that will define your character… who you really are."

He never allowed my brothers and me to play organized games until we entered high school. And, by the way, the purpose of high school was only to give us an opportunity to showcase our skills to the scouts. The education process was just a bad side effect that, "could be cured over time."

My father took offense to practically everyone who disagreed with him. And, that was just about everyone, telling him to mend his ways, thereby saving his sons from a life of abuse. But, in the end, events would prove many of his critics wrong.

His rationalization always had an unusual twist but somehow made sense to me. He'd tell me, "In life, you'll have those people who will love you, and then there will be those who won't. That's okay, but when you go through life and no one really knows you ever existed? It's something to think about." It was in those contemplative moments that I saw the genius of his madness, as well as my life most clear. He left me to connect the dots, with mother's help of course. As I searched for answers, I began to find myself.

Looking back now, I see how blessed I was. Was I young and full of hope? Not in our vocabulary. Hope for what? I didn't need hope then. My dream was crystal clear, and my parents provided a detailed map. With that part of my life well cared for, it was the rest I worried about. They left that for me to figure out. Most of the problems that occurred were because I was just too young to care much about what others thought about me. That would all come later. Undoubtedly, with that attitude, trouble always seemed to find me.

So, as the camp began on that first day, orchestrated by my father, a sense of excitement filled the air. We would begin by testing the skills of the new arrivals, some 100 in the lot. Our camp was usually filled to capacity. It became so popular that the Dodgers' legendary Don Drysdale once called my mother to ask for a space for one of his neighbor's kids. When my mother said we had no room, Drysdale suggested his neighbor would buy the camp a new half-tent. She reluctantly accepted the offer, but that would be the exception.

We would see over 500 kids come through our camp over the course of a good summer. Some kids used baseball as a pretense for being there but, in most cases, this wasn't so. The majority of baseball guys had already passed beyond basic ball skills. Now it was just a matter of building confidence. However, for many of the other celebrity-type kids, it would be their first real chance to get away from home. A first chance at independence, and their parents wanted this experience for them. But, more importantly, they wanted to give them an opportunity to grow up, and, in a peculiar sort of way, our camp became their rite of passage.

The sons of doctors and lawyers could now find common interests in these next two weeks with the sons of farmers, bakers and San Pedro's longshoremen. Making everyone feel at home was a priority. My parents knew we had something more important going on here than baseball. Actor Burt Lancaster, for example, sent one of his boys to our camp and, when the sun set the first night, his boy wanted to go home. Worth a call to Mr. Lancaster? I'd say so. But, Mr. Lancaster told my mom, "No, Virginia, you tell my son he's going to stay the full two weeks and you have my backing on that." His son, like so many others by the second week had bonded and didn't want to go home.

Most of the boys only left at the end of the session because of the great mental distress of their mothers or limited family pocketbooks. Many kids returned each summer until enough time had passed and they were ready to move on. Several families that boated over to the Isthmus from nearby Long Beach, San Pedro or Newport Beach would come ashore with their kids and watch us play. Wouldn't you know it, sooner or later their kid would become our client summer after summer.

Billy Tucker was one of those kids. His dad, Cliff, was a highly successful contractor and loved sailing on his first sailboat, the Papoose. But later, after infected by the sailor's life, he bought the magnificent, sleek racing sailboat, the Geronimo. Cliff's reputation for sailing could match up with the best of seaman.

Billy Tucker, or Tuck as I called him, became a camper and, right away, both our fathers hit it off. Tuck became part of our baseball clan and one of my best summer friends. Smaller in stature, quiet and unassuming, Tuck often found himself overshadowed by his father's enormous, gregarious and sometimes contemptuous nature. After a few days of sailing and camp life, his dark tan caused anyone to guess where the stork had flown from the night he was delivered. I can remember Tuck walking over the mountain path that snakes around just above the bluff from Little Fisherman's. Wearing sailing shorts and a T-shirt and barefooted, he'd walked over to the Isthmus while I stood on the end of the pier looking for him to come over that ridge. He was a great companion, not for any purpose, but just because he was a fun guy who was happy to go along. Actually, he looked forward to going along with everything we did.

It was my cousin Jeff who gave me advice about women. Ross taught me everything he wanted me to know, but I didn't really care to know, and was always trying hard to humble me. But Tuck was just Tuck, and that was always enough. He never questioned my most bizarre schemes… he just enjoyed them. Together we were Tom and Huck.

Billy Tuck also had a sister. Patty would have impressed even the most devout Marilyn Monroe fan. When she strolled down the

Isthmus shore in a one-piece white bathing suit with each inch remarkably finding just the right place to profile her natural curves, it made older men feel guilty and young guys, like me, envious. She left me with this image, after looking at her for the first time strutting down the beach…well, it just couldn't get any better. So why even try? But, as far as Billy Tuck was concerned, it was just his sister, and he would pay little attention to her goings-on.

I was always happy to see Tuck. For, it was then that I knew all the guys had finally arrived from the mainland. The chemistry was there. It was time to make plans and get on with the summer.

It was a time in my life when friends shared ups and downs, talked about our dreams and confronted our fears. It was a time when the past was short and the future was an eternity, when we had yet to sense our mortality. That would follow soon enough, once our innocence and naïveté failed us. But, for now, the world resided somewhere out there, out over some mystical hill. And, besides, our plates were full enough. What more was there to offer?

We still had time to play, this last summer. We needed no excuses to play hooky, to get in the game. And, we still could make up our own rules. For, I think we knew we'd never get a chance to do it like this again. It was just too much fun. What do they say after the players come on the field? When the crowd has arrived, ready with refreshments in hand, the smell of popcorn, peanuts and hotdogs, smothered with mustard, relish and fresh-cut onions, after they have found their seats, the referees have taken the field, the sun is out and the national anthem has played?

"PLAAAAAAY BALLLLL!!!"

CHAPTER 15

# The Sandlot

D ust was flying as the camp's grand '57 Chevy truck attempted, once again, to barrel through the cattle gate to the dump. It was a good way to wake up, driving straight into the fog while skillfully toying with life. We'd done it many times before and always won. Once we passed through the gate, I abruptly slammed on the brakes, hoping to avoid an oncoming shadow taking shape in the mist. The truck skidded and spun out of control, flipping out two trashcans from the back, stopping just short of the intruder, now walking merrily across the road.

"You're crazy! You're damn crazy!"

"Not again," I said. "Ross, why do you keep saying that?"

"Well, maybe it's because you almost killed us AGAIN!"

I screamed back. "What? I saved your life AGAIN! You call that crazy? I'm sure some people would agree with you. Maybe I should have just run over that poor critter, just to shut you up." And, without continuing to give any more credence to Ross's rants, I yelled out the window. "Damn bulls. Damn Brahma bulls! Do you think you own the island?"

"Somebody does, and it's not you!" Ross shook his head and looked up to the sky. "Why?" Asking the heavens for answers, he added, "God, why does he always do that?"

"Why?" I asked, jumping ahead of God's reply. "Because, it's a great way to start a day at the Isthmus, that's why! Remember, we're here, and they're there."

"That was a meaningless statement," I thought. That made me chuckle and give out a short smile. Hoping I just confused Ross by simply stating nothing, I moved on.

After picking up the two errant trashcans, I drove on up to the dump that was nested near the mountaintop, stilled by low clouds and poor visibility. We finished unloading the trash among the strange sounds of animals coming to feed in the early hours, always being cautious of running into a wild pig that seemed very fond of the place. We settled in for a more cautious trip back to the camp.

"Hey, Ross," I said. "So, what did you get off of that girl?"

"What girl?"

"Come on, Ross. Man, do you think I'm dumb?"

"Yes," Ross answered.

"Well, you're wrong. Dumb is something you're born with. Stupid is something you earn. Now, do you want to go tell my mother about how she had a dumb kid?"

"Ha-ha," Ross said, as he looked at me in disgust. Then he smiled, finally seeing the humor in that thought. "You will never know. So don't ask."

"Hey, I told you what I did. Come on, Ross, what are friends for?"

"That's what you call yourself, a friend? For the last three years you've caused me nothing but…"

"But what?" I jumped in. "Come on, if it wasn't for me pushing, you wouldn't be this Joe-athlete. I got you to come to camp all these years. Remember what you did in the summer before Catalina? Nothing, that's what. And, what about the girls?

Huh?" Ross finally smiled again. I always knew how to make him smile, and that always made me smile.

The campers were beginning to wake to their first Catalina sunrise. It was always quiet each early morning when Ross and I walked over from our cabin to the kitchen. The pleasant noise of the ocean slashing against the pier made the mornings all the more peaceful. But, soon the Isthmus began to wake. And, as we came up the ramp leading into the building, we could hear the sounds of campers searching about to find their way around this new environment. It was a strange new place, where getting to the bathroom at the end of the hall was cause for concern. There would be no mother or father to give directions. It was simple moments like this, where basic necessity served as a catalyst to perpetuate one's sense of self-reliance and personal security. How well they adjusted to each new condition would define the extent of their maturity.

We walked into the kitchen and my mother greeted us with her usual, "Good morning, sleepyheads." She went about her cooking while giving us our daily assignments, and we continued getting our breakfast before the campers. Ross and I loaded up with some pancakes and sausages and went down to the eating tables, still half awake. I looked into the Mona Lisa window. The shadows of the girls were gone, but the images were still there, in my mind. I pointed to the window and Ross smiled. He got the message. Those days were history now.

Instinctively, we rushed through our meal as the lights and sounds began to perk up. Ross and I took to our morning chores. Jeff and Shane wandered in, just in time for breakfast cleanup. Part of our working crew wore many hats. For most of us, it was cleanup. Coaching responsibilities were given to the junior counselors. John ran the daily operation and all of our counselors answered to him. Each counselor was responsible for a certain amount of kids starting from the time they woke up until lights out at night. Our job, besides the cleaning, was to facilitate the baseball-training program on the field. We had extensive instruction under the tutelage of my father, so we knew his system well. My father would duck in and out, watching each step of the program as the weeks of camp progressed. He was the leader of the band. No question about it.

My mother was the enforcer. Any attempt at non-compliance from any member of the crew was subject to immediate dismissal and a boat ticket home on the Blanche W. Her past experience with swimming and advanced training instruction for ambulatory service companies in Los Angeles made her well-versed in the area. Mother would hire only highly qualified and certified lifeguards. The only time the camp was ever sued was on two separate cases. Kids had skipped rocks in the beach area and both incidents required dental care. Each was resolved in our favor.

Every morning, the campers went through basic calisthenics, like jumping jacks, pushups and leg lifts. Then, it was off on their quarter-mile jog to the back harbor baseball field. What looked like a dirty, sandy beach adjacent to the shore of Cat Harbor just one week ago was now turned into our sandlot. It was the official home stadium of the Catalina Baseball Camp. And, we had a backstop to prove it, along with two benches on each side of the baselines.

After Ross took care of his duties in the kitchen and the bathrooms, Jeff, Shane and the rest of our cabin crew took the truck down to the field and dragged it into a workable, playing baseball diamond. The infield wasn't that bad. Left field was okay. Centerfield, fine, but when you got to right field, well, anything not caught in the air was a ground rule double. We dragged the field everyday, kicking up dust that got caught in the early morning breeze. The smell and warmth of the ocean currents slowly overcame the chilly morning air from the back bay. And, even with the lack of grass, it made for a pleasurable workout. One thing for sure, Catalina, with its natural beauty and remote location, is very conducive for training athletes, especially in the summer.

After we finished up, Ross and I sat down on the sideline bench. I looked down the left line, where the road going to the dump intersects with the field. The road is on a buildup, and a ball hit up onto the road is about 300 feet... over the road maybe 340 feet. That's why I called it "the monster road." The thought of it kept me awake for many nights ever since ...I can't remember when. When I was 13 years old, my father set the seemingly impossible goal to hit a baseball over that road. No problem, of course, he assured us. It would happen, if we stayed with his program.

Two years ago, my older brothers, some 6-feet tall and 190-plus pounds, hit the ball over the road. The floodgates were open. After that, they made it look easy over and over again. But for me, some 150 pounds and 5-feet, 9-inches or whatever, it hadn't happened yet. I dreamt of that feat more than girls, more than racing ridges and certainly more than breaking mirrors on the way to Avalon. It was the most elusive task confronting me at this time of my life. This had to be the summer to make it happen. I broke the silence with Ross. "Yeah, this is the year. I'm going to hit one over that road. That'll do it. That will get me into the pros like my brothers."

Ross, who'd come along step by step with me in football, played less baseball but knew my capabilities well and said, "Forget it, Gilly. It's not going to happen. It's just too far. You have the speed to run there before the ball hits the ground, but the power? No way you're going to ever hit the ball over that road."

"Thanks for your positive support." I looked across at his face and saw a half smile boosting up under his Italian nose. "You really enjoy putting a kink in my plans, don't you?"

"No, but look how far away that is and look at your size. I don't see it happening."

"We'll see," I said. "We'll see." I never knew why I was always being challenged. Maybe if I were 6-feet tall it wouldn't happen as much. Clearly, that wasn't ever to be. But, I must admit, Ross's negative comments might have been just what I needed to beat that 300-foot monster.

As we continued looking up at the road, here came the campers trudging towards us, gloves in hand and metal cleats marking cadence as they advanced closer to the field. We could hear the counselors directing traffic.

Out of nowhere, riding in a Catalina Island company truck, Mr. McElroy arrived with my dad. Mr. McElroy wore all kinds of administrative hats in those days, but the bottom line was he was the Isthmus authority. Over the years he and my dad became good friends. He took great interest in the campers and followed my dad's players in the pros.

Dad jumped out to give some daily updates and make a short speech. "Remember, baseball is a simple sport made difficult only by sports commentators who overplay the game with chatter about how difficult it is to hit a ball going 100 miles per hour with a round bat." The announcers and analytical experts spin out hours of pregame shows stressing the intricacies of the game. Not so with my dad. He broke the game down to four simple components. "All there is to this game is run, hit, catch and throw a ball. That's how simple it is. All you have to do is concentrate and develop those skills."

Then dad turned the program over to John Radcliff. John, in his late 20s, had some professional experience himself. But, like many pro athletes, he never found his way to the top for one reason or another. Fortunately, many found a future as coaches and managers.

Kids of all different skill levels were in each session. It didn't really matter that much because baseball wasn't the only focus of the camp. When we began clocking their times as they ran the bases, the fun started. We would chuckle under our breath at some of the more unusual styles of running. Two of the boys who were a bit plump, and that's an understatement, began ribbing each other about who was faster. With the other boys cheering them on, they started at home plate and ran in opposite directions, one starting down the first baseline and the other down the third baseline, to see who could round the bases and make it back across home plate first. It was quite a show, as neither passed home plate first. In fact, they didn't get past second base.

These two good-natured chubbers took off and ran like turtles, stopping twice at each base, just to reassure themselves that they'd made it. It was at second base where the spectacle occurred. Running as fast as they could in a tight race, they finally arrived at second, but here's where their size created the problem. Nobody planed on this. How could they step on second at the same time? Well they did, and didn't. The crash was an amazingly abrupt impact, and both found the ground as a result.

The staff and campers broke into momentary laughter with whistles and cheers. But, as these two combatants lie motionless on the ground, the levity turned into genuine concern. Our staff medical team stepped in with some smelling salts. And, with encouraging words, the two boys were revived, stood with raised hands and smiled. By the way, I think this was Chicago's first attempt at a nonstop trip around the bases. I'm not sure he lost a bet, but I wouldn't be surprised.

Once practice was over and campers began to trickle back to camp and eventually head down to the beach, the real workout for us was about to begin. Now, standing on the mound and warming up was this 6-feet, 2-inch or whatever, 200-plus pounder. He'd been raised and grazed in California, and his unshaven, scrubby face made him look like he was encroaching on manhood. However, I wasn't surprised, because throughout the years, my father would scout good right- and left-handers and talk them into coming to camp for the summer. Their primary job was to pitch batting practice just to his boys and maybe a few other lucky individuals. This was our time, our practice, with our dad.

I'd seen this hombre getting off the boat, but he was so much older and larger than others, I hadn't connected who he was. Now I knew, as he warmed up throwing to my good friend and also outstanding pro prospect, Shane.

This creature on the mound was left-handed and, as he began to loosen up, I could easily see why my dad enlisted his talent. His jerky kind of side-arm style of throwing and his release was a little hard to pick up. And, wow, did he have great velocity on the ball. That wasn't too intimidating. I was used to that, because speed was the common denominator of all the pitchers my dad brought to camp. They had to throw fastballs. This was, of course, in keeping with my dad's master scheme. "The key," my dad would say, "to becoming a major league hitter is, you have to be able to hit the fastball. Hitting is just that simple." So, from the early age of 13, that's all we got, a steady diet of fastballs.

After my dad put me through a few warm-ups on the hitting tee, it was time to greet this new firebrand pitcher, face to face. As I stepped up to the plate, Shane laughed behind his catcher's mask and then mumbled, "Hey, Gilly, this guy's really wild. He's all over the place."

"Thanks, man," I said, as I took a practice swing.

First ball he threw was inside and really backed me off the plate. With my speed, I usually was the leadoff hitter, and pitchers always threw me tight. So, getting hit by a pitch wasn't that unusual. But tight, inside and HIGH, whoa! Now, that's a no-no. You just don't do that. Welcome to batting practice at the Catalina Baseball Camp.

I got off the ground under a roar of sustained laughter by the onlookers. My dad yelled, "Okay, you've met him, he's got your attention. Now get in there and get to work!" For the first time I engaged eye contact with this guy taunting me on the mound. Even though it was only batting practice amongst friends, guys have a certain competitive element that clicks in. And, this unknown quantity on the mound had just become my worst enemy. He was there to steal a little something from me. Was it my pride, maybe? My future? Maybe. A girlfriend? Well, I don't know about that, but, what the hell, I'd try anything I could dig up to use as a catalyst or motivation to break this guy. I stepped back and said to Shane, "Okay, let's get this thing going." Under my breath, I mumbled, "by the end of the summer, I'm going to own this guy." My dad loved this kind of stuff. That's why this guy was here, to challenge me, make me believe in myself and develop mental strength. "That's the only difference between the Sunday semi pro-player and the big leaguer…mental strength," my dad would say

The next pitch was down the center of the plate. I swung and missed. He threw the next one inside. I was always a pull hitter, pure and simple, and I sat right on top of the plate. I wasn't going to be intimidated by inside pitches. I nudged a bit closer to the plate, giving him less room to pass me. He came inside with the next pitch, trying to let me know who owned the plate.

There it was. I swung and ripped a line drive. I said to Shane, "single." With my confidence building, he threw the next pitch. "There's another," I called out, telling everybody I was getting it done. I was marching on with my goal of hitting the 300-foot monster and fully intended to conquer that hill this summer. It wasn't that pitcher on the mound that stood in my way. It was that mountain lurching out there. Every time I took a swing, the mountain was daring me on.

Seeing my ball falling well short of the road, one after another, I stepped back from the plate and looked at it, way out there. "I'll get you tomorrow," I thought.

"Came up short again," Shane said as I walked away. He knew where I was going.

Next up was infield practice, then base running, then lunch and, finally, off to the beach. This was our free time, our time to plan and scheme. The whole island was in play. It was our slice of paradise. What more could anybody want? We also knew it was a long way from Rancho Cienega Playground.

This was also the opening day of the girl's camp, and their beach site was adjacent to ours. It was a no-no to talk to the girls from that camp. Most of them came from influential, prep school type backgrounds. They were being engineered for a life dictated by social etiquette. Networking was their calling and their future was to marry within the ranks, to become linked in a hereditary chain…keep it all in the family.

So we stayed clear of them, but we could always take a peek at these damsels, and we did from time to time. Ross and I walked down to the beach with our pack of friends. We chuckled and talked on about our adventures. After a while, Ross became quiet, and I could tell something was really troubling him. "What are we going to do with the rest of the summer?" He'd gotten a taste of the opposite sex and decided he would just have to move on with it.

"Move on with it? What do you mean, 'move on with it?'" I asked.

"I don't know. We had a great time when the girls were here so… what do you got in store for us next?"

"Me? In store for you? Dang it, Ross, you haven't even talked about the last girls!"

He looked at me and said, "That really bothers you, doesn't it?"

"Hey, I set you up. Then you won't tell me anything? It's not about some girl story. It's about friendship."

"Riiight," Ross said. We both laughed together while we meandered our way past the snack bar on our way down to the beach.

Our camp beach was located to the east of the pier and preceded by a short bluff, just before the path that snakes over the hill and winds up at Little Fisherman's Cove. The prestigious sailing clubs tie up there and come ashore practically every weekend. After racing their sleek sailing boats while crossing the mainland channel, they put on one continuous party until they wash back out to sea.

The Isthmus bay is full of power boaters that scoot around trying to find a mooring. Then they jump into skiffs and row ashore, landing either in the snack bar restaurant or on the sandy Isthmus beach. The more adventurous types often wander to the back bay/Cat Harbor, taking in the Catalina air, hoping to see some wild island animals roaming around.

But today, Ross and I were oblivious to the goings-on around the Isthmus. It was our beach time, our time to relax in the sun and plan our next adventure. Because, without a next adventure, what is there to look forward to? Just as we were about to come to the bluff overlooking the beach, Ross said, "Look, Gilly. It's the Boy Scouts unloading their goodies from the Blanche W., and look who's giving you the stare." I looked over and, yep, there was my good friend Randall, who seemed to be glaring at me from the rail of the pier. I asked Ross, "Is he throwing me gang signs or something?"

"Not really. I think he's giving you the bird."

"Who me?" I asked jokingly. "Gosh, I thought everybody loved me."

"No way."

"Oh yeah! Where did you get that idea, Ross?"

"They hate your guts. They think you're nuts!"

"What?" I asked. "Even you?"

"Yeah, you dip, sometimes even me."

"But I'm such a sensitive guy."

"Riiight," Ross added sarcastically. "Who told you that, your mother?

"Ha-ha," I returned fire now by laughing and smirking at Randall. "The bird? No way… not a scout. It must be his way of telling me I'm number one."

"Wrong again, dipshit," Ross added.

My cousin Jeff always said, "Life has a way of abruptly changing the conversation." And, it did just that. I glanced up to the path on the bluff above our beach and could see the shadow of a figure walking toward us. As it got closer, I was delighted. Yeah, really delighted to see him coming our way. He never waved or gave a welcoming gesture, but I knew it was Billy Tuck. That meant the Geronimo had landed after a morning of racing and Tuck, tired of playing sailor games, was looking for me. I hadn't seen him since last summer. Yet, I knew there would be no fond hello or catch-up talk. It would be just like the next day's weather report: Sunny, and we'd be back to usual.

Billy Tuck had the appearance of being shy, but don't let that fool you. He was, but he harbored poignant unforgiving opinions for just about anything. Tuck had this way of expressing himself by using the least amount of words possible. A "yes" or "no" would do. An adjective could become a complete sentence in Tuck's vernacular. He let few people into his world, and I was proud to say I was one. Tuck was smaller, more like a miniature of his father. As usual he was walking barefoot, in shorts and a boating crested sailing T-shirt and burdened only with a backpack, probably filled with clothes. Enough, I figured, for a few days. Tuck's complexion was always blackened by the sun on the sailing trip from the mainland, so I nicknamed him "the pigmy," which always made him laugh.

When he approached, I just nodded and said, "Hey, Tuck, long time no see. His response of course, "Yeah." No need to go beyond that now. There seemed to be little reason to talk about the past eight months, for that was in another life.

The gang was complete with his arrival. All the chess pieces were on the board, and I really liked the prospects for this summer. This was going to be my last and best summer at the Isthmus. And, I wasn't going to let it get away without something dramatic to remember it by.

Then, yes, there she was, now coming off the bluff, still some distance away. She stepped from the path to the beach and, like Tuck, was already barefoot. I stopped and stared; it was his older sister. She wore her white, one-piece bathing suit half covered by jean shorts. Patty was like fine china...don't mess with it, don't get too close, don't try to handle. It may lose its gloss. Images are that way.

Tuck laughed seeing me hypnotized by his sister. "You just have to live with her for awhile." That broke up my gawking and brought me back to reality. She raised her hand and waved to me, letting me know somehow I existed in her life. Finally, she was close enough to say a soft, "Hi, Gil." Wow, that was enough. I returned with, "Hi, Patty." And the case was closed again.

So Ross, Billy Tuck and I scrambled down to the beach. While swimming, Ross caught Tuck up about our episodes with the girls and the confrontation with Randall and the scouts. Tuck responded, "That spazz? He's still around?" We sat there on the beach for awhile, noticing the new bikini styles on the girls parading about in their exclusive area until they all started to look the same and we got bored. We got up when I suggested getting back to the camp to see what was going on.

On the way, we meandered through the snack bar. Linda always greeted us with a stern, "What do you guys want?" We'd say, "Nothing, just looking around." She'd then suggest with a smile that we look around outside.

Linda was always kind of like this semi-mother type. She'd give us some sharp conversation, but she would always slip in a smile. Much like her father, it was all business in the snack bar and restaurant. But, she always let us know we were a bit more special than the regular boaters or occasional tourists, pouring in daily from the Blanche W. excursions. You see, we weren't islanders like her family, born and raised in Avalon. However, we weren't entirely mainlanders either. After years of spending summers at the Isthmus, we were looked upon as some kind of half-breed, caught somewhere in the middle.

This made us stand apart from the rest, an exclusive status bestowed only to people who had a right... a purpose to be there. We could never be the Taylors or the Bombards. So, who could we be? Just the Lefebvres from the baseball camp. We were happy with that, to be there, to be a part of and contribute to the Isthmus history.

We walked up the freshly whitewashed rock pathway leading to the camp, then up the ramp and into the kitchen. "Billy, good to see you," mother said. "How's your family doing?"

"Fine."

"Well, I'm happy to see you, and I know Gilly is too."

I smiled. "Gee, Mom, don't get too sentimental now."

"Billy, look who else is here,." mother continued as she pulled us over to the door that led to our craft room. There he was, Clyde. Mother said, "Clyde, look who's here," as if I'd just stepped off the boat. "It's Gilly!"

I jumped in, "Hey, Clyde," never expecting to get a response. I noticed he was engrossed with drawing a picture and coloring it in. Clyde really didn't fit into the category of the mentally challenged. He was beyond that. At 13, it was obvious he was a deranged psychopath. Well, maybe that was going too far. Maybe he was just wired into some other planet. He'd stayed at our house on the mainland for a brief period. His parents hoped that hanging around us would be a good antidote for what he had. But, it seemed no one could ever figure out what that was. I called it an obsession with trouble. My mother wanted me to take him under my wing and guide him back to sanity.

"Wow, Mom," I sighed. "Not again." Looking now at Clyde drooling on his drawing and my mom's pleading eyes, I agreed, "Okay. Okay I'll try."

"Now, Clyde," mother said, "you do what Gilly tells you." I looked over at Ross and Billy Tuck smiling. Then, I mumbled under my breath, "He'll be out of here in a week."

With mother back in the kitchen, I asked, "Hey Clyde, what ya drawing, some animals? Let me see." After looking at the picture I said, "Dang, man, why so much bleeding? Looks like a blood transfusion or something. Do you want to be a doctor?" As usual, Clyde didn't answer. "Well then, maybe a vampire?" Ross and Tuck attempted to conceal their laughter.

"I am hunting them down," Clyde said, coming back to our world.

"Why, Clyde? Are you hungry or something?"

"No, that is what they're for, to hunt."

"Okay, dip. At least keep the crayons inside the lines."

"No, I won't!" he said.

"His first act of defiance," I thought. "Here, let me show you," I said, as I took his crayon, sat down on the table and attempted to impose order into his drawing. He grabbed his other crayon and scribbled over my suggestion. I snatched the paper from him, and he cried out so the whole building could hear, "VERRGINNNNYAAA!"

My mother rushed in. "What's the problem?"

I just shook my head and walked away saying, "Why me, Mom? Why me?" Mother allowed me to stoke out my fire.

While we finished up the dinner pots and pans, mother came in and introduced a new worker. "This is Billy Hawkins, big Ben's younger brother," she said. He was a lanky kid that always seemed to be smiling, even when he really wasn't. Since his ribs were the most prominent part of his physique, we just called him "Billy Bones" or "Bones" for short.

After campfire, we rested back in the cabin. Ross, me, Billy Tucker, Shane, Jeff, Dennis and Ret Taylor (Linda's cousin) began talking about the summer ahead of us. The radio played while Ret spread out on the top bunk reading his new Playboy magazine. At 8 p.m., we heard someone call out, "Lights out!" We knew the rule didn't apply to us, or did it? Just then, bam! The door was kicked open and in came the new disciplinarian, Tauso. He was like some kind of martial arts expert and an ex-military guy. "You turn out those lights, or…"

"Or what?" I asked.

He snapped back directly at me and said, "Hey, you little shithead. I know your father owns this camp, but that doesn't mean a thing to me. You question me again, and I'll shove this boot right up your ass!"

"So much for nepotism," I thought to myself as he pulled out the radio cord from the socket and threw it across the cabin. He walked over and yanked the magazine away from Ret, then turned out the light and slammed the door. And, that was it. He left. Everybody sat in stunned quiet and then started laughing. "Who in the hell was that guy?" Ret asked. Then, just as abruptly as he left, he returned. "Did I hear a word out of you bastards?"

Somewhere from the corner of the pitch darkened room, a squeamish voice responded, "No."

"Remember, the next time I come in here, I'll be wearing my boots!" And, with that he left again. We began to fall sleep, already thinking, how we had to put a stop to this guy. Complain to my dad? No way, too punk. That's not me. No, we had to deal with him on our own terms, and that would have to wait until the morning. In the dark I whispered to Tuck, "Good to see you here." There was no reply. I began to dream as I fell asleep thinking of Patty.

CHAPTER 16

# No Diving

With summer in full swing, the Isthmus became a splendid montage of sounds and smells. The boaters scurried about their moorings and then hustled to dry land to stretch out their limbs. They talked in the snack shop patio about the wind, sails and tides that brought them there. Overhead, the roar of Channel Airlines signaled its steady hourly schedule had begun. Most of the tourists onboard came over to this special place for the same reason, to find a few days of prescriptive relief from their stressful existence overtown.

Campers from the different coves came to the Isthmus regularly now. They arrived in small trucks to gather supplies, meet new arrivals or just mingle with the locals over a Coke or a beer. Looking back, we all had a tendency to overstate the part we played there. Actually, more was going on besides our adventures. But, that's the way it is, when you can only live one life at a time.

So it went, boats passing in and out, people going about their own way, all of them having something in common. Yet, they kept a certain distance from each other, except for a few moments at 11 a.m. each day. It was a time for this bustling micro-metropolis to come together and catch the arrival of the Blanche W. She carried with her tourists, looking to view the scenery in the most remote parts of the island. The trip took about an hour to travel from Avalon, along the shores of the west end. It gave the sightseers a good look at the coves and crannies that led into the island's interior. Once docked, the boat was greeted by divers, who beckoned passengers to throw coins into the clear blue water. The pier was always full of spectators waiting for someone or just gawking and observing with interest these new arrivals.

When there was time, we'd join the divers at the end of the pier. On a good day, we'd get a handful of coins and quickly spend them on delicious malts from the snack bar. Otherwise, in our free time, you'd find me, Billy Tuck and Ross just kicking back on the beach, letting summer overtake us. Oh yeah, we had big plans. But, for the moment we were evading them by laying back and soaking it all in from the water's edge.

Overtime, the beachfront began to get crowded. Tuck announced, "Invaders! We're being invaded by all these tourists."

"Okay, Tuck. So what should we do?" I asked.

"Let's take a flaty out for a cruise."

"Good idea, Tuck," I said and looked at Ross for a response. He agreed but with one condition. "As long as it's Tuck sailing that thing, not you, I'm in."

"I'm good, with that," I replied. So we jumped up, dove in and swam out to the float where the camp sailboats were tied up. We climbed aboard one and settled in. There was just enough room for the three of us. With Tuck at the helm, we set sail. It's truly something to look forward to on a hot day. Out toward the open bay of the Isthmus we sailed. Out where there were no rules to follow and no one to tell us where we could or could not go. We were free to sail to the horizon and beyond, sometimes dreaming that maybe, just maybe, we'd never come back. Like many times before, we sailed about a mile and a half out, around Bird Rock and then into open waters, trusting Tuck's sailing skills to get us home.

Out there, we relied only on our own discretion. We did these things knowing full well they carried with them responsibilities and consequences that were entirely ours and unforgiving. It was a natural recipe for maturity. I would later discover that traits like mistrust, suspicion and doubt were also needed in order to survive. But for now, this was another time and place.

And, yes, there were signposts along the way. Signs like, "NO DIVING" and others that cautioned about this or that activity. Rather than view them as blanket prohibitions, we preferred to think of them as discretionary warnings that gave us license to make a choice in the matter. Isn't that what being independent is all about? We weren't going anywhere, just somewhere. A safe place meant nothing to us immortals. To follow a prescriptive life tarnished the lust for it. Here we could sail into danger, just to see how we would deal with it. We somehow knew it would make us better, make us come alive, and no signs would dare keep us from that.

Ooh, maybe we'd get a scathing rebuke from my mother now and then. But, I could tell she understood. For, she was never really concerned as much about where we'd gone. She was just happy to see us come back safely. Mother was that way. "Life is yours to live. So live it your way. It's playing in the game, that's what's important. How it all comes out… well, that's just the way the ball bounces." I'm not sure if she was referring to divine providence, but, at this point in my life, I don't think it really mattered.

In the end, Ross, Tuck and I created our own memories to talk and laugh about. It also gave us a cause, a noble purpose to our daily routine, and we bonded over these shared adventures.

CHAPTER 17

# A Lobster Tale

Catalina is filled with a plethora of animals. Most of them have found their way to the island by natural migration. Others were left behind by motion picture studios, while some were just allowed to wander off by weekend boaters. The conservancy has a prodigious list of species that inhabit the island. Without being too specific, the list includes bats, birds, frogs, lizards, rodents, American bison and foxes, trailing in with mules, deer and goats. You can also add the wild pigs, which were coveted by the locals for numerous festive Isthmus luaus. They were wrapped with indigenous herbs, ironically brought from the mainland, then slowly baked underground with hot burning coals and served to the tourists for a few dollars a plate.

Of course, we wouldn't want to forget those damn Braham bulls. Whether intentional or not, they garnished and controlled the roads from the Isthmus to Avalon. One afternoon, Buzz, our camp dog, chased a small gathering of bulls right through the ball diamond. The game was suspended while they passed through. Plus, our campers needed time to dry out from diving in the shallows of Cat Harbor in order to flee from those unwelcomed beasts.

However, the island's most abundant creatures are not the ones who live above the sea, but the ones who live beneath. There, an entirely different world existed, one that provided provisions for Wednesday's Fish Night. What made this such a personal endeavor was that most of the seafood was caught, shot or gathered by the campers themselves.

On Tuesdays and Thursdays, our boat left at 5 in the morning and traveled out to Bird Rock, where the fishing began. The idea of catch and release wasn't in vogue back then, a least not at our camp. If you caught something eatable, you could guarantee it would end up in some kind of fish and chips recipe. We'd bounce around out there until 7 a.m. Then, we'd take back our catch, gutted and filleted.

Tuck never really had any interest in fishing, and I never had the patience for it. It just took too long. All that waiting in a rocky, smelly boat full of fish bait kind of turned the stomach. So, we made the best of these required, supervised trips by taking the dead fish and secretly placing them at the end of camper's lines while they snoozed. Waking them up with applause, now that was fun. And, the "catch" made the camper feel that getting up early and fighting through the fog and the cold chill around Bird Rock was worth the trip.

But, as far as Clyde was concerned, the week had just begun and we became entirely committed to rid the island of him. We stuck a dead boned fish on his hook while he played Rambo, attempting to jab a sharp knife into a dying fish. Something was definitely missing with that kid or, maybe he had too much.

Tuck and I wrestled with him and finally confiscated the knife from his cold callous hands. He wailed, "I'm going to tell Virginia what you did!"

"Go ahead, wacko. Do that," I said.

"You're supposed to be taking care of me!"

"Right, we'll take care of you." Now looking at Tuck, I added, "We're about to do just that." Tuck and I grabbed and propelled him out of the boat and into the water. After a few seconds, I dove in, just to make sure our tactic appeared at least semi-appropriate. I pushed, and Tuck pulled, Clyde back into the boat. As usual he yelled, "I'm going to tell Virginia!"

"Shut up, Clyde. I really don't care. Besides, who dove in and saved you anyhow?" Clyde didn't quite know how to take this disclaimer I'd just thrown his way. So, he calmed down and went back into his normal insane mode as we pressed back to the pier. Tuck looked at me. I knew what he was thinking. Dang, we're really starting to have fun again.

Our camp divers spent most of their leisure time doing want they liked. That was skin diving for fun and food for the camp. Abalone didn't have to be in season back then. "Pinks" were the delicacy of the species and could be picked up in the shallows. Lobsters were so plentiful they were also easy prey. In the afternoon, I went to Tuck and Ross and suggested we go spear some lobsters ourselves. "That's a pretty easy feat, right?"

"No, it's not," Ross said. "And, where are you going to get a spear gun?" Tuck and I looked at each other and chimed in at the same time, "Jimmy Brown!" My fond friend and camp counselor had one. He had everything. Ross dampened the mood with, "Hey, guys, he's not going to loan it to you."

"Why do you say that, Ross?" I asked.

"He knows every time you borrow something, it gets lost or broken."

"No way, you're making things up, Ross. Let's just go ask him." We trudged over to his room, getting all excited about our spear fishing quest, but it wouldn't be that easy because his roommate said, "Brownie's down dragging the infield, and I don't know when he's coming back."

"So, later on?" I asked.

"Yeah, that's about it, Gil."

"Hummmm, okay, well," I reached over and grabbed Brownie's arbalete. "I'll just use it for awhile."

His roomy jumped in. "You know how Brownie is, Gil." Then, he raised his hands and shook his head. "Hey, remember. I know nothing about this."

Ross added, "Not a good idea, Gil."

I looked over to Tuck. "What do you think?"

He smiled as always with a little smirk. "Why not, Big G.?"

"Well," I said. "Tomorrow is tomorrow; today is today." Again, it made no sense at all, but, unlike Ross, Tuck and I needed no sense – it really had no purpose here. We just wanted to go spear fishing. As we turned to leave with Brownie's arbalete in hand, Ross continued. "No way I'm going along with this."

Down to the beach we went. Tuck swam out to the float, untied one of our boats, climbed in, then rowed back to shore to pick me up. Ross refused to get in and said, as he threw up his hands, "Not me. You're both crazy. I don't need any trouble with Brownie."

You see, Ross lived a measured life. It was a strained recipe of adventure simmered with caution. Unlike Ross, Tuck and I couldn't follow a recipe, not for lack of talent, but primarily… we just didn't care. What fun we'd miss if we did. Oh, we might pay for it later, but that would take care of itself…later. Right?

Off we went with our borrowed arbalete. Clearly, "borrowed" may not be the appropriate word here. However, it was the best we had. While rowing over to Little Fisherman's on the point, where the water shallowed above the reef, Tuck and I talked about his friends back in Long Beach. But, it didn't matter much because what was happening in our lives was here. Tuck and I never talked about purpose or goals. We let those ideas filter in from somewhere else. Maybe we'd let some suggestions from his sister, Patty, into our conversation. But, besides getting a little input from the opposite gender, we didn't let it take up too much of our time. Tuck and I were like the right and left hands. When one moved, the other helped out. No need to talk about where we were going.

Dressed in our diving gear of masks and fins, overboard we went, bubbling our way around. Tuck stayed a safe distance behind. Maybe it was because I was equipped with a lethal spear gun, which at the moment was not all that endearing to him. We looked like a takeout from a James Bond movie, as I propelled around the reef with Tuck serving as my navigator, steering me around by pulling on my fin. Experience with the spear? None, neither one of us. Therefore, the task became more of a co-operative endeavor. Yeah, that's the operative word.

On Catalina Island the concept of entitlement also goes beneath the surface. What one sees down there is appalling. There are these bright orange fish called garibaldi that have an attitude. They must have paid off some state legislator because they had a unique status as an endangered species. That's okay, but they all knew it! In my attempt to navigate around the reef, they enjoyed slowly passing in front, blocking my line of vision. Kind of like saying, "Ha-ha you can't touch me." After a few frustrating minutes of their abusive indulgence obstructing our diving, I surfaced. Tuck intuitively read my thoughts and asked, "Why don't we just shoot the suckers? That'll teach them a lesson." I liked that idea, and it did cross my mind. But, then what would we do with a dead garibaldi? I'm sure there could be a hefty fee for a garibaldi fish and chips dinner. I knew that's what Ross would say. So, I avoided the temptation and dove down.

Orange, just orange, that's all I saw again. But, then I saw it – something orange but clothed in a shell with tentacles. It was big, really big! I resurfaced and garbled to Tuck. "Did you see that?" With a big smile, Tuck gave me the thumbs-up sign. Our moment of truth and the completion of our diving exploit were just a few feet away. Like a pilot fixated on the enemy target, I plunged back into the deep, searching. I saw it dart into a crevice, guarded by flowing kelp that shielded it from my vision. I knew it couldn't get away. I could see it on our plates right now. Enough for Tuck and me, and let Ross eat crow as he begged to sit in on this feast. I pulled the trigger. The spear sliced through the water like a torpedo. It headed straight for the target and entered through the crevice, just as planned. I waited for an instant, knowing I had it. All that was needed was to surface with my line still attached to our prey.

"We got it, Tuck!" I muffled through my snorkel. Then, I immediately dove back into the shallows to capture this beautiful entrée. However, as I tugged the line, the lobster refused to give up. I pulled harder, but to no avail. Now, I'd had it with this crustaceous prey. I gave it one last jerk and, finally, it broke loose. The first thing I noticed was how it disguised itself when threatened. For, it came out not orange but brownish and thin as it slithered out of the crack. By now, I was thinking that Tuck's idea of shooting the garibaldi wasn't so bad. I continued to reel in the rope. Oh my God! There on the end of my line was not a delicious lobster dinner but a very angry 6-foot eel! And, to make matters worse, I'd shot him in the tail. That allowed his crushing jaws all the flexibility they needed to treat us in an unkindly manner. Immediately, I gave into discretion rather than valor and dropped the spear in order to quickly surface toward a safer world. Tuck and I quickly retreated back into the boat.

Keeping my mask on, I hung over the side with my face in the water. I had to see what was going on down there! "Big G.," Tuck said between heavy breathing. "How are we going to get Brownie's arbalete back?" The situation had clearly taken on some new issues. Neither Tuck nor I was about to dive back in the water and attempt to retrieve it with the angry eel attached to the end of the shaft.

It was decision time as we sat safely in the boat. "Got any ideas?"

Tuck replied, "One thing's for sure, we can't go back down there."

"Okay," I said. "That's a good start. So, what about Brownie's arbalete?"

"Maybe he won't miss it for a couple of days, and it's not going anywhere for awhile."

"Maybe. Okay, let's go back to shore, back to camp, get a string, come back, dive down, tie it to the arbalete and pull it up from the boat. Then, we can drag it back to the beach." Now, that sounded like a good plan. Actually, it was the only plan we had, so there was no other choice.

After making a mental note of the spot, we rowed back to shore. By now, it was getting late and dinner was just a short time off. Ross and I had kitchen duty, and my mother was becoming a bit strained over my repeated late arrivals. Plus, Clyde followed through on his threat and had passed on his low regard of me to my mom. Consequently, I had a lot on my mind that night.

Patty came in to tell Tuck his dad wanted him back on their boat. So, off goes Tuck. As I entered the kitchen, Ross jumped right on me. "You know your mother is ticked off about throwing Clyde into the water this morning. You should have heard him crying." With that, he began to act out the scene for me. "'Virginia, Gilly and his dark friend tried to kill me!'" Ross laughed at the drama of it all.

"I already know about that, Ross. So what's new?"

With a sarcastic smile Ross said, "You've got the pots and pans tonight."

"No problem," I said, warding off Ross's delight.

"So, what did you great divers haul in today?"

Now remember, Ross always said he could see it in my eyes when I lied. So, I answered, "We had an uneventful day."

"Uneventful day? Did you look up 'uneventful' in the dictionary? I know you didn't find that word yourself." Ross laughed.

"No. I got it from Tuck."

"Riiiiiight," Ross said, now continuing to drill me like he was the prosecutor and I was on the witness stand, under oath. "Okay. Now I know you're lying!"

"No, I'm not!"

"Yes, you are! So what happened? Come on. Tell me!"

"I'll tell you if you tell me what you got off that Kimberly girl last week."

"No...no you'll never know! Anyway, what's that got to do with anything? Oh and by the way, did you get Brownie's arbalete back to him?"

I kept quiet, refusing to get into the heart of that matter.

"Bull's eye!" Ross exclaimed, now in full taunting mode. "You didn't, did you?" Pressing the point, he continued. "I told you that would happened. I never lend you anything because you either lose it or break it. Always! Sooooo, what happened to Brownie's arbalete?"

"Okay...okay. Geez, Ross." Hoping not to let the cat out of the bag, I tried quieting down the conservation and said, "Let's go back into the bread room and I'll tell you what happened." That side room had refrigerators on one side and, on the other, rows of cardboard breadboxes stacked from the floor up. Just coming from the kitchen and in the middle of cleaning the utensils, I had a dirty butcher knife in my hand. As I made my point about this afternoon's blundering, Ross began to laugh. "There you go. See, that's why I don't go along with you and Tuck on your crazy ventures. Something always gets screwed up!"

"What? Did I screw you up with the girls last week? You seemed to have no trouble going along with THAT venture!"

He smiled. "Okay, okay, what are you going to tell Brownie about his $100 arbalete that's at the bottom of the ocean, somewhere between Little Fish and Bird Rock? Man, he's going to kick your ass!"

"I would really like to," I said and, without thought, hurled the butcher knife at the breadbox just to show my frustration. Unfortunately or fortunately for Ross, it whizzed by, far too close for comfort, and stuck into the breadbox next to his head.

"Some circus throw," I thought, relieved. That wasn't supposed to happen. Ross's eyes attempted to escape from his head with fear of the possibilities of what could have occurred if the knife had just been a few inches closer. This didn't, by any stretch of the imagination, refute the deranged persona held by my skeptics. As a result of this close call, Ross let out the obvious response again, "You're crazy! I'm telling you... crazy! You could have killed me!"

"No way!" I said, in my defense. "I'm too good to have hit you. Let me try it again," I pleaded to distract him from what had just happened.

"Hell, no!" Ross answered. "And, you would do it, wouldn't you?"

I tried to keep a straight face but couldn't. "Come on Ross. You got to trust me, dude."

"Yea, right," he mumbled and went back into the kitchen to finish up. Sometime later, Ross's humor was revived. "So what are you going to do about Brownie's arbalete?" I told him our plan.

"What if you go out there and it's gone? Then what?"

"Well, I'll worry about that when it happens."

Just then, mother walked in. "Gilly, what's this about you throwing Clyde in the water this morning?"

"Mom, Clyde, had this fishing knife and was stabbing all of the catch 25 times just to make sure they were dead. Then, he was cutting campers' lines when they weren't watching. Mom, this guy's a nut... no actually a loony, and he won't listen to anything I tell him. He gets dumped into the water, and did he tell you I jumped in myself and pulled him out? No, I bet he didn't tell you that!"

"I know, Gilly. Clyde is a little unusual. But, his parents have been good friends of ours for a long time and they want Clyde to be around you... hoping that he'll pick something up. You always take such good care of the homesick kids by getting them involved. So please try some more, and if it doesn't work out, okay. Let him be just one of the boys."

"Okay, Mom. I'll try. But...."

"I know. I know. You will."

"All right, Mom."

"See you in the morning, boys." As mother walked out the door, she noticed the knife stuck in the breadbox. "Who did that?"

"Don't forget, Mom, Clyde's been around here."

She took a deep breath. "Okay, well, put it back in the kitchen. Good night again."

Ross started to laugh. "Clyde? You and Tuck are the loonies. And, your mother wants him to be like you? Now that's just crazy! Two, no three running the cuckoo's nest."

At our first break of the next day, Tuck and I, along with a hand spear, ventured back out to sea. After finding the arbalete, we became excited. It was as if we had discovered for the first time the Titanic resting at the bottom of the sea. I dove down cautiously because the eel was still lurching about, attempting to free itself from the arbalete's shaft. After grabbing the line with the spear, we swam back and climbed into the boat. Then, we began to reel in Brownie's arbalete. Sure enough, the eel was still on the line. We didn't even try to bring it up into the boat, for fear of its flaying about and those frightful teeth, looking to lock onto something. So, we towed it to shore and laid the deadly creature on the sand. Passersby stopped to see our catch, stumbling their way down the beach taking pictures and asking peculiars about our quest. To us, the eel wasn't the prize that day. Retrieving Brownie's arbalete was.

We sprinted back to hide Brownie's arbalete in the back of our cabin, along with Ret Taylor's Playboy magazines. Those magazines added to the cabin library. However, our most valuable literature would still be Sports Illustrated and College Football Review, which were now scattered about our unruly cabin. It was our intent to put back the arbalete discreetly, without Brownie ever knowing he had loaned it. Of course, Brownie, up to this time, was fully unaware of ever having loaned it to us in the first place.

That afternoon, we played ball on our sandlot. Ross was managing his team and Tuck served as my assistant manager. In the late innings, Tuck looked over to Cat Harbor and noticed the sand sharks were sunning themselves in the shallow waters. So, after the game, we took the campers over to view the shark fins moving around the bay.

After the workouts were over, I suggested Ross, Tuck and I go down and see if we could play with the sharks by running in and grabbing their tails while they swished about. "Good idea," I thought, and if this didn't work, we had Brownie's arbalete to further entertain us. Tuck agreed that it was another good idea, but Ross, as always, had reservations. He disagreed with the feasibility of the plan and instructed, "You'd better get that arbalete back into Brownie's room before he knows it's gone, or he's going to kick your ass."

"Not a problem, Ross. You always worry too much. Come on, don't miss the fun."

Off we went, down to Cat Harbor. Our first attempt at pulling the shark's tails became far too difficult a task, so we went with Plan B and it looked as if it would be another great idea. However, here's where the problem really began. As I raced across the water holding Brownie's prized weapon, I pulled the trigger. Mind you, it was only the second time I ever shot the thing. It was like throwing rocks at flying sea gulls… you really never think you'll hit one. It's just something to throw at. But, this time, unfortunately the spear struck the tail of one of these peaceful creatures. Some days later, we'd consider the inhumanity or humanity of that action. But, not at this moment, for it was the cause of our undoing.

Once the spear hit the tail of the shark, it began to escape toward deeper waters. Small detail, we forgot to retie the line to Brownie's spear. The shark now owned the spear, as we chased him about, trying to grab the shaft embedded in its tail. No such luck. The last time we saw that shaft, it was slowly disappearing, like a submarine periscope. It submerged inch by inch until it completely disappeared from the surface, along with the shark. Now, we had a problem. The question was whether it was Brownie's problem or ours? And, of course, Ross was about to have a ball with this one. He'd keep this story as ammo for a long time, countering me with a defense for any dumb thing I said about him.

As far as Brownie was concerned? After a period of outrageous descriptive expletives about my personal character, in the end, I gave up one of my finest baseball mitts in exchange for the lost arbalete. I'd named it affectionately, "Mickey," after Mickey Mantle of course. This was just about as far as I would go to make him happy again. No further. Tuck and I had a philosophy of sharing, and I told

Tuck, "We would have let Brownie borrow our arbalete if we had one. Wouldn't we?"

Tuck smirked and said, "Big G., we don't have one."

I said, "But Tuck, if we did, we would have." That was the kind of dog-chasing-its-tail sort of reasoning that always worked for us. As far as Ross was concerned, he really never understood that sort of logic. His world was a just little too rational to understand ours.

CHAPTER 18

# Operation Cherry Cove

T he island had fallen into the night, and the Isthmus was fast asleep. But, inside our cabin, all of our comrades and co–conspirators wrestled with flashlights as we went over our plans. Ross, Jeff, Tuck, plus Press's son Tay and his cousin Ret, along with our newest recruit, Danny Watercutte, had been working on this for some time now. We had a mission to carry out tonight. Preparation was key to success, so we carefully walked through it one step at a time. Timing, surprise and the escape plan were the most crucial aspects. That's what always made it work. We knew they would look for us first. Who else would it be? But, without any proof, there would be no case.

We carried on through the late hours of the night, going over every detail. Ross suggested we wear our baseball cleats, and, for the first time since the girl thing, I thought he had a good idea. We needed to dress for speed, because that would be our advantage. Tuck provided us with enough firepower to let Cherry Cove have a good wakeup call, that's for sure. Tuck had a large collection of fireworks he'd pilfered from his dad's boat club parties. So we had at our disposal a variety of pyrotechnics. There were some 180s, which gave us lots of pop, then a few conventional low-grade generic firecrackers for effect. Yep, that should be enough. But again, Ross leaned on caution as we scrambled about with preparations. "So what happens if they find out we did it?"

"Hey, that kind of attitude never stopped us before, Ross. Relax, they'll never prove it! Unless... unless..." I slowly garnished my thought. "Unless you screw up! You weren't so worried about sneaking out and messing with Kimberly, now were you, Ross?" He'd rather forget the question, as a low chuckle came and anchored the frenzy for just a few moments. Jeff said, "Randall will be let off his leash after tonight." I disagreed. "Randall, no, he's too well trained to do anything on his own. He's like one of those German officers in WWII movies; great soldier if he goes through the right door, but he has trouble, stumbling over his feet, when he has to act on his own."

Ret, like Jeff, had little experience in these matters but knew the Isthmus was our territory and we needed to do things like this every once in a while if we wanted to carry on with the boat girls on the weekends. The scouts would never dare come into our neighborhood and do what we do. Ret needed some reassurance that the ammo would work. Tuck quickly replied in the positive, and that's all he needed to hear. Matches and explosive devices were handed out to our designated commandos. Yeah, now this was real fun, and the thought of getting caught only made our adrenaline flow faster. No need for Red Bull in our day, just a grand daring idea served the purpose.

It was time. Out we went, all seven of us. Without a sound we slipped from the cabin and traversed over to the main road, being careful to say little and use our flashlights only sparingly, trusting on past experience and the light of the full moon. We found the road. It was partially patched with oil, but most of it was hard-packed dirt that led from the Isthmus to Parson's Landing, some seven miles down the road. We weren't going that far, just two coves over, just beyond 4th of July Cove to our target, Cherry Cove, home of the Boy Scouts.

Cherry Cove Boy Scouts Camp was one of the most popular scout programs in the western United States. The camp had been in that same location since the 1920s. It's 1.3 miles from the Isthmus and the home to scout leader Randall J. Cunningham the Third for the summer. It was our time to remind him we were here too.

As the night led us closer, I reviewed our plan. Jeff, Danny, Tay and Ret would traverse to the western side of Cherry and light their fireworks as diversions. Once the camp lights begin to come on and the scouts begin to fumble around, half awake and turning toward the noise, Ross, Tuck and I would let go with the 180s on the east side of Cherry. If you've ever heard one of those 180s go off, especially in the quiet of night, in a cove that carries an echo, what a blast. You'd think it was Pearl Harbor all over.

Eventually, we found the path heading in to Cherry Cove and quietly descended into the valley. Once in the cove, we hid in the brush unnoticed. Now, all we had to do was wait for the others to get into position. When they lit up the first firecrackers, then things would begin to pop like popcorn. That will be our trip line to let go with the 180s. Ret, Tay, Jeff and Danny were to stay put for a while, then come back home, but only after everything begins to settle down. Ours was a bit more ominous. We would hit them and then retreat back to the Isthmus. Sounds easy, except for the fact that we knew the scouts would chase us by truck.

All went off like planned. The fireworks created a distraction on the other side of the cove., We heard, "POP...POP...POP... POP..." as we lay still in the bushes. We could see the scout leaders running about, flashing lights in the other direction. Once the campers' lights began to come on, one by one, it was time for act two. Our hands were shaking as we carefully lit the 180s, placed of course in an area where the explosion would be out of harm's way of anything flammable. We certainly didn't want to bring in the fire department or actually hurt any of the slumbering scouts, only to jolt and deny them of a few hours of sleep.

BAAAAMMMMM!! BAMMMMM!! BOOOOM! BOOOOM! The whole cove lit up! The 180s brought their music home. Even the moored boats were flipping on their flashlights and shouting out into the dark. Now the race was on! We had to get back to the barracks undetected. To do this, we needed to beat the ensuing scouts, who'd gotten the message and began jumping into their trucks. They knew the way back to our camp as well as we did. But, to their disadvantage, the trucks needed to go to the back of Cherry Cove in order to pick up the main road. As planned, this would give us the time we needed. We cut down through 4th of July, then up the side and raced toward the Isthmus trailhead.

Once we finally reached the road, we looked back. As expected, there were two trucks in pursuit. It was only a quarter of a mile to reach the Isthmus trailhead. However, fatigue was unquestionably beginning to hinder our performance. We were just baseball players and, even though we had our cleats on, this wasn't the 90-foot run to first base we were used to. The last quarter of a mile began to kick in, and the bear quickly jumped on our backs. We looked back again, just for a moment to see the headlights turning the last corner on their rush to the Isthmus.

Luckily, we made it to the trail some distance ahead of them and dove down the path, hiding in the bushes as the trucks passed. They had to go to the back of the Isthmus first, giving us a good head start. Our hearts pumped as we scampered down passed the Groves' house on the western hill and then on across the brushy field, tripping over dead tree branches and whatever else was in the shadows. Finally, finding relief in our darkened cabin, we continued in silence mode, slid into our bunks and caught our breath. Sometime later, a soft knock came on the back of our cabin. We opened the door for Ret, Tay, Jeff and Danny. With their safe return, all that was left was our silence and denial to make the mission a success.

Our door was abruptly kicked open. Head counselor Tauso stepped in like some German Gestapo guy out of another war movie and yelled, "All of you guys, get out of bed!" As we pretended to be waking up, we rubbed our eyes and slowly climbed out of our bunks. He continued, "Look, you may think this was a funny thing you pulled tonight, but we had the sheriff, the fire department and the scouts going crazy looking for the people who pulled off the prank. Also, some of the boaters are driving Doug crazy thinking some boat exploded in Cherry Cove. They even radioed the Coast Guard. Soooo, what do you know about this thing? Everybody's pointing the finger at you!"

I spoke up first, "Man, we don't know anything. We…" Before I had time to finish with my planned denial speech, he snapped, "Shut up Gil! Do you think I'm a damn idiot?"

Since he brought up the subject, I was ready to show my arrogance by saying, "Yeah, I do." Except the timing was wrong. Tauso turned to the rest of the guys. First to Ross, thinking he'd probably be a good target to confess our guilt. No, not going to happen. He pleaded the fifth. Tauso went into another rant. "I don't know where you guys are coming from, but this is serious business and I need some answers! And Gil, your dad isn't very amused with your little escapade." Trying again, he stared down at Ross, who again refused to budge. "What about you, Jeff?"

"Hey, the only thing that would get me out of bed…"

"Yeah, I know, some hot girls, smart ass. What about you two Taylors?"

Ret explained, "Hey man. I just came to visit my cousin last night and crashed here."

"How about you, Danny? What do you have to say for yourself, son?"

"Son?" I thought. That seemed to be a little strong on desperation. I began to fight off a laugh.

Danny replied, "I was sleeping and reading."

"You, reading?" Tauso reached under the top bunk mattress and pulled out the latest Playboy magazine, then said, "This is what you call reading? Pervert."

Ret jumped in, "Hey that's mine! Don't take that." I thought it was about time to intervene and said, "You know, master counselor, Ret's having trouble adjusting to girls."

Tauso looked over at me. "You think this is funny? I told you to shut up, Gil. Your father's not happy with this, and he's not going to back you up this time. So I'd wipe that cocky smile off your face." He looked over to Tuck. "And you, why do I take the time to ask for your answer? Whatever Gil does, you back that dumb shithead up, no matter how idiotic his ideas are. They tell me he's been trouble since the day he was born. You know, someday I hope all of you get drafted into the military. You pull these kind of stunts, and you'll find someone who'll put a boot up your ass!"

With that dramatic finale he turned and was gone, of course confiscating Ret's Playboy on his way out. "Our denial rests, your honor," I said.

"That guy scares the shit out of me," Jeff added as he climbed back in his bunk. "Why did you dad hire that maniac anyway?"

I replied, "To scare the shit out of us. That's why."

We began to enjoy the night, what a caper. Now that our alibi, for the moment, hadn't been broken we burst into laughter and began to retell the night's raid. Ret told how he'd fallen off the trail and landed into some cactus. Then, he went on to size up the disposition of his rights about the stolen magazine. But, all in all, we came to the conclusion, mission accomplished.

Early the next morning, a small knock came on the door. Ross opened it carefully. "It's Clyde," Ross said with obvious disappointment.

"What?" I asked. "What does he want?" Clyde walked in and said, "Well, I just wanted to know if I could borrow a firecracker."

"Why?" I asked.

"Because I want to blow up this frog I found yesterday," he said as he held up a bottle to show us his intended target.

"Listen, wacko. First of all, why would you want to blow up a frog? Everyone knows what they're good for." Not pandering to his nonsense, I asked "And, what do you mean 'firecrackers?'"

"I mean the ones you guys hide in the backroom."

"Clyde, how do you know we have firecrackers in the backroom?"

"Cause, I seen them, that's why. And, Virginia is all mad. She thinks you threw them at the Boy Scouts last night."

"Hey, look, wacko. You're not allowed in our cabin, never and I mean never! So get out of here."

"Okay. But I'm going to tell Virginia about the firecrackers."

"You do that dummy, and we'll make sure you'll be very sorry. Just remember that!" I said as I pushed him out.

I heard him yell when I closed the door, "I'm going to tell Virginia you shoved me!"

Once he left, Ross asked, "What if he does?"

"So what. We know nothing about it, right? And besides that, what are my parents going to do? Send me home? Hey Ross, worry about your girl, Kimberly. Now that could be a real problem up the road."

"What do mean 'problem?'" Ross asked.

"Never mind," I said, hoping just to plant some worry in his mind, to keep him at bay.

Back into the kitchen we went, ready for breakfast detail.

Mother was there to greet us all, this time before we came in the door. "Ross, I know you would never do something like what happened last night." Then she turned to me and said, "Dad is furious with you. But, he's still not sure you and your bunch did it."

I began to break a smile and mother smiled back. "Well, let's just say it wasn't you and go from there. But, Gilly, you'd better watch your Ps and Qs for a while. Oh, by the way Clyde, said you have fireworks in your cabin. That's quite a coincidence, don't you think?"

"Mom, the guy not only walked into our cabin when we weren't around but searched the place, and he brought up the fireworks because he wanted to blow up a frog he'd captured in a glass bottle. The guy's a sicko, Mom! Better get the guy out of here, before somebody really does something to him."

She took a deep breath and sighed. "Okay, but until then, don't give him any other reason to want to go home. We'll just weed him out, sooner or later."

"Well, I hope it's sooner rather than later, Mom."

"Dad's overtown. He'll get a laugh about this one, but not today. So keep a low profile, Gilly, a real low profile. Your dad is tired of making excuses for you. But, I know he always says you put fun into his life."

"What about you, Mom?"

"Oh, what are mothers for anyway?" she said with a smile.

The day went on as if the night before had never happened. As Tuck, Ross and I walked down to the field for workout, I said, "Wow." And, with a sense of relief I added, "We could have been in some real trouble on that one. But, it'll never happen again." Ross shook his head, knowing better. Tuck looked at me with a smirk on his face that turned into a cheek-to-cheek grin, saying nothing. We all knew it would happen again.

CHAPTER 19

# In The Line of Fire

B y now, Ross's sense of caution had taken his attitude on a downward trip. So, before leaving to work out the campers on the field, I went by the shower room to see how he was doing. Each one of us had specific jobs outside our regular kitchen duties. Cleaning the bathroom was Ross's. The camp's enclosed toilets were alongside a massive shower area and both got Ross's special attention. While passing by, I smiled and said, "So how goes the latrine detail, Ross?" There was no response to my sarcasm as he continued to work on. I tried again. "We had a great time the other night."

"Yeah, you wait," Ross said, now breaking his silence, "until somebody squeals and I 'am on my way back home.'"

"Hey, dude. It's me you're talking to! When did I ever get you in trouble?"

"Let's see. We've got Tauso on our backs. I've had to lie to your mother. The sheriff and Coast Guard are doing some investigation, so you've probably got me violating state, federal and international laws. And, I'm sure that's not going to look very good on my resume!"

"And cleaning toilets will?" I asked laughing. "Come on, Ross.

You always look to the downside. If you want something to worry about, you might want to think about that girl. She loooovesss you. I could see it in her eyes."

Ross stopped and looked up at me. "Don't start on that again! I'm getting pretty damn tired of you bringing that up."

"Well, did you or didn't you?"

"Don't ask."

"Yeah, I will, when you have to marry her. Now that's something to really worry about, Ross."

"You know, the only thing that worries me, Gil, is that, for whatever reason, I always go along with your pranks. And then, trouble finds us."

"That's a good thing, Ross or you'd have a dull, boring life."

"Riiight. I'd rather have it dull than end up dead. That would be better than some kind of penitentiary or insane asylum like where you're going to end up."

"Get back to work, Ross," I ordered as I moved close to the shower window. I thought it was time to remind him. "Just think, a little over a week ago 60 girls stood right here," leaning against the window, I continued, "giving us a wonderful show every day. "See what I got you into. Not bad, hey? For the rest of your life, you'll remember that window." Finally, Ross couldn't help but laugh. "Well, enough talking to the help. Carry on," I said cheerfully as I walked out of the bathroom.

Now, Ross wasn't really a hypochondriac, but his mother must have thought he was. For, she took him to the doctor for everything and, when he came to camp, she must of thought he was going to war in the jungles of New Guinea. Ross had something for everything. Also, Ross was so meticulous about his clothes that, to messy friends like us, it became a rather obnoxious ritual. Consequently, Tuck and I decided when he left to clean up the heads that morning to take a couple of his shorts and socks, along with a few bottles of his medicine, and hang them like Christmas bulbs on a tree just outside our cabin door. Jeff, Shane and Danny got a kick out of it, and we laughed all the way down to the ball field.

During each two-week session, we broke the campers into teams and played a tournament. My team would be the Reds while Ross managed the Dodgers. We did our best to make the teams as equal as possible with the talent we had, in order to make the games competitive. Coaches gave their teams infield practice, and then it was, "play ball!" At the end of the session, there would be awards for everybody. Kind of like elementary school, where everybody became Student of the Month sooner or later – it was the same here.

So there we were, in the middle of the game, and here it came. It must have been around 10 a.m. because, once again, Channel Air sounded out the call of a sputtering engine just about to break the Isthmus apex. Everyone on the field stopped as usual to look up and see if the plane could, one more time, make it safely into the back bay. We saw it, barely tipping over the trees and, sounding like a balloon losing air, gyrate toward its landing zone without hitting any other obstacles. "It's just a crapshoot." I explained to one of the campers sitting on the bench next to me.

With the game now stopped and all eyes looking up to this daily drama, the plane whizzed overhead and bucked like one of those Braham bulls as it entered the water. After that, the plane revved its engine, as if in pride, letting everyone know it had made it once again.

About the fifth inning, Tuck came over, sat down next to me on the bench and said, "Ross took his stuff off the tree. He didn't look very happy."

I laughed. "Really?"

As the game progressed, Tuck pointed over to the barge at

the back bay. "Look, some weird guys are running in and out. What do you think is going on?" I looked back and, sure enough, there were a couple of dinghies tied up to the covered barge. I suggested, "You know, the next time we hike back into the harbor, we need to take a look as what's going on inside that thing."

After the game ended, the counselors walked their kids up to camp and then on to the beach. My dad stepped behind the backstop to control my life for the next hour. After a few warm-up swings, batting practice began. His newly hired, right-handed flamethrower decked me on an inside pitch, again. I was getting used to that. My dad specifically hired these pitchers to throw hard, but accuracy apparently wasn't a primary criteria. While I dusted myself off from the red dirt clay and sand, my dad waited to see my response. "Where did you get this guy, Dad? His glasses are so thick he can't even see me."

Shane tossed the ball back to the mound chanting, "Mercy, mercy, mercy, this guy's going to kill you."

Uh-oh, here it came. Dad began his rampage. Actually, I'd rather refer to it as his mantra. "Okay, Gil, this is what's going to happen if you try to hug the plate. Remember, when you play in front of 40,000 people as leadoff hitter, they'll always try to intimate you. They're going to try and take you off the plate with the fastball. If that intimidates you…well I guess you can try and make a good living playing the piano."

At that moment, I was thinking, "Yeah, maybe that's what I'd like to do."

"Get back in there. Here we practice and practice on the basics. It should be instinctive to you by now. The key is to keep the lead hand down and pop those hips." The next pitch found the plate, and I pulled the ball down the left field line. I knew it must be over the road this time. But, no, it simply ripped into the side but not over the road. "Patience, Gil. It'll come. It'll come." That thought continued to echo in my mind. It'll come someday. It'll go over that damn road. I finished my hitting and looked out to the road. It was only 300 feet away, and I'd barely even hit a ball that threatened to go over. The hill became animated in my mind, smiling at me, challenging me and then daring me. I knew my life in baseball depended on defiling that geological spectator.

Getting back to reality, we finished our practice then went back to camp. On my way back to the cabin for a rest, I passed Ross on his way to the kitchen. "Really funny...really funny," he mumbled. I saw his things were no longer hanging from the tree. And, as I stepped into the cabin, Jeff said, "You got his goat this time."

"Really?"

"Yeah, Ross told us,." "Damn Gilly and damn his pigmy sidekick. They're going to drive me crazy!'"

Ret was up on the top bunk reading his newest edition. I said, "Hey pervert, let me see what you're looking at." Jeff remarked, "Thank God for clothes. Clothes creates the suspense and lets the mind imagine what there is to see without them." But for Ret, I guess his creative appetite was just too short and direct. No fine connoisseur of women, just lust.

Ret laughed at my pervert reference, so I added, "Remember, that's what Tauso called you. Why aren't you like your suave cousin Tay? He knows how to appreciate fine women. Now Jeff and Tay can really teach you something." Just then Ross walked in. "Funny, just talking to Ret about you, Ross. I told him you knew how to close the deal with your Italian stallion charm. Like with Kimberly."

"Who's Kimberly?" Ret asked.

Ross waved his hands in the air. "Forget it, Ret. It's nothing. Just Gilly's B.S. as usual."

Now, with the tree-hanging thing over with, head counselor

Tauso again impolitely exploded through the cabin door. "Who taught you manners?" I asked sarcastically.

He must not have heard me because he barked, "Gil, your mother wants you to light the water heater. It's gone out. So get on it. And, by the way, this scout thing isn't over, and you're going to fry, Gil."

"What scout thing, master counselor?" I asked innocently. "It's like we said, we know nothing. Right?" I looked over to Tuck for support. "All of us were here sleeping soundly until you rudely kicked in the door and threatened us with a boot up our ass."

"Listen, smart ass, if your dad didn't own this camp, you'd be up shit creek!"

"But, my dad does own the camp," I reminded him. "So, I don't think I'll see shit creek in the near future."

"I'll get you, you shithead... sooner or later, I'll get you," he growled. While storming out of the door, he added, "You'd better get over and light the water heater....now!"

Lighting the water heater pilot was always fun and a bit of a mystery. You had to press in on the thing and allow for just the right amount of gas to come out, then light a match and stick it in at just the right time. The trouble was, how much gas did you need? We'd always pump it a little too much. Then, when we put the match to it, a burst of flames would shoot out, producing a small explosion that always caused us to jump backward.

So onward we went, over to the side of the building where the heater sat silently waiting. Since this was always a surprise, Jeff, Tuck and Ross came along for the show. After a few unsuccessful attempts, Ross stepped in and said, " You're not doing it right. Let me show you."

"No, I've done it before; you haven't." After a few more tries I decided, "Okay, Ross, your turn, but let me prime the gas pump."

"Fine," he replied, as he grabbed the matches.

"When I tell you… light it!" I said, as I pumped some more. When I could smell gas coming out, I pumped just a little more for effect. "Okay, Ross. Light the match and put it next to the pilot." Sure enough, he did it. A loud BOOM came out of the pipe and, like a dragon spitting fire, it flashed across Ross's face. He was now in a state of shock. We were reluctant to laugh until we saw if he was hurt from the explosion. Seeing that his tan face was looking far more tan, his eyebrows singed and his curly dark Italian hair frizzing but that he was still alive and cussing, we thought it would be okay to let loose with laughter. Not seeing the humor, Ross continued his cursing. I think it was a prayer… something about Jesus Christ? Then he switched over to me. "You damn idiot! Gilly, you almost killed me! Why do I ever listen to you?"

"Good question, Ross," I said. And with that, we all began to laugh uncontrollably. Ross looked like a character out of a Tom and Jerry cartoon. Hearing the explosion, out came mother, all the way from the kitchen. After seeing the possibility for a much more catastrophic result, she got my attention and began to berate me for my stupidity. Rightfully so, however, I think Ross's survival minimized her contempt, but it never rose to the spectrum of our humor…yet.

Ross needed some immediate tender loving care from nurse Lyan. Later, my mother contacted his mother, explaining the mishap and calming her fears, knowing all too well, it could have been far worse.

Clyde felt justified. "You see what Gilly does!"

I explained to mother, "I'm sorry, my mistake. But, if it had been Clyde holding the match… I would have pumped more gas out and blown that kid up." I added something to the effect that the world would have been proud of me for ridding it of the wacko. Mother found little, if no amusement in my Clyde comment. I think for the next few days she held me in contempt for being born. But, it was like my mother to give in to unconditional love. Sometime later, we'd revisit this incident, like so many of our escapades, with a more amorous attitude.

As for Ross, he recovered within hours after assurance that his burns were only minor. Then, he took off after me once again, making false claims against my sanity. To wit, I replied, "Hey you asked me, no begged me to let you light the pilot. Right Tuck? Right Jeff? You were there." All nodded in agreement. "Sooo, it could have been me. Then what, Ross? You'd have lost a good friend. No…no, not a good friend, the only friend you have. Remember that."

"Yeah." Ross laughed then said, "With you as a friend, who needs enemies?"

"We've got Randall," one of us added and then went on to laughing and joking about the raid. "Well Ross," I said, after we'd slowed down on the stories. "It's dump run time!"

"I've got shotgun!" he yelled.

"No way, Ross. Not today. I'm going solo. Got to go quick and fast. Got to beat those gateposts once again."

"I'm going with you. Just wait!"

"No way, man. You've already got me at odds with my mom over that gas thing."

"I'm coming," Ross said in a direct and demanding tone.

"No you're not, not today. You'll be bad luck!" I shouted back as I jogged over to the rear of the kitchen, picked up the trashcans, threw them in the truck and jumped into the driver's seat. As always, the keys were still in the ignition. Because, who would steal a truck out here anyway? And, where would they go if they did? I began to drive away when Ross ran alongside and jumped onto the running board, persistent as ever to make sure he would have his way. I told him to get off the truck. But he said, "No way.

I'm going!"

"Okay. You'd better hang on tight then!" I advised. As we picked up speed, he began to sense the predicament he gotten himself into. I turned the corner at the end of the tennis courts, where our hitting cages were set up. Next, I addressed the quarter-mile straightaway leading into the back bay. Ross, holding on tighter now, sensed what was about to come next and shouted, "STOAAAP the truck!"

"You wanted to ride to the dump. You pushed for it, so now hold on!" I slammed the gas pedal to the floor. The dust started kicking up behind us. I'd done this many times before with Ross, but not with him hanging on the outside of the truck. As we picked up speed, those gateposts began to look very precarious. The closer we got, the bigger the obstacle appeared. Ross, looking into my eyes, now realized I was actually going to do this. Thinking his life would end shortly, he transformed into a hysterical rage.

By now, I was extremely confident, maybe a little overconfident, of my driving skills. And, I could scare Ross to death, which was better than the other alternative, and make it through with ease. But, I must admit, the pressure was on and, by now, it was too late to change my mind. We were moving too fast. I yelled out to Ross, now hugging the truck as if it were his last lifeline to this world, and, at that moment, I believe it was. "Hold on tight!" I advised as I held steady while approaching and accelerating through the posts, with just enough room not to tear the pants off Ross. I stepped on the brakes, making an amazingly quick stop. Ross jumped off and immediately went into a tirade, "You almost killed me, AGAIN! Twice in the same day!"

I waited for the dust to settle and said, "Don't sweat it. Look around. You're still alive aren't you?" That didn't seem to help. He sounded off with the, "You're crazy! You're crazy!" thing again and then started back to camp. I got out, came alongside and thought it was time to remind him, "Hey, I told you 'no,' and you wouldn't accept no for an answer. I didn't tie you up on the running board. Remember, you jumped on and refused to get off! It was you who put yourself in the line of fire."

"Okay, maybe it was, but you're always there when it happens."

Feeling he might have a point, I said, "Okay buddy, I'm sorry about today." However, like usual, he refused my apology and continued walking back to camp. I turned to finish the dump run with a sigh of relief. We made it, and that's all that counts. Anyway, the walk back would be good for Ross. Getting away from me gave him a chance to cool off.

Later that night, the fog settled into Cat Harbor. The Isthmus breeze brought in a chill, and clouds threatened to cover the stars. Ross, Tuck and I went walking down to the beach, then eventually found our way out on the pier. It seemed to be resisting the pounding of the ocean surge as it creaked at each wave passing beneath. The dinghy dock let out an eerie curling squeal, just enough to pierce the harmony of the cool summer wind. The pier lights were partially dimmed, and only the lights streaking out from the snack bar illuminated the Isthmus. As we as left the pier, a peculiar odious feeling came upon us. We went into the snack bar for a retreat from the night. While walking up the steps, we could see Linda huddled in the corner all alone and reading. She looked up at us and asked, "What's up guys? What do you want?"

"Nothing," I answered and waited for the usual buy or leave request. I jumped in before she made the stipulation. "So, Linda, what are you reading?" While she closed the book and started to answer, I got close enough to see the cover, "GHOST OF CATALINA."

"Wow, didn't know we had them here."

She became serious and asked, "Do you believe in ghosts, Gil?"

Sensing she'd begun to open up here, I egged her on. "On a night like this, who wouldn't? It's in the air."

"Well, let me tell you guys…" And, for the next half-hour, foreboding tales about sightings and paranormal activities going on right here in the Isthmus mesmerized us. I'd been around for some years, but this would be the first time I'd ever heard of this stuff. Oh, maybe a few stories about the Indian burial grounds but somehow that didn't bother me. Heck, I'd been to my share of cemeteries before.

Linda went on to tell the story about a Civil War soldier, Jeffrey Higgins. He'd been barracked in buildings that were now the yacht club, just below the Banning House. It seems that poor old Jeffrey Higgins had fallen in love with an officer's daughter. Her family lived in the yellow house next to the tennis courts, just a stone's throw from our camp. He was sent off to fight at Gettysburg and never returned to the island. The daughter became so despondent, she left the yellow house in her white dress one chilly foggy night and simply disappeared, somewhere on the island.

There were tales of tragedies throughout the years in that yellow house, but no one knows for sure what really happened. Sightings of young Higgins wondering about looking for his "Lady in White" late at night were passed on through the years. "She's been seen several times looking out the window of the yellow house and on the bluffs above the Isthmus, looking for Jeffrey's return," Linda explained. "People see them, but never together. They wander here, looking for what they lost long ago."

"People really see them?" I asked.

"Yes they have," Linda said with certainty.

Linda's stories perked up our senses as we left the snack bar and stepped into the dark night. And, on the walk back to the cabin, each tree, each slight noise, now posed a haunting presence.

Once inside our cabin, Ross seemed to forget about his own traumatic adventures of the day and broke the silence. "So, what do you think? Is it true?"

"No way," I declared. "I've been around here for some years now, and that's the first time I've ever heard that story. Who knows? Anyway, I've always worried about the living ones, let alone the ones who are dead. Though, I have to admit, sometimes, when I walk down the pier or enter the fog bank at Cat Harbor, I feel an eerie thing coming on. The yellow house, Jeffrey Higgins and the Lady in White, never saw them, but, then again, I was never looking for them either."

Deciding to do our part to keep the story alive, Ross and I retold the story over the next night's campfire. When the campers began to show signs of becoming true believers, we turned our flashlights down the hill and onto the main road, leading to the yellow house. To the shrills of the campers, we announced, "There she is!" And there she was, dressed in white, swishing down the road. Of course, it was just Shane dressed for the occasion. Later, I did have some reservations and thought to myself, "Was it really a good idea to mock the ghost?" Now that was a scary idea. But, what a great tale to tell the campers, to help keep them in after lights out.

While falling asleep that night, I thought about the possibilities of Linda's story. I hoped the Lady in White didn't pop up in my dreams. And I shivered thinking what might happen if I had to go for a nature break in the middle of the night and walk to the restroom, into the dark, alone.

"Hey, Ross. You still there?"

"Yeah, go to sleep, Gilly. I've had enough of you today."

Simply to have the last word, as I drifted into sleep I mumbled, "No way."

CHAPTER 20

# The Grand Recipe

At exactly 11 a.m. every day except Sunday, the Isthmus attracted a crowd from all over the west end.

Gathered together on the pier, they'd wait patiently for the first glimpse of the majestic Blanche W. She finally became visible while turning into the Isthmus bay. That's when the crowd's anticipation was released, and they began to point and yell, "There she is!"

Mind you, this elongated craft looks more like a stretched version of a shore-boat or a floating Cuban cigar, yet the Isthmus locals hold her in high esteem.

They make claim, "Avalon may have the Great White Steamer, but we have the Queen of the Fleet, the Blanche W."

The Queen holds the regal name of William Wrigley's granddaughter and her birth date gives her seniority even over the iconic Avalon Casino. The Blanche W. was built and registered in 1924. While, the casino went into construction a few years later in 1928. The Blanche W. in some ways was the lifeline to the Isthmus. But, most importantly for us, the Blanche brought in the mail. Mail was terribly important to a young lad, separated for three months on the island from his girlfriend. It seemed like years, and not knowing whom else she might meet during the summer made it even worse.

So, it was great reassurance getting letters from a girl. With a few squirts of perfume, she'd leave her special scent and might even sneak in a few extra love notes on the back of pictures. Plus, if you were really lucky, she sealed it with a kiss. But, what made it even more entertaining, years ago we came up with the idea to conduct a contest between the campers over who had the best looking sister. They'd send for their sisters' photos and, of course, we'd prompt them to write about their wonderful counselors. We got to know a lot of great girls through the contest. Wow, anticipating a letter was like a birthday every day.

Dad made it part of his usual routine to pick up the mail from the cove office at noon. After lunch, he'd yell out names and hand the letters out. That was the one time the entire camp needed little prompting to pay full attention. Once your name was called out, you grabbed your mail and ran to find a quiet, safe place. There you would sit and mull over the letter, again and again, making each word say what you wanted it to.

As the Blanche advanced toward the Isthmus pier, Tuck and I watched the young divers putting on their fins. Then, while holding their mask in hand, they jumped off the pier and into the ocean water below. Once masked, they immediately began yelping like seals, pleading the Blanche passengers to throw some coins.

"Tuck, remember when we did that?"

He smiled. "Yeah, just for a few dollars' worth of coins."

"Amazing we survived all that kicking, grabbing and fighting down there," I said.

"Yep."

"Bought a few delicious malts with those coins," I added.

"Yes we did," Tuck replied.

"Wow, summer's really here. Look at all the boats that came in last night. Yesterday, half the moorings were empty. But now look. Man, they're here, summer's here," I said with excitement.

Billy Tuck and I watched the passengers emptying from the Blanche and then looked over to Little Fish to see if his dad's boat had come in. Yep, there she was, the Geronimo, the starship of the Long Beach Sailing Club, and around her sleek presence was the rest of the fleet. They'd raced early that morning to the island. Those boats never meandered their way over. No, they always raced, and, once here, the crews would party all day and into the night. Then, on Sunday, they'd race back to Long Beach.

"Hey, Tuck, the family's in."

"Yeah, my mother's bringing me some clean clothes. I need to go get them."

"I'll go with you," I offered, hoping to get a glimpse of the girls that usually sailed over with them. Tuck and I started to retreat back down the pier, wearing only our T-shirts, trunks and flip-flops. That suited us well under the morning heat of another beautiful summer day. Halfway down the pier, I looked over the rail leading down to the dinghy dock. Tuck looked at me, and, as usual, read my mind. "Big G., you can't make it." He loved to challenge me.

"Oh yeah?" Seeing a space open between two dinghies tied to the dock, I glanced around, just to make sure I could go undetected. While taking off my shirt and tossing it to Tuck, I quickly climbed up onto the rail. And, like I'd done so many times before, I bent my knees, spread my arms wide, pushed off and dove out over the dock and into the water, right between the two dinghies. I swam back to the dock, pulled myself up and walked up the ramp.

"Not bad," Tuck said, as he handed back my shirt.

I pulled it on over my wet body and allowed the sun to dry me off. "I still have it, Tuck." Then, acting as if nothing special had gone on, we strolled off the pier.

I looked over to him and said, "You know Tuck, one time when I was diving in the shallow water a tourist challenged me. He said he'd give me 50 cents if I would dive off the pier at the shoreline, just down there. It gave me only about four feet of water to make it. Luckily, my mother taught me how to belly flop dive to start swimming meets back in L.A.. Now, landing shallow dives are no problem. I just waited until the surge came, made the dive and the guy gave me the 50 cents. Not bad, huh?"

"Right, Big G. And, if you had hit bottom?"

"Man, it wasn't even close." Now bragging on to my friend, "That's called confidence, Tuck, believing in your capabilities."

Looking straight into the Isthmus as we walked off the pier, we noticed people bustling about. Some were going into the snack bar for lunch, while the local beach crowd, the Hawkins boys, Ben and his younger brother, Billy Bones, played volleyball with Big Al. We turned the corner and walked behind the cove office, where Doug, along with his wife Audrey and Carol Ostach, did their business with the arriving boaters. Carol worked a variety of essential jobs throughout the Isthmus. Next, it was on to the bluff just above the beach, then past the roundhouse where the "girls of the snack bar" stayed and eventually the Wild Goose Lodge. A few summers ago, legend has it that John Wayne rented the place out and carried on some rather raucous festivities with his Hollywood and USC crowd.

We moved on to our camp's beach and through the private girls' camp beach area. They were just arriving for their day in the sun. Dad maintained a strict prohibition on any socializing with them. Also, the camp manager, Lady Cruikshank, was a stern cookie who impeccably watched over those girls. The story was, she would prosecute anyone ever attempting to toy with her girls. So, we paid little attention, besides, no need to. There were enough girls to go around for all of us.

Tuck and I climbed the mound beyond the girl's' camp leading to Little Fisherman's trailhead. We chatted about his buddy, John Cherry, who was a wrestler from Millikan High and, according to Tuck, quite good. Our conversation carried us over the crest.

As I looked down into the cove, I thought we might have stumbled onto Peter Pan's hideout. All sorts of young family members were going about having fun, doing all kinds of contests. Some were climbing poles, others tying down sails, rowing about and even swimming. The parents were drinking and hooting it up after their long morning of sailing. By the end of the day, the kids would be set free to wander into the Isthmus, while the parents would change the site of the festivities, most likely finding their way to the Isthmus for dinner and then closing the night out with Ernie in the bar.

Tuck and I dropped into the cove and were quickly greeted by his sister, Patty. She always smiled at us. Actually, I was never sure if it was a smile, maybe just a wide smirk, as if to say, "What trouble are you guys planning today?" But, it was all good with Patty. She quickly said, "Hey, Gil, I've got someone I want you to meet."

My head and heart sort of stopped when this tomboyish looking girl in cutoff jeans appeared. She seemed to be a pint-size version of Tinker Bell in a halter-top. Her skin was sunbaked and contrasted well with her short-cropped blonde hair. She stared up at me, sizing me up. I stared back at her. Her hand rose slowly to lower her sunglasses, exposing her eyes, and there she was. There's something to be said about chemistry at times like this.

"Gil, this is Jody, and, Jody, this is Gil," Patty said, with that funny smirk.

Jody had a presence about her. When she smiled, you could immediately tell she had fun written all over her. There was this sparkling appeal with personality that just jumped out at you. We kidded over small things. Patty, seeing there could be something happening here, suggested, "Let's get together today."

Normally, I'd jump at the idea, but on Saturdays we always had the campers play ball against the counselors at the sandlot. So I asked, "What about tonight in the snack bar? Or, you can come and watch us play."

Without conferring with Jody, Patty answered, "Okay."

"Okay to what?" I needed to know.

"Okay to coming to watch the game and we're also on for tonight. But, we have to leave early. My dad wants to race home Sunday morning."

"Okay then," Tuck picked up his clean clothes and put them in his backpack, and away to camp we went.

On the way back I asked, "So Tuck, what do you know about this Jody girl?"

"She's a friend of the family from way back and a lot of fun."

Knowing Tuck would never offer his advice unless I pumped him for it, I went on. "Do you like her?"

"Yeah, I like her. She's just normal. Not like some of Patty's other friends. And," he added, "she's a kick."

I didn't say any more, hoping to curtail my interest in her. She was different, all right, clearly not a sexy thing but still rather attractive nevertheless.

Once lunch dishes were finished, we raced down to the sandlot for the afternoon game, campers against counselors. Our handicap… we had to bat from the opposite side of the plate. As the game went on, the sun blistered down on the field. Dust kicked up in all directions every time a play was made. The campers had a few exceptional players. There was a 15-year-old on the mound that threw hard, and a catcher who was a real prospect, Pete Beathard. Yeah, the same guy who later played quarterback at USC and afterward in the NFL with the Kansas City Chiefs.

My dad made all his boys switch-hitters. But, to tell the truth, I was never very good at it. When I came to bat, I went to my left-hand side first. After spotting Patty and Jody sitting on the side of the hill, I naturally wanted to make a good impression. But, the first pitch hit me. I took my base as everyone laughed at the beaning. The next time up, I batted from the right side.

The pitcher tried his fastball on the inside of the plate, and I crushed it. I stood there, knowing the ball was going over the road. This was it! This was the career-changing drive. This would be the first time over the road. More than 18 years it took me to do it. I finally made it!

Or did I? Playing far back, Chicago sputtered and stumbled as he approached the hill, all the while appearing to have his eyes on me. He was actually grinning at me, saying "no… no… no way." The shot came about halfway up the mound of the road and, to everyone's surprise, he made an unbelievable, Willie Mays one-handed catch!

I tossed my bat down hard. Damn. I almost made it. Ross, waiting a few cautious moments, walked over and said with certainty, "You're too small."

"Say what?"

"Yeah, you'll never hit it over the road. You're too small."

I shouldn't have been surprised. Ross always had the trump card ready for moments like this. It was his way, I guess, to get back at me for all the jokes I'd played at his expense. I said, "I'm thinking I should've hanged you on the gate or blown-up your feathers in the heater room."

While he walked up to the plate, Ross answered back, "You'd miss me. Besides Tuck, I'm the only one that puts up with your crazy stupid ideas."

To my pleasure, Ross proceeded to strike out. That brought a big smile to Tuck's face and I yelled out, "You bum!"

The game ended abruptly for two reasons. One, the catcher with the rifle arm threw the ball to second base while a runner attempted to steal. The second reason, the ball arrived on time but the shortstop missed, and it ricocheted off the runner's head, knocking him out. Fortunately, after a few seconds, he recovered. To be sure, they decided to put him in the truck along with nurse Lyan.

"Great arm," my father said to Pete and then turned to me. "You almost did it today." One thing about my dad, he was my number one critic but also my number one fan. He believed in me. He could be flexible, consistent, critical and positive all at the same time. I always admired him for that.

While sitting back down on the bench, Tuck said, "The back bay, we've got to go explore that barge soon.

"We will...we will before the end of summer," I said, gazing back at the barge, suspended in thought. "Yeah, you're right... soon."

I looked back around. The game was definitely over for today. All of us were covered with red dirt and sand, attached to the skin by our sweating, reeking bodies. We got up and started picking up the gear when Tuck asked, "Hey Gil, what's that crawling around out there?"

"Maybe Clyde," I joked.

"No look. It's a seal, a baby seal, and it's coming our way!"

"Yeah, you're right." I got the campers' attention and pointed to the young seal plodding along. "He's coming right to us. Gosh, he must be really hungry," I said sympathetically. Sure enough, he was. With Patty and Jody looking on, the little guy allowed us to pick him up and gingerly place him in the truck, alongside our injured camper and transport him back to the camp. Later, we would fill the shower with water, and he seemed to feel right at home. Mother called for advice from Ben Hawkins and Big Al on how to feed the critter. We named him Cecil. I think one of the campers came up with the name, and it just stuck.

As the rest of us walked back to camp, we passed the infamous yellow house. The kids came up with all kinds of remarks. "Did you see her?"

"Yeah, she's waiting at the window."

"I saw her too, and she was topless."

The joking was getting a little over the top, so I said, "Hold it back guys. You're going too far. Who knows who she'll be haunting tonight? Better watch out or it might be you." They quieted down for a moment, but then went on. "You're brave now. But tonight, when lights are out? Good luck," I warned. Once we reached the barracks, the campers hurriedly changed and ran down to the beach.

After dinner, I rushed back to the cabin to spruce up for the evening. "What are you up to?" Ross asked.

"What are you talking about?"

"Well, you've spent more time than usual getting ready for the snack bar. That's what I'm talking about."

"Patty set me up with her friend, remember?"

"What does she look like?" he asked.

Attempting not to directly answer his question, I said, "Well, it's like Jeff says," looking over at him for assurance, "she's a 7 who has a 10 personality."

Jeff laughed as he explained to Ross, "It's the busty ones, like the ones you like, Ross, who are defective. They rely on their trimmings while the others... they compensate with a good personality."

"You hear that, Ross? The operative word here is 'com-pen-sate.' You know what that means, Ross?"

"Yes. It means she's ugly," he flatly replied.

I jumped back. "No it doesn't! Didn't you see her down at the ball field with Patty? You can't by any stretch of your feeble imagination call that ugly! It's a different idea about girls than you have, Ross. You just get what you want and then leave them. Let me educate you a little. You know, you can enjoy just being with them.

"Riiight," Ross said. "So now you're a convert to morality?"

"You just don't get it. Jeff and I are trying to teach you something." Ret, sitting on the top bunk, attempted to enter the conversation. I interrupted and said, "Don't even try, Ret. You're a little out of your league here. You see, Ross. You and Ret think alike." I turned to leave. "Any final advice, cuz?"

"Yeah, remember, skinner was no beginner…he knew her before dinner."

"Thanks, Jeff," I said as they all laughed. I became serious and came to her defense. "This is not that kind of girl. This is something different. So guys, I'll see you on the patio and you'd better be nice to this girl or…"

"Or what?" Ross asked.

"Or, more hours in the shitter for you. That's what. See you later." I stepped from the cabin into the dark night and headed toward the distant pier and snack bar lights. Funny thing, guys pretend they don't make decisions about girls based on what their buddies say, but I'm afraid we do, more then we admit.

The nights in the Isthmus are made for comfortable romance. The warm air crossing the channel from the Southern California deserts and the Santa Ana winds tempered by the Pacific breeze, make it extremely pleasant for such an occasion. Plus, when the sun drops down beyond the horizon and the city lights of the mainland turn on, it becomes a brilliant spectacle that illuminates far out to sea. Then, there's the silence of the night that allows all the other senses to come into play. The rush of the ocean as it crashes against the shore or the billowing of the palm trees as they flutter in the wind and even the creaks of the pier as it resists the oncoming tide all becomes music to the ear. Add to that the smell of the sea and the taste of salty air mixed with open campfires and it creates a blend that, together, is truly a grand recipe, a rhymester's dream, the essence of Catalina's romantic mystic.

Any mention of the Isthmus social life would be remiss not to mention Ty Ewing. He was one of those rare individuals who didn't complicate life. He just lived it. You could find Ty outside of the snack bar any Friday or Saturday night. He always wore a smile that seemed just for you. Gracious and fun to be around, he made you feel as if you could always share a story and it would never be lost in idle conversation. Ty knew all the nuisances of boating. It was a big reason he came to the Isthmus in 1953. For some 40 years he lived, loved and eventually married here. I had the opportunity of knowing and passing time with him on those balmy Isthmus nights in front of the snack shop. I would find him talking with the locals, playing with the Bombard kids or just welcoming a new arrival to the Isthmus life. I'd usually start my night by running into him. He'd ask how things were going, and I'd tell him about upcoming plans or about a prank we pulled. He'd laugh with me and enjoy the stories. Always, in his timely manner, Ty would slip in some good commonsense advice. This night it was about the girl Patty Tuck had introduced that morning. He asked, "Well, what do you think about your first meeting?"

"Well, it was different."

"How different?"

"She seemed fun and comfortable to be with. The others… they were something you had to work on." Ty nodded, as if he knew exactly what I meant. About that time, a pretty girl with the same first name of Patty stepped in out of the dark. She was a great admirer of Ty and, after saying a friendly "hi," she pulled him with her toward the pier. He waved goodbye as she wisped him away. I was now on my own, no entourage to give me encouragement or to lean on. Just me. What an unusual predicament, making a case for myself, that is.

As I walked into the snack bar, Linda greeted me and asked what I was doing out all by myself. I explained that I was waiting for Billy Tuck and Patty. She'd brought a friend of hers over whom she wanted me to meet.

Linda smiled and asked what I thought about the yellow house story the other night. I shared what I did to the campers, and we both had a good laugh. About that time, in they came. The Boy Scout guys from Cherry Cove, and, yeah Randall was right in front of the pack. He pounced on the chance to get in a few words with me. "What are you doing out here without your groupies, or should I say your protection squad?"

"It makes no difference, Randall. Cause I need none when you're around." I felt happy I could come up with a smart line. Linda, sensing the tension stepped in, "Okay guys, not around here. You baseball guys and scouts can do it some other time and some other place. Now, put down the attitudes. There are enough girls to go around tonight. They'll be in off the boats in a little while, and I'm sure you'll want to be here, instead of back in camp. So, what do you say?"

While we shook our heads in agreement, to move our issues on to another day, in walked Patty, Tuck and Jody. Feeling something in the air, Patty asked, "Any problems, Gil?"

"No, just jostling with the natives." We all smiled and sat down to order malts. Patty directed the conversation. Then, as easily as an Olympic track star, she passed the baton to Jody. She was ready to take me on, from the point of my birth 'til this very moment. She raced on for an hour, keeping me entertained. I became so engrossed in her, I hadn't even noticed Patty and Billy Tuck not only backed out of the conversation but were gone. I chuckled and questioned where they went. "Doesn't matter," she assured me. "I'm having fun with you tonight."

With that, Jody took the night away. I rarely met a person so engaging and focused on knowing me...no dangling conversations. She acted as if she was in command. Without a doubt, she was quite capable of orchestrating the evening. There would be no hunting, no feeling each other out. We simply let ourselves be.

Then, after her lengthy prying, she pulled me out onto the patio for a slow dance and then another and another. She was warm, sensitive, yet stern and most definitely in control. She knew where she was going and, for the first time, I really didn't. Clearly, I was just happy to be going her way. The night ended with a walk on the pier. At the end, we gazed out to sea, where one could dream beyond, look into the crest of darkness and wonder at the stars as they came out, one by one, to greet the night. The stars flashed down their light from the heavens to sparkle and flicker across the rippled water. The moon came in, making a grand entrance.

We stood for a while, just enjoying nature's part in this thing called romance. I reached out for her hand. She greeted it, actually welcomed it with a firm, grasp as if she knew it was about to come. I didn't need anymore. The warmth of her hand said enough. Anything else would have spoiled the night. We talked in silence, the only noise we heard.

It must have been about an hour when the silence was broken by the clutter of drinkers coming from the bar. They felt their way down the ramp to the dinghy dock, hoping to make it home and not drown along the way. This made us both laugh. It was late. We had to go from each other. I walked her back to the end of the pier and, as if rehearsed, Patty appeared. "Ready?"

Jody nodded and said, "Goodbye, Gil. I had a very nice time."

Knowing she would set sail early the next morning and not

knowing if this would ever happen again, in desperation I asked, "Write me?" That's all I could say. She smiled and began to walk away, took a few steps then turned and said, "I will."

CHAPTER 21

# A Cliff Hanger

A piercing light woke me as it radiated on my face through a crack in the cabin curtain. I resisted this untimely intrusion as long as possible by turning over in my sleeping bag. I noticed Jeff staring at me with a glazed smile. Lying in his bunk, still half asleep, he whispered, "So, tell me about this new fling you have going on." I stared back, fully intending not to talk about it, wanting to keep it to myself. I felt I had something special brewing here. However, he was persistent and continued prying. "You know what your problem is, Gil?" I resisted the chance of saying, "I really don't care." I'd heard it all before.

He wouldn't stop. "You never learn do you? Your problem is, you find these girls and you get tattooed. You get all involved, and you let them control you."

"So what? Why does that make a difference?" I asked reluctantly.

"Because, you see, there are a whole bunch of girls out there, okay? You've got to get out there, test as many as you can. Noooo commitment. Shop around the marketplace. Most of them are the love-'em-and leave-em' type." He chuckled. "So don't ever take yourself out of the game too soon by going steady or whatever.

With that attitude, you're never going to find the right one."

"What's your motto, Jeff? Take the girl to dinner, and how does the rest go?"

"Well, that's the only way you're going to get to know if she has any values, right?" he asked

"All I know is, the last time I took your advice, she ended up talking about marriage."

Jeff wouldn't stop. "Just tell them what they want to hear, get on with it, then drop her. Move on and scratch it up to experience."

"Yeah, but what fun is that? I want a girl I can really share things with," I said.

"Okay. Just forget it. I guess my vast experience and advice doesn't fly with you. But, remember one rule, just one rule. If you ever like some girl more then she likes you, drop her."

"Why?"

"Because, she'll always be in control. Now, if it's the other way around, she's a keeper, for a while. Cause, if you're always in control, you're never going to get hurt."

"Humm…not bad, Jeff, not bad. I think I like that one."

"You never answered my question. So what does she look like?" he continued.

"She looks like a girl with a pleasant personality you'd love to be around."

"Yeah, I know what that means." He laughed but, after seeing my defensive mode backed off. "Okay, I know what you're saying."

Dramatically changing the subject, I said, "Guess who's going hiking with the campers to Little Harbor today?"

"Since we've been allowed a few more hours of sleep, my guess… it's us."

Once each session we take an overnight trip to Little Harbor. It's about three hours of walking through the hot Catalina interior, supported by our kitchen crew. They bring us our meals in the truck and pick up some of our straggling hikers along the way.

We finally closed in on Little Harbor around 11 a.m. By that time, the morning shoreline fog of the windward side was in the process of retreating back into the Pacific as the sun broke through. After walking in the heat, everyone was looking forward to ending the trek.

"Can you believe it's been only a few weeks since we were here with the girls?" Ross asked as we arrived on the mound just above the bay. We weren't able to see the water yet but smelled the ocean and heard the crashing of the surf. We sat the campers down for a short break, allowing us to scout out the beach below. I cautiously moved to look over the bluff.

Spreading out all over the beach, enjoying its pleasures, was the private girl's camp. Our eyes locked onto three older girls. They looked like counselors and were lying on towels a short distance from the girls. Protected from vision by some rock formations, we climbed closer to the edge. I motioned to Tuck and Jeff to come over and check it out. Two of the girls were enjoying the sun… topless. We smiled and sat there for a moment, taking in their natural beauty. They fit in so well with the white sprawling sandy beach and the rolling surf, spraying the harbor as each breaker met the shore. "Gosh," I said to Ross, who just discovered what we were looking at. "Think about how David, the guy in the Bible, must have felt seeing Beersheba." We all laughed, took in a few more looks, just to remember this by, and then moved back to the campers.

"Boys, it's our time!" I proclaimed as I raised my hand in the air and pointed down to the beach. It looked like a cavalry charge as the campers rushed over the bluff. The girls' camp quickly took notice. Finding a suitable place a good distance from them, the campers concealed themselves in towels and stripped down to change into their bathing suits. They scrambled down toward the water's edge to play with the oncoming breakers. Now, it was back to work. Our lifeguards kept vigilant, watchful eyes on our swimming campers while they frolicked in the crashing waves, riding one after another throughout the day. Later on Ross, Tuck and I walked down the beach to where the nature-loving girls sat, finding them now with their tops on. They smiled then waved at us. We continued on across the mound that separates Little Harbor from Sharks Bay and found a good place to bed the campers down for the night.

The sunset portrait from the Pacific on that part of the island is extreme. The day closed into night, and our camp truck returned, this time to bring our dinner. Tuck said sarcastically, "Look who else came with the dinner, if it ain't our good friend and shit-kicker Tauso."

The moment the campfire was in full bloom a sense of finality charmed the scene. Late into the night we sang camp songs and told stories until totally exhausted. Then, all of us finally fell asleep.

Morning broke at Little Harbor with the first dash of light. It peeked over the mountaintops from the west. Funny thing, how the locals refer to the west end as Parson's Landing and the other end at Avalon as the east end. Yet the island is really fashioned in a north-south direction. Somehow, you just go with the local's logic. It makes more sense.

Mornings are always chilly here at Little Harbor. So, we stayed in our sleeping bags a little longer. At least until we heard the honking of horns on the bluff, giving notice that the breakfast kitchen crew had arrived. After our famished group consumed our ration of hot chocolate, dried cereal and sweet rolls, we put some of the younger weary campers into the back of the truck. It was obvious they were not looking forward to the long three-hour return hike.

On this day, a few of the campers suggested we take a different way back to the Isthmus. Someone heard about a trail that leads along the beach side of the island. From there, we thought, all we needed to do was follow the rugged Catalina shoreline, then eventually end up at the entrance to Cat Harbor. After that, it would be only a short walk through the Isthmus and back to camp.

Ross, Tuck and I jumped in, "Yeah, let's do it!" We'd never gone that way before. It was virgin territory where maybe only a few goats had traveled. Beautiful shoreline, rather than desert-like interior, sounded like a great idea. This would turn out to be one of the most irresponsible and almost fatal decisions we ever made.

My father was back at camp and, as always, relied on our good judgment in these matters. We'd taken the campers to Little Harbor and back so many times before, it had become routine. But this new hike would be nothing like I'd ever been on. Looking back, I think we were so beguiled by the adventure of climbing around the jagged cliffs of the island's backside that we simply overlooked any hint of danger. On top of that and what clinched our fate… Tauso, our head counselor threw, his lot in with us.

So, there we were, looking for a goat trail with about 20 daring campers. Laughing, singing and full of spirit, we pressed on like an encore to The Sound of Music. On the north side of Little Harbor we found an unmarked trailhead. Actually, it was more like beaten down bushes that hinted someone or something had passed this way. That didn't matter. This was the fun of it, going as pioneers on a trail less traveled. We concluded this was the path back to the Isthmus. Somehow, somewhere, it would wind around the edge of Catalina's raw windy coast and find its way to Cat Harbor. We were sure of that as we continued chattering along the way. Ross and I began joking about the two half-dressed sunbathers. "Gosh, I'd never seen them on the Isthmus beach before."

"Maybe you had but they were dressed then, and you were focused on something different," Jeff chimed in. "Yeah, remember what I always say about clothes…they have a way of keeping the good things enticing."

"What does that have to do with anything, Jeff? The girls had no tops on, and that's what made it enticing. See, Jeff, you have no image to go by. It's just unwrapping a present to you. Then you go on to another, then another."

"So what's the point?"

"You've got to communicate with these girls, Jeff. You'll learn. Just stick with me for a while. At the very least, get to know them." Ross started to add his two cents. I quickly interrupted. "And you, Ross, what happened to good old 38D Kimberly? Heard anything yet? Sorry to hurt your feelings, Ross, but where did she go? What, no letters? Huh? See, there's something more to this girl thing."

"Oh, and I guess you really know, Gilly. How many times have you been screwed by girls?"

"No. No. No. That's not it, Ross. Look, it's all about images and timing," I said.

We continued up the side of the mountain and entered a fog bank at the crest. It began as a slow creep and eventually covered the mountain in front of us. Once we reached the top, the cloudbank suddenly lifted and exposed the valley on the other side. It looked like a page taken from early pioneers crossing the western plains with thousands of buffalo grazing on the prairie. But, instead of buffalo, there were what looked to be a thousand goats content on chopping away at all the island had to offer. They took little notice, maybe knowing they outnumbered us. We sat on the peak gulping water from our canteens.

On the top of that unknown mountain, with the fog in full retreat, the blue Pacific gave us a view of its horizon. We were besieged and overwhelmed with the wild and rugged terrain of the island. The raging ocean plummeted the island coast, carving itself a place on the Catalina shores. The scene was tamed only by the presence of animal life that also shared this place.

The fog appeared to be playing games with us now. It seemed to say, "I'll let you see what I see every day, but just for a brief time." This was the real wild brazened heart of Catalina that, up to now, we were oblivious to, where its seductive forces became so imposing.

We sat there for some time, realizing too late that things around us were closing in. "Tauso, let's get out of here," I said.

"Yeah, let's get going guys," he agreed.

We began to press on to the next valley and then to the next peak, thinking just over it would be Cat Harbor. Once there we would be safe and sheltered from the stormy elements, now beginning to pose a daunting threat. Again, the fog began to roar back in. On we went, but when we reached the next peak, we only found another. This wasn't how it should have been. But, how did we know? None of us, not even the lead counselor, had taken this route before. And then it happened. A mountain stood in our way, way too steep to climb and blocking the route to the interior.

It was just too far back to think about the alternative. We'd come to a dead end and were walled in on both sides. We sat down to take in our dilemma. Our carefree casual hike had now torched our legs, outspent our canteens and forced us to reappraise our judgment. Fear began to creep in, as slowly as the fog had earlier. We attempted to challenge it with reason. But, for the first time, we knew we'd need more. With each moment, the trust and confidence we had in ourselves began to pass away. Our safety and lives had become a tenuous proposition.

I searched for God in prayer. It's not that I was religious. No. I wouldn't admit to that back then. It's just that there were no other options. My mind strained to remember Father James's conversations about divine providence. Then, it echoed back to the predicament we found ourselves in. Was this something God dreamed up... His plan? I stumbled deeper in thought. Or, was this just the product of our own indiscretions? And, was that even important now? I went back and forth, cross-examining myself. But, all that really mattered was to squeeze out a spark of hope, that God would do His part, give us a hand and help us make it up that mountain.

So, what to do next to minimize our risk? Tauso was now huddling and counseling with me about this dire situation. I could see the concern on his face as he spoke. He'd been in combat before and knowing that didn't help dissuade my anxiety. Panic? No. That was lost on concern for our campers, and the urgency of the circumstances gave us little leisure even to consider it.

The one thing we knew for sure... going back wasn't an option. We needed to confront the elements on our terms, press ahead, slowly, carefully, skillfully and in concert as a team. Cat Harbor must be out there, just around the corner. Our best bet, we concluded, was to give up on going straight over the peak and try to go around from the ocean side. This meant keenly scaling the bleak and dangerous cliffs that hung over the roaring ocean below. Any slip was an unacceptable prescription for our survival. It could not happen.

Before advancing, we carefully laid out a strategy and placed a counselor within every four boys. There would only be room for a single-file passing. We also did this in the hopes of keeping the younger guys calm, and, if one were to slip, we could help. We moved on with this maneuver. Ever so slowly we advanced farther, yet it became even more precarious. Now, there could be no turning back, even though the trail led higher up the cliff. Rocks began to tumble under our feet, not stopping until they smashed into the hillside, then finally finding their way into the ocean below. We stopped for a moment. Tauso yelled, "Hold the line!"

The jokes and banter were gone. I leaned out, looked down below and saw seagulls in flight, blurting out calls, looking up at us, seeming to say, "What are you doing up there?" We'd run out of answers and instinctively knew we had to move on. For the first time, my mortality instinct poised questions. What would be tomorrow's headlines? "Campers Stranded On Mountaintop"? But, would anybody even know where we were? My father would be going bonkers, knowing we put these kids at such risk. Then, for some reason I thought about the Boy Scouts and Randall. Did he know something that could help us up here? Maybe I was a little too harsh with my attitude of those guys. Or, maybe a helicopter would fly by and rescue us. We just couldn't stay and let it all happen. No. We needed to press on. And, that meant to climb even higher.

We directed the campers to, "Hold on, listen to us and don't look down. And, please, no talking. It'll be alright." We progressed ever so slowly. But, as we did, rocks began falling more often and at a faster pace. The sound of seagulls, the crushing sea and the bouncing rocks below now became dominant threats to our concentration. We prayed on each move. Each individual rock had its own meaning as our hands grasped at it, ever so tightly. Finally, lead counselor Tauso gave us some badly needed hope. The top was just in front of him, so he announced, "Pass it on! Hold on. We're going to make it!" He reached the top and began to pull each camper, one by one, slowly over the peak to a safe area.

But, it soon became apparent, there was another steep valley to descend. And, this time cactus gingerly tainted our path. No one dared to complain and, after taking only a few minutes of rest, we slowly traversed downward into the valley. And, that's when it happened. Billy Bones, worn out by fatigue, tripped and began tumbling down. Having the gall to grab a cluster of cactus and then hang on to it is the only thing that stopped his fall. There he sat, in the cactus, screaming with pain. Immediately, we rushed to pull him free. But, his body was full of punctures from thorns still entrenched in his flesh.

Then, something unusual and unexplainable happened. One of the campers looked up the valley and asked, "What in the world is that?" He pointed to a dark moving object on the side of the hill.

"We've got another problem," I said while looking at what appeared to be an enormous black cat glaring our way. But, it couldn't be a cat. It was way too big. This big black something looked the size of a lion. A panther? No way! Could it be?

The animal began to slowly move along a path, showing us the way out. And, then, we saw her in the distance. Someone at the top of the hill was actually waving in our direction, motioning us to come her way. "They've found us!" I yelled. Our eight-hour journey from Little Harbor was almost over. No one had the energy to cheer, but you could hear a collective sigh of relief. We would stay out of tomorrow's newspaper headlines. The sun would rise after all. Some bruising and scarring and other unpleasant memories would persist. But, for now, we could dream on about our future, talk about girls and, for me, look forward to Jody's letters arriving on the Blanche W.

Over the last mountain we went, then we scaled our way down to the backside of Cat Harbor. "Gil, look down there." Tuck pointed. The clouds had settled over Cat Harbor, and a light illuminated from the barge. A small skipjack was tied alongside. "You're right, Tuck. Something weird is going on down there. That's next on our list. We're going in there at night."

"At night?"

"Yeah when they're gone. We'll find out what strange things

those smugglers are doing."

"Why do you think they're smugglers?"

"I don't know. Why not? They've got to be doing something wrong. 'Smugglers' fits."

However, all that had to wait. For now, we had other, more pressing things to take care of, like getting these kids back to camp and facing dad. And, that was something I always tried to avoid, facing dad when he was upset. I could already feel that lanyard stinging my butt. Finally, the local sheriff and some of the search party greeted us. They'd been looking for hours after we didn't return on time.

All was put to rest, and Billy Bone's rump was attended to by the tender loving care of nurse Lyan. Of course, it became the pun of the week and the butt of our many jokes, at every campfire that summer. Yet, we knew we were very lucky to still be around. Or, was it luck? There would be no displays of arrogance about the incident, just relief. I tried to explain this large panther-like cat to my dad and the authorities. They disregarded the sighting as nothing more than a large stray cat. So, we let it go as well. I personally thanked the officers for getting us out of the mess.

"What do you mean, 'getting you out of the mess?' We never found you guys. We had a helicopter searching for you, and trucks on the other side of the Banning House, from Little Harbor to the Isthmus. We first saw you coming over the mountain in Cat Harbor."

"Well, what about the lady officer that waved from the crest of the valley, showing the way out?" I asked.

"What lady officer? We don't have a lady officer on the west end, or, for that matter, anywhere on the island, not even in Avalon."

There seemed little reason to go on with what we saw that day. Years later, the panther and the lady were still a mystery. But,

I know what we saw... and we're here in part because of them. And, as to Randall... I gave up on my efforts to accept him as better person than he was. No. I couldn't let that happen.

So, finally, in the safety of our beds, Ross suggested, "You better say a prayer, guys. We were goners."

"Hold on, Ross, we made it because we made it," I argued.

"But, what if we didn't make it?" he shot back at me. "Where would we be?"

"Not here, dummy," I answered. "The only people who have to worry tonight are those stupid smugglers in Cat Harbor and, of course, Randall Cunningham the Third. And, Ross, if you're afraid to fall asleep, remember your butt isn't filled with cactus. Too bad you didn't fall into that instead of Bones. Right, Tuck?"

"Right."

"Just go to sleep and dream about Kimberly kissing your toes or something. Remember her. Because, that's all you have left... just memories. No letters, no nothing." That silenced him. "And while I'm at it, Jeff, turn off that damn music. Ret, turn off that flashlight, you pervert. You've read that edition so many times the colors are off the pages. And, last thing, anybody got to take a leak, go to the outside head, don't even attempt doing it around the tree. If my mother sees you, she'll go crazy. Night guys."

With that settled, I began to pray.

CHAPTER 22

# Avalon

Once we loaded the campers on the Blanche for our trip to Avalon, it took less than an hour to reach Long Point then settle in toward the east end of Catalina Island. After passing White's Landing and Toyon Bay, we turned the corner and one of America's finest resorts came into view, a favorite of the rich and famous, the St. Catherine's Hotel.

If you were well known, you must have stayed there. We never did. The St. Catherine, like much of Avalon, came to life in the '20s. However, like the rest of island commerce, it became a casualty of the Big War. With the advent of air travel to other more exotic destinations, she was left barren and became another relic in American history.

Nevertheless, Avalon's investors weren't willing to let the St. Catherine go by the wayside that easily. They attempted to see if she could still hold her charm and gave her a facelift. In the process, we found it an inviting proposition to sneak over construction barriers and then wander around her endless hallways, where some of the most prestigious people of that era had come to play.

Then, just a blink away, located at the point of Descanso Bay, the Avalon Casino appeared. Giving sightseers a little history, the

Blanche tour guide continued his monologue. "The Avalon Casino is to Catalina what the Eiffel Tower is to Paris, the London Bridge is to England or the Golden Gate Bridge is to San Francisco. On a smaller scale, of course, but as important nevertheless."

Wrigley had the casino built in 1929 by the same people who built the world renowned Grauman's Chinese Theatre in Hollywood. In her heyday, anybody who had musical talent played there.

When we turned into Avalon Bay, the S.S Catalina greeted us. The Big White Steamship left everyday from Wilmington at 10 a.m. sharp and returned at 4:30 p.m. During the summer about 2,000 passengers would arrive daily to "The Island of Romance". By now, the moorings in Avalon were full and beaches were bustling with sun tanners, lying out on their towels to meet the warm Catalina sun. While we were docking on the pleasure pier, we looked up to the left and got a good view of Mt. Ada. William Wrigley Jr. built a home and named it after his wife when he purchased about 99 percent of the island in 1919.

SWOOOOSH came the sound of propellers sputtering overhead as Avalon Air found its way into the bay, skimming along until it finally stopped, then revved up its engine and pulled to the end of the pier to unload passengers. I had to shake my head and laugh. "Man, Tuck, those pilots are crazy!"

"As crazy as Channel Air back at the Isthmus?"

"You bet. They all come from the same school of river runners and bootleggers." A loud explosion interrupted me. That sound was the signal when somebody caught a marlin. So, we climbed out of the Blanche and hurried up the ramp to see it weighed in. After that, on down the pier we went, telling the campers they had three hours in Avalon to buy gifts for their parents, have lunch, look around, then meet back at the entrance to the pleasure pier.

The streets were full of tourists excited to spend a fun-filled day, spurred on by the backdrop of mariachi music playing along Crescent Avenue. The enterprising locals readied numerous shops that lined the streets, hoping to lure in as many visitors as possible. The people of Avalon made their living in the summer, and they thought of all the ways to give tourists an opportunity to help then in their pursuit. What a feeling contrasted with the solitude of the Isthmus at the west end. It was like spending a day at the Long Beach Pike. So many people with so many vibrant colors… the aroma of hamburgers, fries and Catalina taffy crept into your nostrils and taunted your palate. This was Avalon. Okay…but Tuck, Bones, Ross, Jeff and I took off for another adventure. We were about to disembark from the Main Street crowd and search out the real heart of Avalon. Since it was Jeff's first time here, I began to spout out everything of interest he might overlook. As we walked along, a giant clock on the side of the hill began to chime. I explained the noise was coming from the tower just above the casino over on the west side of Avalon. The bell chimed each quarter of an hour from 8 in the morning until 8 at night. It's been doing that since 1925.

Jeff asked, "What? Did it ever stop?"

"Heck, I don't know…probably."

We moved on, and I pointed just below the clock to the Zane Grey Hotel. I explained it used to be the home of Zane Grey, a well-known author of western TV episodes and novels.

We continued on to the backstreets, where tourists mounted excursion buses headed out to all over the island. Waiting taxis lined up for trips to the Bird Farm or Wrigley Botanical Gardens, hidden in the back valley. Visitors could also take a trip to the Catalina Airport in the Sky, have lunch then travel on to Black Jack or Middle Ranch. There they could gaze at Wrigley's fine breed of Arabian horses. Only a few lucky ones might make their way over to Little Harbor but most never did. And, that was a good thing. It's too fine of a place for mere tourists.

Having been to downtown Avalon many times before, I wasn't about to be distracted by attempts to gobble down hamburgers or spend time in the magic shop. Nor would I be cajoled by the smell of the taffy. No, there would be none of that. We'd do that later. For now, we had to keep going. There were other things we must do first. After finding Catalina Street and traversing through row after row of golf-cart lined residential areas, we finally arrived at a familiar gray house. This was the winter residence of the Taylors. Why there? Because Tay said he'd introduce us to some local Avalon girls whenever we got to town.

I could see a gleam in Ross's eye as I knocked on the door. This was the first time in the past week he seemed to sense that I had a direction in life. Ross always felt that way when girls were brought into the picture. Otherwise, he thought what I did was really pointless. Tay opened the door. After seeing all the friendly faces, he said, "Hi guys! Welcome to Avalon."

As we remained out on the steps, you could hear someone clamoring about in the house. Tay went back in, and we overheard him explain, "They're buddies from the Isthmus." He yelled to us, "Come on in." We did and were greeted by a gorgeous girl, dressed in a loose halter-top and cutoff jeans. "Hi," she said with a pleasant smile. Without hesitation, he started introducing us. "These are my soon-to-be famous friends from the Isthmus." He finished with Billy Bones, "named because of his slim-to-nothing build." We all laughed. "So, listen, I'm going to make some calls… see if I can round up some friends. We'll catch you guys in about an hour at the back of the casino… next to the steps where they certify the scuba divers."

"Okay. We'll see you then, in about a hour."

Tay smiled, pulled the girl back into the house and shut the door. Now feeling good that something was in the works,

I said, "Let's go over to Lolo's barbershop and get the load on who we're playing against next week. Lolo and Frank Saldana, for as long as I can remember, have had their barbershop on a backstreet of Avalon. The two brothers, who've lived here from birth, graduated from Avalon High as All American baseball, basketball and soccer players. Throughout the years, the brothers' barbershop became more popular than the TV show Cheers as a place to scrape out what's going on in Avalon. Rarely is there any talk about the outside world. No, their specialty is baseball. After that's exhausted, it's on to the rest of the world of sports. They both rambled while attempting to cut your hair.

Frank has been known to leave men bald while talking over all sorts of issues with his buzzing machine whispering in your ear. At the end of the conversation, he'd introduce you to the mirror and ask how you liked the haircut. Looking like a marine recruit just out of boot camp, you'd laugh to yourself and say, "That'll do." With that, he'd wisp you out of your seat and you'd hand over a few bucks. It was well worth it to be able to stand around all the time you wanted. A small price to pay for browsing the faded photos on the barbershop walls, gawking at all the celebrities who had passed through Lolo's over the years. But, by far, the most prominent wall space was given to baseball stars, especially to some of the old rendition of the Wrigley family's Chicago Cubs.

From 1921 to 1951, the Cubs set up their spring training camp in Avalon, where they built a small version of Wrigley Field. All of this history of Avalon sports can be found in one form or another on Lolo's walls. Caps and autographed this and that take up every inch.

Cutting hair was not the only thing Lolo and brother Frank kept busy with. They were also proverbial coaches, leaders or what have you of the youth baseball programs since, as they tell it, the Civil War. So, when my dad started the baseball camp in the '50s, no doubt there was keen interest in Avalon toward his new enterprise. Some of the finest young talent from the mainland came every summer to our camp at the west end. Five times each summer our best would come out to play the "Worlds Series of Catalina Island," as it was known. We'd compete against the formidable talents and rival east end team, the Avalon Boys. The deal was, every session we'd compete in Avalon's Wrigley Field or they'd come to the Isthmus and play in our sandlot. There would be no mention of this momentous occasion in the LA Times but, on the island, this was big.

It was also a treat for young guys who dreamed of baseball, even before girls. Avalon's Wrigley Field was it and always fun to take our friends to. It was a piece of history, and we were a part of it. Maybe a small piece, but a piece nevertheless.

The Saldana brothers coached the Avalon team, and my dad and Lolo cut the deal. So, that's why I had to come by and see Lolo with my entourage. Always happy to greet and jostle us about the upcoming game, Lolo said, "Hey Gil, good to see you. In town for the day?"

"Yup," I replied then pressed on. "So Lolo, who are you guys going to pitch next week at Wrigley?"

"Oh Gil, you know we're just lucky to field nine guys."

"Right," I thought. He always played down the effort.

"But we did have a good baseball year in Avalon, as you know."

But, I didn't know. So he went on.

"We've got two good pitchers with a lot of zip. So you can tell your dad we'll be ready for next week's game."

"How many kids do you have coming over from the mainland to play this game?" I asked jokingly. He laughed without missing a cut on the guy sitting in the barber chair. "Come on, Gil, you guys at the Isthmus think we always bring in ringers for the game."

"Maybe it's the goatees and tattoos on the players that bring those thoughts to mind."

He now smiled and stopped to chuckle. "Well, remember, you have all of California and even a few other states to recruit from."

"But all our boys are under the age of 15," I shot back.

Lolo laughed. "I don't know about that, but a lot of your 15-year-olds are holding major league contracts. And what about you, Gil? When are you signing on like your brothers?"

"My dad seems to think never. He says I need to hone in my temper, whatever that means."

He smiled and said, "Hey, we'll see you here at Wrigley next week."

"Looking forward to it," I said while breaking the guys from wandering around the shop in disbelief. "Let's go guys. Got to give Lolo and Frankie some time to make a living," I added as customers began to queue up for their share of Lolo's humor.

We paraded ourselves down the main street where the local pharmacist, Dr. Klein, had his store. He'd been a good friend of my father's since their USC days. I told the guys to take off because I had to get some stuff for my dad. The Catalina Taffy Shop was just across the street, so they hustled over.

"How's your father, Gil?" Dr Klein asked as he looked up from his work.

"The same. Thanks for asking."

"How're your brothers doing with the Dodgers?"

"Fine, I guess. I don't hear much from them these days."

"Well, I keep track of them in the sporting news. Good stuff. It's always good when I read about Benny's boys doing well."

"My dad always talks about you and his days back on USC's campus."

"Yeah, those were good times, and your uncle Henry... phew... what a football player, but of course all your dad's brothers were.

What can I do for you today, Gil?"

"My dad's prescription?"

"Oh yeah, I almost forgot. I have it for you right here." He reached over his counter and handed it to me. Then asked, "Is the camp coming in to play Avalon next week?"

"Yep."

"Good, I'll take off a few hours from the store and watch you guys."

"Great. Root for us."

"Well now, Gil, nothing personal, but I've got more customers here in town." We both laughed. "Tell your dad, 'hi.'"

"I will. Bye, Doc." I stepped out of the corner store into the crowded pedestrian traffic and found my way across the street into the taffy shop. I'm always amazed at how many people stood outside, thoroughly entertained by the giant machine spinning and pulling taffy in the window. I looked around the shop and found the guys in line about to pay for their choice of candies.

We then proceeded back out to the street, and they looked over at me as if I were their tour guide. I suggested that we go ahead and find Tay at the casino. While we strolled down the esplanade that runs alongside the sandy beach, we carefully scanned the girls lying out on their towels.

The casino is about a quarter mile out. Getting closer you realize how immense it is. I said, "The guy who designed this thing must be happy. You can't come into Avalon without seeing it. Unless you're blind, and I think you could feel it even if you were."

"What are talking about?" Ross asked sarcastically. "If you can't see it, you can feel it?"

"Whatever, Ross. Obviously, you aren't deep enough to get the point."

We went to the back of the casino and walked over to the stairs leading down into the dark water. "Hey, look at that." About 100 feet out, bubbles percolated to the top. "If you want to be certified as a scuba diver, you can get tested right out there. It falls off here to over 100 feet down." Just then, two divers surfaced. We watched them swim to the stairs and take out their mouthpieces, anxious to talk about the dive.

"They made it," I said.

"What do you mean, 'they made it?'" Ross asked.

"No bends."

"What bends?"

"You know, the air bubble thing. If you come up from way down there… the pressure makes bubbles inside your body. You can die if they burst. But if you come up slowly, your body works out the bubbles. Something about decompression."

"Are you crazy or something? You don't know what you're talking about, Gil. Since when did you get all scientific? You just tell stories. Have you ever seen someone with the bends?"

"No, Ross. But I've read about it."

"Right, that means you don't know what you're talking about AGAIN."

Not wanting Ross to continue with his raving review of me, I announced, "Here comes Tay and some girls." His golf cart stopped right in front of us. Out stepped Tay, who introduced two more girls. Not that it mattered, but I think he enjoyed giving the impression he was the man around town. We juggled into meaningless conversations and sized each other up. Then, back into the cart and away they went.

"Okay…so that's it?" Ross asked.

"Hey, what do I look like, the Pony Express? Don't talk to me about Avalon girls. Talk to Tay when we get back to the Isthmus. Let's go have some real fun," I said while leading them over to the St. Catherine construction site. Work appeared to be at a standstill with only a few people moving about. We walked around to the back and saw an open delivery door. I asked some guy, "Do you mind if we go in and take a look around for a few minutes?" Surprisingly, he shrugged his shoulders and said, "No problem, but just for a few minutes." He came along and seemed to enjoy pointing to this and that, as if he were showing us a hidden jewel. "All the famous, from Gable to Monroe, used to come to this place in the early days, before the war. Go ahead and have a look," he prompted.

It wasn't that St. Catherine's looked different than any other hotel we'd been in. It was just knowing you were walking in the rooms that somebody special had walked in before that kind of made you part of their world. I was getting a little nostalgic about the past. But, how could I? What past? I was a mere 18 years old. "That's not a past... that's a beginning," I thought.

"Okay guys, we're out of here."

"Where now. Not more girls?"

"Nope. Better. They're not even on our list for the rest of the day, something way better!" I said as I rushed out of the hotel, making sure to thank the guy for the look-see.

We raced back toward town, past Lolo's barbershop and on to Descanso Ave. Then, when we got to the end of the street, past a few palm trees... they caught their first glance. "Yep that's it. Avalon's Wrigley Field! There it is, guys, Wrigley Field!" Now, for kids that grew up in major league cities, this wasn't such a big deal. But, remember, the Dodgers had just recently come to LA. So, to us, this was big stuff and the closest we'd ever come to a famous icon of baseball. This was as good, no, even better, then wearing a Mickey Mantle jersey.

The gate was open, as it always was. We walked reverently into the quiet stadium and onto the field. After a few minutes we mounted ourselves on the bleachers and began to yell out baseball talk. The sounds echoed back. It was like being in the Notre Dame cathedral, screaming out noise and hearing it reflect back, recognizing we were there. You could imagine the smell of the popcorn, the jostling of the crowd and the crack of the bat as it made contact with the ball. Also, the hushed sound of the crowd, following the ball out of the stadium. Then, the collective roar as it floated over the fence. This was baseball paradise. They played it all right here.

I went back down on the field and ran over to home plate. "It was right here, guys, believe it or not, I got my first hit in life. I was 13, playing against Lolo's Avalon team. Yeah, right here," I said going back in time. "It was a fastball. Yeah I hit it, just like my father said I would. It didn't get me. I got it." Now looking out to where the short stop would have been, "There… right between short and third…a line drive double!" I stepped up to the abandoned plate, took a swing and began to run as if I had hit the ball. Down the first baseline I sprinted. I rounded first and slid into second with a perfect hook slide. Then, I yelled back to the bewildered bunch, "That was it! Yes it was!" I looked back at my friends gathered around home plate, gazing at me as if I were a loony.

Now beaming with arrogance and pride, I walked out to center field, laid down in the weeded grass and looked into the stands, crowded with ghosts, actually thinking I could find a familiar face. Soon, we were all lying down, telling baseball stories. Little did I know that only two years later I would be in a locker room playing cards with Ernie Banks and Ron Santo, two of the most prodigious players in Cub's history. But, for now, it all started here at Wrigley Field in Avalon. Next stop… the magic shop. It always honored our campers' donations to its prosperity on every visit to Avalon. This was a fun place, continually jammed with camp kids. The store clerk took pleasure in giving a magic show and, afterward, giving away the secret ingredients to each trick for the price of a sale. The kids bought in and, for the next week, the nightly campfires would be all about two-headed coins, marked cards, hats that had pockets and ropes with four ends. Other than rabbits or airborne white doves, they had it all.

Now, stuffed with postcards of every building in Avalon, Catalina taffy and magic tricks, the cash-strapped campers began to gather at the end of the pleasure pier. Some found just enough money left in their pockets to purchase a juicy hamburger from the stand. The smell was just too enticing to reject a taste. After counting heads and concluding we had no escapees, we marched them in no particular order down the ramp and into the waiting Blanche W. Once they found their friends, they climbed aboard and parked themselves with their loot well protected under their seats. The head counselor stood up and began calling out names.

Everyone was brought to a complete silence. It was mail call. After some minutes of reading off names, John Radcliff said, "That's all folks." But, he quickly gave a smirk and finally called out some of the counselors' names. Wow. I got one and reached over to grab it. I really didn't care if the others received anything, so I tuned them out 'til I heard everyone laughing. And, to my surprise, I got two. No way! I quickly jumped from my seat, snatching the extra letter from John's hand. "Looks like Lefebvre is getting more than his share of letters from your sisters. What about me?" he asked with a mischievous smile. "Don't you guys love me?" The campers responded by yelling out tame expletives. He sat down, chuckling at their response.

I moved away from my friends, as they got lost in their own mail and looked at the return addresses. One was from my girlfriend on the mainland and mailed from a cruise ship somewhere in the Mediterranean, the other from Jody. For the moment, I became a forensic expert, attempting to find clues that would give away what the envelopes contained. I smelled both of them, letting my senses dictate their priority. There was a subtle difference, telling me something more than what I already knew.

Betsy's was familiar with a sweet tingling kind of cotton candy touch to it. You wanted to eat the letter rather then read it. On the back, I could see evidence of red. Betsy's frilly, girly pink envelope fit her. It was so neat and nice and all girl. Next, I attempted to pick at the back of the letter, finding cause for the red. Yes, as I peeled back and broke the seal, I could see the red became an impression of her lips. Yep, it was sealed with a kiss. Okay, at least it's not a Dear John letter. Betsy loved to flirt away the day with just about any male, but especially with foreigners who would love to reign in an authentic California girl. Without opening it completely, I rushed to examine Jody's letter and put it under my sensory test to see what conclusions it would reveal. No cotton candy smell or pink-colored envelope this time. Something more subtle and germane, yet a detectable scent never the less. Not entirely Old Spice but something close, telling me it was female. But, what was it? I had no clue. This clearly was something new for me.

I slipped back into my seat hoarding these letters as if they were my last link to survival. No way was I going to share them with Ross or Jeff. Okay, maybe Billy Tuck. For whatever reason, I opened Betsy's letter first. She went on about her daily activities and those wonderful foreigners…"so nice and respectful, never too demanding". I read between the lines. With every sentence, she hoped to put doubt in my mind and make me jealous. "Betsy, I know you too well," I thought. "I won't let that happen. Nah, that's not enough for us guys back here," and I began to chuckle at her attics. She ended with some stuff about the sunset reminding her of us. Okay, that's fine but I've heard all that before from her. Finally a few Xs and Os and "Miss You …Ever, Betsy."

"A lot of cheesecake," I thought and placed the letter in my back pocket. I began to fondle my other letter, the surprise of the summer. In total suspense, my hand moved slowly around the edges. Will I be accepted, rejected or asked to resign? Who knows? All this was so new. The envelope offered no clues. I looked for hints of red. None. Oops, that might not be a good sign. I peeled back the envelope, took a deep breath and dove in. I could hear her voice as I read, "Dear Gil," so formal…it continued, "I had a wonderful night with you on the Isthmus pier. My heart began to give me away. I'm glad that no one else could feel or hear it pounding the way I did." She went on talking to me in letters. Not about other things, just her and me. Maybe it was because I really didn't know her that well, but there was no second-guessing, no reading in between the lines. She was direct and poignant, plus signed off with no "forever" or "thinking of you" stuff. Just simply, "I'll be coming to the Isthmus next weekend. Hope to get a chance to see you… Jody."

And that's when I began to think, "What does she mean, 'a chance to see me?' Does it mean that there may be no chance to see me? Why not give me a more definitive answer? Like, do you want to see me? Not just…chance. What's with this chance idea?" Maybe I was so used to reading Betsy's letters that I'd become too callous and, yeah, a little suspicious. I tried to vet out everything and got nowhere. Why am I so bothered by this girl with so little to clue me in on her intentions? Well, it'll work itself out. BOOOOM! I was brought back to the moment at hand with a slashing of the ocean, crushing against the Blanche W. while we turned the corner to pass Long Point. The small boat was now open to the insults of whitecaps rolling in from afternoon Pacific storms.

Rounding the corner, going back to the Isthmus in late afternoon always reminded me of the old WWII movie series Victory At Sea, where fleets are plummeted by huge sets of waves, causing ships to bob up and down as each one hit. The Blanche corkscrewed her way through, attempting to navigate each blow. Since her christening, Blanche always prevailed, but her passengers, like us, got soaked. We did our best to protect the new investments we'd acquired in Avalon. When it seemed all was lost to the wet and cold, we made the turn into the Isthmus, finding immediate relief behind Bird Rock's protection from the westerly winds. Finally inside the bay and shielded from the weather, the sun once again tumbled down on us.

Wow, what a great day. Maybe someday I'd never let it end and sail away to anywhere. But, for now, I greeted my mother and dad on the pier as we docked. Everything was complete. Life couldn't be better, and I had this Jody thing snuggled safely in my back pocket, the way I wanted it to be.

And, Betsy? "Have a good time. See you in September."

CHAPTER 23

# A Sherlock Day

If you don't like sailing to nowhere, never come to the Isthmus because that's where you start. But, if you dream of idyllic surroundings, hope to find antidotes to civilization or want to rediscover yourself, as travel ads promote, you don't have to voyage to some far-off, remote corner of the world. It's all right there, just 26 miles offshore and 55 minutes on the Catalina Express.

The way I see it, Catalina has two different attitudes. One you'll find in Avalon, with all sorts of places to go, people to see and things to do, all pre-wrapped and identified artfully in tourist brochures. You'd be remiss to overlook them. But, just down the coast, at the west end, is an entirely different thing. It's canvassed by exotic tints of natural beauty but with little protocol. No tourist maps to keep you moving. No, that's up to you. I asked a sailing friend once how he liked the Isthmus. "It's okay, but when you get there, there's nothing to do." What? Nothing to do? His statement told me less about the place and more about the type of person he was.

Not so with us. As each morning's sun came up, we planned our day. We created our own fantasies and images. That's what made them exceptional and exclusive. We took on the challenges of our time and accepted the results, whether good or bad. For, in the end, isn't that what defines character? Years later, maybe we'd regret some things. But, in those earlier years, there was little time for that.

Ross, Tuck, the bunch and I made idle day's play. We sought out adventures, always pressing on to something new. Not looking for fun but creating it instead. We'd ponder away on hot summer days, planning our next episode. And, one episode still on our mind was the back bay barge. Yeah, the one in Cat Harbor. Our imagination began to explode at the possibilities. That barge hung out there, half in the water, half out, dangling like a cigar ash ready to drop off into the sea, sometimes like a seal enjoying the sun in late afternoon, yet always surreal. We decided it was time to find out what secrets were hidden within its bowels.

"Strong stuff," I said to the guys.

Jeff bowed out. "No romance in that, Gil."

Tuck, he was always ready to go. Ross said nothing but the same old, "You're crazy," then consented, "I'll go. Besides, what'll I laugh at you about?"

"Great. Go ahead and come along as an observer, brave one," I jabbed.

Okay, the lineup was set and, after our late workout, off to the barge we went. "Do we need any flashlights?" Ross asked.

"No man. Let's not wait till dark. Look, we need to get in and out as quickly as we can. No need to go in there looking like we're going to camp out all night or something. Let's give the impression we're just taking a hike, zoom in and look around… then out we go."

Ross laughed. "What do you think this is, some Special Forces operation?"

"Well, just maybe it is. Do you know what those goofy

looking guys are doing in there? Could be drugs, gun smuggling or whatever. How many times have they eyeballed us? You have to admit, there's definitely something fishy going on. So, if I were you, I'd be a little more concerned than you are right now, Ross."

"Wow," he said mockingly. "It's some sort of national conspiracy. Ooo! Ooo! Maybe aliens or ghosts are in there like Linda talked about. Or, maybe that's where the Lady in White hangs out."

"Okay, maybe you're right, Ross, but, at the end of the day, if you have the gall to…."

"Relax, Gil, I'm in. This is going to be fun."

Sometimes the afternoon fog plays a funny game in the back bay. It comes in and then retreats with the tide, while the front bay usually stays clear and sunny. Ross, Tuck and I marched our way toward the target, taking the high road that passed between the yacht club barracks and the Banning House. We crouched low to the ground on the hills for about a half mile and moved into the clutches of the oncoming mist. Darn, I hadn't planned on this. With the thickening fog, my nerves needed some reassuring. But, if Ross detected any kind of reluctance building up inside, I knew I would never live it down. No way. I started this thing, and I was going to finish it.

As we closed in on the barge, the sun finally laid into the fog and pierced its veil, lighting up the bay. All right, this was a good sign. The mysterious aura was about to falter. We plunged off the road, running quickly to the side of the barge, hoping to go unnoticed, listening carefully each step of the way for clues as to what was inside, secretly wishing nothing would be found.

But, as we slid up alongside, something weird happened. The barge seemed to vibrate, tempting me on. What was it? All stopped and my heart fluttered as it took in what was going on in my mind. Instinctively, I stepped back and looked for a breach in this creaking creature. It seemed to challenge me to come on in. Why? What was there to hide? Maybe I really didn't need to know. Maybe it wasn't any of my business. But, again, there would be no losing face here. I was going in. This despicable barge would never beat me. I let go of the procrastination stuff when I said, "It's on. It's go time!" With that, we pulled ourselves onto the deck. So far, so good, but my heart called out for relief. We saw an opening and moved forward. I stuck my head in first. Nothing, nothing but darkness, but, as my eyes adjusted, I saw a stream of light coming through a corner of the dilapidated wooden shell.

Not a word was spoken. Silence ruled. We pressed on into the darkened chamber. Still no clues... Water. Water? We felt it oozing between our toes. It seeped slowly into the half-sunken barge. We kept on until, out of the dark, everything underneath us started to move. Eerie creatures invaded our feet. "Oh my God!" I yelled. "What's..." My question was drowned out by a deafening noise. The room became alive! The floor turned into a burst of frenzied energy. Whatever it was, it consumed the room. This senile barge seduced us in and was now about to thrust its secret on us. We froze, reeling from all the chaos. Someone shouted, "Let's get out of here!" As we began our unplanned retreat, Tuck ran into a piling that gave way. I attempted to grab him, and we both fell face first, unable to brace ourselves from the fall or the unknown creatures that were lurking beneath us. Then, up from the broken piling, light suddenly illuminated the scene. To our amazement and enormous relief, the brightness revealed hundreds of lobsters flipping and snapping about the room. It was like an indoor aquarium!

Okay, now we're getting somewhere. I said, "Guys, this must be a holding spot for lobster poachers." My smile was contagious as we stood in awe at the abundant display of captured creatures. Soon, panic set in. "We'd better get out of here before those guys return." In half the time it took us to get in, we escaped the barge, vaulted to the road and then climbed the mountain above the bay. After overcoming an oxygen deficit, we sat on the top of the hill, looking down at the crime scene. Seeing there were no witnesses to our daring act, we laughed with relief and reviewed the events. There would be no need to embellish. This was great stuff. "Hey, Ross, you should have seen your eyes. You were so scared back there, weren't yooouuu?"

"Not any more than you and Tuck," he said with a wide grin. "I have to admit, Gil, this was a good one."

"Well, Ross, there you go. Another episode you'd never have experienced without me."

"Gilly, you've almost gotten me killed so many times. It's about time you got something right."

"I'll give you that," I said.

We all jumped up with raised hands and shouted, "Yeah! Yeah!" And, like Irish highlanders scrambling across mountain peaks full of energy, we began our descent. Our day was a success. We'd met the enemy, looked it in the eye and didn't blink. Testosterone was boiling over. Not even Randall Cunningham III, the trailblazer, could match our day.

Remembering it was his day in the kitchen, Ross raced on ahead. Tuck and I sauntered down to the solace of the deep blue water and sun-baked Isthmus shore to just clown around.

Following a little post-adventure analysis, we decided it was about time to go about our favorite pastime – besides looking for girls, that is. So, we jumped into the warm Pacific water and swam out to the float. After catching the line that held our flaty, we pulled it in, jumped into the boat and off we went.

Coming from a family with legendary boating credentials, Tuck's navigational skills were mastered at an early age. Staying just inside of Bird Rock, we sailed effortlessly while crisscrossing between it and the shoreline. As he attacked from side to side, I questioned him relentlessly. His answers were typical, spontaneous and simple. "Yes," "no" and "I don't know." He never even suggested my line of questioning made little sense. Just conversing, without really going anywhere, was enough for Tuck. We sailed the day away.

Then, unpredictably, Billy Tuck made a big mistake. He broke in between one of my dissertations about girls. "Gilly, it's about time you learned how to sail." Mistake? Yep, that's for sure. I took over the keel. And, while looking up at the sail, Tuck began to guide me into the breeze. He broke into a spirited monologue about sailing into the wind, off the wind, attacking this way and that way. Something about flutter sails and full sails... far too much information for my un-navigational mind to pick up. Clearly, it was a side of Tuck I'd never seen before. He was in control and secure in a world where he belonged.

For those brief hours at sea, Tuck was Admiral Nimitz, taking command with me sitting on the tiller, taking orders. We could have been anywhere during those times...the South Pacific or islands around New Guinea...anywhere. But for now, we had control of the bay. And, nothing could match that feeling, looking in from the horizon to the Isthmus, appearing like pictures taken from a spaceship as it looked back toward Earth. Even Bird Rock became animated by the day's charm. We passed the white stone, while birds rambled about with their young families, chirping into the ocean air. Waves muffled their cries while crashing on the rocks surrounding this geological anomaly. The strong odor of bird droppings kept us safely out of range.

Eventually, it was time to find our way back to Isthmus life. So, we slowly began our attack back to shore. I was happy while opening up again with a barrage of questions, this time about Jody and her upcoming visit, trying to get a sneak preview and entice my spirits. "Yep, she's coming," Tuck called back to me. "You like her?"

"I don't know her yet. How about you, Tuck?"

"I mean, like I said she's a good friend. But not really."

"What do you mean, 'not really?'" Tuck stayed firm on his answer. Again, through the breeze, I asked the same question.

"Well, she's kind of a tomboy type, but fun… yeah fun. But, I never looked at her that way."

"What way?" I asked.

"You know, not like the other girls."

"Okay, I get it! But isn't that what makes her special?" I asked, trying to find additional reasons to like her. The conversation abruptly stopped. At that very moment, a burst of wind put the flaty into an extreme heel. Tuck started laughing at how the airstream surprised me. I jerked the keel abruptly to break off from the wind. It worked, but overboard went Tuck. Next, I made the fatal mistake of tying down the keel. Another gust of wind threw me out into the water.

Now, both of us were in the bay swimming alongside the abandoned flaty, tied down on a course heading directly toward the mainland. No way were we able to keep up, and we began to laugh at the situation. What a sight, the ghost ship sailing straight to San Pedro, some 19 miles away with no one aboard. We swam our way over to Little Fisherman's, then plopped ourselves down on the shore. The flaty was nowhere in sight. After laughing it up some more, the reality of the situation began to sink in. Uh-oh. What are we going to tell my dad? That one of the camp's flatys is going to end up on the mainland shore, somewhere…sometime tomorrow? No, I don't think he's going to be very happy about that.

"Plead ignorance?"

"Well, hey, Tuck. It worked with Brownie's spear gun, at least for a little while.

"So, what are we going to tell him?"

"Nothing. No one saw us take out the boat, so who would know?" As I began to cook up our alibi, Tuck smiled. By now, we were used to these kinds of situations. The plan was set, and off we went. While walking back and passing the camp's beach site, I said, "Oops, here comes Clyde."

"Gilly, what happened to the flaty you took out?" Damn Clyde. What's this guy do, follow everything? "What are you talking about? What flaty?" Now Clyde knew he was on to something.

"I saw you and Billy Tuck take it out. Where is it?"

"Well, Clyde, the mast had a problem and we shored it at Little Fish. We'll pick it up later."

"Okay, I'll tell Virginia."

"What? Why would you tell my mother you little kiss ass? You'd better watch out, Clyde. They might find you at the bottom of the ocean someday."

"You wouldn't do that! I'm going to tell Virginia you're going to drown me!"

"Now, Clyde, I didn't exactly say that. Let's just keep this between Tuck, you and me. Oh, and how about a chocolate malt tonight at the snack bar?"

"You're just trying to keep me from telling your mother."

I jumped back and poked my finger at the pitiful looking guy's chest. "Do you want the malt or not?"

"Okay…Okay," he said cautiously.

"Then, we'll see you later, dude. Tonight… and keep your mouth shut!"

Dinner went off without a hitch, and I finished my dishes while Ross still talked about the barge thing. "Really? Ya think that was such a good idea? Wonder what would have happened if those poachers had been there. Then what?"

"They weren't, Ross...so there. And so what?"

Ross walked back for a loaf of bread, and, again, I heaved a kitchen knife right into the nearby breadbox, only this time quite a ways from him... just for fun and effect. He turned back. "Someday, you're going to miss and..."

"And what, Ross?"

"You'll see. One of these days."

At that moment my dad walked in and looked straight at me. "The flaty? Have you seen it in the last couple of days?"

"Now that you mention it, Dad, I don't think so," I replied as I cringed and made ready to make my defense of today's folly.

"Well, Big Al said that he saw a flaty on the rocks off of Bird Rock. Could it be ours? Must have broken loose from the rope line."

"Maybe," I agreed, feeling a bit more comfortable knowing there were no witnesses except Clyde, who had just walked into the kitchen and caught the end of our conversation. I quickly interjected, "Don't worry, Dad, we'll go out there tomorrow and check it out."

"Okay, but make it early. We'll need you to get the all-star team ready to play Avalon on Thursday."

"Got it. See you in the morning," I said as dad left. Clyde began to speak, but I didn't let him get started. "See you at the snack bar in about an hour, Clyde." I turned to leave with Ross and under my breath muttered, "You little rat fink."

The next morning, Ross, Tuck and I puttered out to Bird Rock. And, there it was, the flaty, grounded on the shore nestled between two rocks, while the sea surged below the bow. How it got there was anyone's guess. It was turned on its side but otherwise surprisingly okay. Now, the only problem was how to extricate her from the sharp rocks. The sun broke through, and the nauseating stench from bird droppings began to pierce through our nostrils. But, after a few minutes, the caustic ammonia smell became tolerable.

Getting onto Bird Rock is a tricky proposition. However, we found a place just big enough and pulled ourselves up. Once landed, we went over to the grounded flatly and happily saw that it looked pretty good, considering the circumstances that put it there. "Great," I said to Tuck. "Better than I expected. Should be easy getting it back to shore." Since this was the first time any of us had ever actually been on the rock, we took some time to scout around. The seagulls, which found this place home, hovered over our heads, keeping a keen eye on us. "Watch out for those guys. They think we're invading their homeland," I said.

"But we are," Tuck added.

"Yeah, I guess we are." When we came over the sticky mound to the other side, we walked ever so slowly out to the backside. From there we looked directly toward the mainland. It was fun sitting on the top while the Pacific roared all around us. The ocean breeze tousled our hair about. As we moved around the edges of the rocks, suddenly we came to a ledge that hung over the Pacific straight down below. It must have been a least a 100-foot drop. I looked at Tuck. "If we can get Ross to bring the dinghy around, I can make this dive."

What a dive that would be; I could do it. I knew I could. We hustled back to the other side to call out my idea to Ross. While we scrambled back to the ledge, Ross brought the boat around and began surveying the area. Then, he yelled up at us, "Don't do it, Gil. It's too high, and I can't tell how deep it is! Besides, you'll have to clear those rocks." He kept looking down in the dark blue water and yelled again, "I guess it does drop off here. Yea. It's deep enough. Really deep, but you're still going to have to clear those rocks!" His shouts echoed from the walls of the grotto that encased the cliff.

"I can do this, Tuck." And then that feeling came. You know the one that comes into your gut when you're on top of high bridges or on the edge of Half Dome in Yosemite? They're high all right, but I needed to know if I could make it. Could I dive, under control, fighting my nerves and hit it? This had nothing to do with a death wish or an adrenalin kick. I wanted to challenge my abilities. I needed to know if I was good enough. It was all on me, not a challenge from somebody else, not even the cliff. It was a disturbing proposition and for the first time, Tuck said, "No Gil. Don't do it."

I stepped closer to the ledge, now mesmerized at the pending prospect. My head became light and dizzy as I put both feet together and extended my arms in preparation of the swan dive, same as I'd done so many other times. It was as if I'd been preparing for this very moment all my life. My mind flashed with previous dives. From railroad bridges into Kings River, the Merced, tall piers and more, but this was different…far more remote and much higher. Ross yelled louder, "No kidding, Gil! It's not worth it!"

But it was…straight to the big leagues in one dive. If I can overcome this, I can overcome it all. Yet, as I inched forward, something stopped me. Then what? What's next? Even if you make it, what's next? I shuddered at that thought. We'd done some crazy things, but this was different. Was I making this thing too dramatic? It was just a simple dive. The panorama and theatre of it all was intoxicating. I heard Tuck say, "Gil, think about it." And, with that thought, I took one step back, away from the precipice. Interestingly enough, that was all it took to break free from the trance. My mind let me go…freed from the lure of danger.

Back in the boat, while Tuck sailed over and returned the flaty to the float, Ross said, "Come on, Gilly, even you're not that crazy."

"No, man. I could have done it… easy."

Ross was just happy to move on to shore. But that day on the rock would haunt me. I knew it was something I needed to do, just for me. All during the rest of the summer, every time I stood at the end of the pier and looked out to Bird Rock, I said to myself, "I will be back, and I will take on the challenge."

Often, it's not the people or places or circumstances that present the most troubling issues in life. It's the issues you create all by yourself that can become obsessive and delusionary. The remedy? Re-evaluate the situation. Unfortunately, when you're young, that's not good enough. You must face it head-on. Overcome it, and that will make it disappear. That's elementary my dear Watson...elementary.

CHAPTER 24

# Searching For God

Sometimes when you don't go to God, He comes to you and says, "Where you been all your life?" Sometimes, that happens to me...being visited by God, that is. I'm sure He wants to meet me, except I really don't know why. But what I do know, there are times when there are no other answers, so I attempt to find them in Him. Some people find this simple. They say God talks to them every day. Since He hadn't done that yet, I found it to be a scary proposition. If God said, "Gil, I'm talking to you. I'm God. Here I am," I'd probably do what Moses did, find a bush and hide. But, it would be the events of this day that would prompt a life-long journey in search of Him.

Early in the morning, Tuck and I were hiking back down the path from Little Fishermen's Cove, getting a good look at the girls on their camp's beachfront. I felt pretty chipper while sneaking a peek at the new recruits and counselors. Tuck confirmed that Jody would be over this weekend on the Geronimo. That certainly lifted my spirits. With everything under control and the sun out, all was good.

I looked beyond the beach to the pier and noticed a large group of people gathering. It was too early for the Blanche. I threw out a question to Tuck, "What's the deal?"

"Maybe it's those divers from the national contest that's been going on for the last week. They probably shot a big one!"

"Let's go see!"

The moment we arrived on the pier, we detected a somber mood. It quickly impaled the delights in our mind as we slowly walked toward the crowd. News got around like the flu and echoed through the Isthmus when something noticeable happened. Obviously, something noticeable was going on. We stopped moving forward when we saw Birt and Big Al standing almost at attention. That certainly was unusual. All eyes looked at a small boat puttering toward the platform at the end of the pier. No doubt it held something inside so sacred that not a peep could be heard... not even a shout out from the moored boats that shouldered the shore as it passed by. They stood still, also as if at attention, until the vessel passed. Once it reached its destination, some men climbed out to tie up. Mr. Bombard stepped in with authority and, along with Big Al and Birt, began to move about, clearly attempting to get the objects in the boat secured and comforted. The large hushed crowd hindered Tuck's and my view.

After a few moments or more, who could tell how long, for time was never in question, the men moved away from the objects that were at the center of it all. Suddenly, the unspeakable was revealed. The bodies of two young men, light blue and ghostly white appeared. I'd never ever seen faces like that before. Were they dead? They must be. Their lifeless bodies just laid there hopelessly, lost to the care of others. But what were they doing with them? Little, except bundling them in blankets. Was it to keep them warm? If they had to keep them warm, there must be a possibility of life, right? I mean... keeping them warm was an act of desperation to sustain someone's life, wasn't it? I heard the jingle of talk from some of the bystanders. "It's the bends."

What? The bends? No, it couldn't be. Weren't those some of the best professional divers in the nation? How in the world did they get the bends? My mind began to take in, digest and sort out the predicament. The bends...that's when divers come up too fast and some kind of bubbles enter their bloodstream or something like that. All I knew for sure, it was horribly painful and probably fatal.

A helicopter invaded my thoughts as it passed overhead, landing in front of the snack bar. Two or three uniformed men jumped out. Then the chopper quickly ascended and flew off, disappearing somewhere out over Bird Rock. These new arrivals began to scurry around the bodies of the afflicted divers, appearing to do nothing special but probably doing more then I knew.

Around the point, like a scene taken from Bogart's African Queen, came the Coast Guard, huffing and puffing its way into the bay. The boat seemed to know it was in a race with death, trying to get here as soon as it possibly could. Every minute gained was a lifeline that could remedy the situation and evict these guys from certain death.

The crowd cheered as it found its way to the dock. I prayed in silence, again. This was becoming a repetitive matter for me lately... this praying thing. The divers were quickly shuttled to the back of the boat where large decompression chambers sat with opened doors. Their only hope to live another day was inside those contraptions. As they slid them in, the Coast Guard set off screaming toward the mainland. People stood around, sharing information, then gradually went on their way.

Tuck and I sat down on the end of the pier, really not saying much, but an air of doubt began to filter into our conversation. Remember, this was long after the Big War had been won. The Korean War was over and Vietnam was just mounting its horse. The U.S. and other parts of the world had the bomb and knew better than to use it. In fact, it wasn't until much later, halfway through the '60s, when war was introduced with honor, glory and pride by movies like The Green Beret. Our homes were decorated with rabbit ears, collecting airwaves for the latest TV shows. Ozzie and Harriet was a favorite. American Bandstand was in everybody's living rooms, and the drama of the day was Leave it to Beaver. So, in this climate, our attitudes, this excess of immortality, rarely came under attack. Ours was a safe zone with little concern of consequences, except the self-inflicted ones. Very rarely were we ever faced with the possibility of dying. After what I just witnessed, coming face to face with the prospect, all kinds of questions begged for answers. Death…no one wants to talk about it. What happens then? Does anybody really know?

I looked at Tuck, and he looked at me. I sensed that we were both bothered, at least for the moment, about what we had just witnessed. We walked back down the pier, clearly in a far different mood than when we had walked up. But, let the rest of the day come, because, "At least it wasn't us, right?"

"Right," Tuck said softly.

"That's enough of that," I said.

It wasn't until the late of night, in that dark cabin, while the rest of the guys slept, that my mind began to wander, like it always did, this time back to the pier. Thinking of those ghostly figures that came from somewhere out of left field now plagued me for answers. "Did I have one? Did I really need one? Why? I was going to live forever," I thought. But then, maybe not, so I began to arrange a credible way out of my dilemma.

The way I saw it, dying had two major problems. One, how you die. The other was... what was it like to be dead? Did anybody ever tell me about death? I could hit, throw, run and catch, but death? What's that got to do with me? I had questions, but no answers. Okay, I needed to get to sleep, but first I needed to unravel this thing. These guys, how did they get there? Was it because they made a stupid mistake? They were professionals, right?

It was entirely their own undoing. Or, was it just their time? Well, they should have known. It was their own fault. It could have been prevented. That's it! They could have stopped it from happening. Since I was smarter than that, this thing wouldn't happen to me. Now, I was getting somewhere with this. "Everybody dies," I thought. "So what if they do," I countered in my brain, "but it's usually when they get old. I'm not old yet so that's not a problem. Let's see… I'm smart and I'm not old enough to worry about it. Not my problem, at least not tonight." I figured it was something like dental work…don't need it today, so no need to worry about the needles now. Maybe a little brevity might quiet my concerns. Still, my mind continued to taunt me. Father James, I bet he's got answers. Maybe I should've listened to him on the beach instead of putting those rocks in the sand while hunting out those girls. That thought gave a momentary smile. I needed that. Let's see…what did Father James say? "God is in control." The church had given me all the rules of the game since I was born. Do something wrong, confess, then say a Rosary or two. I've got that down pat, just like Ross. Guess I don't have to do anything else. I'm cool with that. So, what am I making all of these decisions for, if God's in control?

So tomorrow, now erasing all my earlier revelations, if I end up… not here... it's God who did it. That's okay. But now where's God going to take me? And why? Oops. I'm back to the same situation that woke me up. It must be God, but what about me, God? He's never talked to me. Although somehow, when I find myself in trouble, I talk to Him. In a way, that makes things easier to understand, without really understanding. I just leave my problem on His doorstep. And, "praying" is the operative term. He'll always be there and look at the situation in a more favorable light when I pray about it. That will do. I gave up for the night after finding enough distance between the guys with the bends and me, thanks to this God thing. Off to sleep I went. Not knowing, at the time, I'd just taken my first undeclared step in the search of God.

CHAPTER 25

# The Betrayal

Friday finally arrived. I had this feeling deep down that something special was going to happen, and it did. You know it's funny when a defining moment takes place in your life, sometimes it's difficult to recall names or the exact sequence of events, but you remember it happened just the same.

I was up before sunrise and rushed out of the cabin before any of the guys awoke. I dashed into the kitchen, and, as usual, mother was wrapped in her apron, preparing breakfast. "Well, Gilly, you're up extra early and perky this morning."

"Yeah, Mom. I couldn't sleep."

"Good, because I've got some work for you to do. It's fish night, so I need you to get the abalone out of the refrigerator and start pounding."

Our camp divers, Big Al, Ben and even Ty, had been busy all week diving for these tough critters. Think about it. With 130 hungry mouths to feed, my dad made out like a bandit. Every single one free from the sea and all that was left to do was a little labor. They were hammered to tenderize them then breaded and chicken fried. What a treat. Labor cost…practically nothing with me, Ross and Billy Bones happy to just get a free meal out of it.

Dad walked through the door and, like mom, was surprised to see me up so early. "Got something special going on?" he asked with a smile.

"Not much. How about you, Dad? Something going on with you?" Usually, dad would stay up late and put the camp to sleep while mother finished up the kitchen. So, he'd sleep in and she'd come in early, but today was an exception. Dad explained, "It's your brothers. They're flying in on Channel Air."

"What? They get released?" I asked jokingly.

"No, no. They're on All-Star break and have some hitting problems. I told them to fly in for a couple of days, and we'd work it out. We've got them for the weekend."

"Sounds good, Dad."

"Yeah, this is the first summer you guys have ever been separated."

My twin brothers are just 11 months older than I am, but it seemed like at lot more than that. For most of our lives, they were a few years ahead of me in school, partly because I'd had problems adjusting to school in general and my temper kept me in trouble. They, on the other hand, had each other to depend on to work through the issues of growing up.

Dad and mother were always happy to see their boys coming home, and the Isthmus was, in a way, our second home. "So, Gilly, after breakfast let Ross take over your team. Your brothers are going to need the pitching machines to be in good working order today."

"What time are they coming in?"

"Sometime in the afternoon. I think around three or four."

"Do you want me to pick them up?"

"No, I'll take care of that," Dad said as he grabbed a fresh cup of coffee on his way out to sit on the deck.

My parents had a routine of sitting out there while reviewing the day's schedule. Up the path strutted Big Al and Ben. Big Al's muscular physic was impressive, especially contrasted with Ben's sleek thin body, both were barefoot, wearing trunks and, as usual, no shirts but, as always, broad smiles. They came up occasionally to sit with mom and dad, talk about the news around the Isthmus and enjoy a good breakfast together.

Ross walked in the kitchen and began to taunt me. "Well, Gilly's got a special day coming up."

My mom jumped in. "Sure does. His brothers are coming in on Channel Air."

I looked at Ross and made a cut-it-out gesture by slicing my hand across my throat. Saying in sign, "you better not talk about Jody." Smartass, he knew he got my goat, and that made him smile. But, he held off and didn't say another word until my mother walked out.

"You owe me," he said.

"For what?" I asked.

"For keeping quiet about your new flame. That's what."

"What are you talking about, 'my new flame?' She's just a friend. It's nothing like the Kimberly thing, hey, Ross?"

"What about the Collin thing? You do remember Collin, don't you Gil?"

"Can't say that I do," I answered, egging him on. "Besides, this is different, Ross."

"So what makes this so different?"

"It just is!" I said while raising the abalone mallet high above my head, as if it would be thrown at him any second, knowing that would shut him up just in time for my mother's return. "Gilly, I need you, Ross and Billy Bones in the kitchen early today to fry up this abalone. So take off after lunch but be back by two o'clock."

We finished up and Ross went up with the campers to play

games, while I worked with dad on the machines. When I got a break, I rushed down to the beach to see if the Geronimo had come in. It looked like it was going to be a big weekend. All the moorings were quickly being filled. But, it was Little Fisherman's that got my special attention. I looked from the pier toward it, but it was too far away to see who was in. All I could see were just a bunch of bobbing masts. Just then I turned to see Billy Tuck walking up the pier. I was really happy to see him because this time I knew Patty and Jody couldn't be far behind. I waited anxiously while Tuck got closer. Working hard to disguise my enthusiasm, I greeted him. Too late, Tuck knew me better. I didn't even need to ask. "Jody's coming in on Channel Air this afternoon," he said.

"Okay. So, Tuck," changing the conversation, "are you staying with us this week?"

"I hope so. It's boring at home," he replied.

"Well, it's fish night tonight… stick around."

"No, I can't. Not today. The club's having contests again, and my dad's got me in them all."

"Okay, dude," I said as we walked off the pier. "See you later then."

I went into the snack shop just to look around, then walked back to camp. The campers returned from their morning game and were on their way down to the beach. I went over to the cabin where all the guys were lying on their bunks reading either Sports Illustrated or Sporting News, with the exception of Ret, who held tight to his, by now, stale magazine. I said, "Man, you need to get rid of …." but I was interrupted by the sound of a horse galloping on the road behind our cabin. I looked out the back window and said, "Now that's a picture of pure beauty."

"What is?" Ret asked.

"Shirley, she rides like the wind. It's poetry in motion."

"You ride, so what's the big deal?"

"I ride, but not like her and certainly not on Joey, that wild horse of hers. The point is, Ret, she fits into the picture better than any of those girls you're sweating over."

"Oh, yeah," he mumbled, without being distracted from his reading.

"So, Gilly, what's the story on your new flame? Is she in?" Ross prodded.

"Geez, she's not my flame." I tried to parry the conversation away from her. "The harbor is full, and it's going to be a big weekend."

"How do you know?" Ret asked.

"Cause, Linda told me."

Ross wouldn't let it pass. "So what's her name again?"

"Shut up, Ross. No need to mention it…just a friend."

Out of nowhere, Jeff tried to get a penny's worth of his wisdom in. I stopped him cold in his tracks. "Shut up. I've heard it all before."

"OOOOh, Gil's stressing. I forgot this girl's his special one." Seeing that from here on, I would be pleading the fifth, Ross conceded, "By the way, I heard your brothers are coming in."

Shane said, "Yep, on Channel Air. Been reading about them in Sporting News…maybe about you, next year."

"No way," Ross pointed out. "With his attitude, he'll probably kill some umpire or something. No one will put up with him. Besides, he's never going to hit the 300 road… never."

I just shook my head and said, "My mother wants us in the kitchen early today, so let's get over there. We'll be pounding abs until dinner." Billy Bones, Ross and I got to the kitchen just in time. Mother put us right to work hammering out more abalone. Billy Bones fired up the oil in a huge pan to get ready to fry. As I continued talking and banging away, the unexpected happened. While attempting to move that large pan of hot oil to the next burner, Bones hit the corner of the stove, lost his footing and fell. The boiling oil splashed down the front of him, and he screamed out with pain. While the rest of us stood stunned, mom rushed in and immediately took charge. She gave orders to get the nurse and calmed the situation. Surprisingly, even though Bones was in extreme pain he hadn't lost control. After nurse Lyan arrived, mom made some calls, and we realized the urgency of the situation. His chest down to his stomach had been burned, so mom made arrangements to take Bones to the nearest doctor. The Boy Scout Camp at Cherry Cove had one. After providing basic first aid, they got him in the truck and away he went. Mother said, "Gilly, you, Ross and Jeff need to stick around for dinner. We need Jeff to take over for Billy Bones in the kitchen." I was concerned about Bones. But, since he was alert and talking, I felt that he was probably going to be all right.

Suddenly, the thought crossed my mind. "What about Jody and the Friday night thing?" Great, I'd been working on this for over a week now, and I'm going to be stuck here in the kitchen. So what about Jody? Pushing back the Bones issue, I thought, "What the heck am I going to do?" I guess I can see her later tonight. She's worth the wait. I just needed to get a message to her. But she wasn't expected to arrive in the Isthmus for another hour. So I pressed on.

About an hour passed, and Big Al stepped in and said, "What you're cooking sure smells good. By the way, your brothers just landed at Cat Harbor, and they're getting a celebrity welcome from some of the locals."

"Really?" I asked.

"Yeah. Seems they like having two of their own sign major league contracts."

"I'm sure they like all that."

"Who wouldn't?" Big Al agreed. "I'll bet Benny's a proud

father. I remember when you guys were about that high," now putting his hand out, showing our height when we first came here. "He always talked about you guys making it in baseball. Well, see ya, I'll be back for dinner."

"Okay. Oh, did you hear about Billy Bones?" He hadn't, so I described in dramatic detail what had happened. While leaving, Big Al said he'd run down and tell Bones's brother, Ben, in case he didn't know. Just then our truck pulled up behind the kitchen and in walked my brothers, looking like they had just stepped off a movie set, clothed in colorful floral Bahamas shirts, Florida loafers, dark sunglasses and followed by a few of our counselors, helping with their luggage.

"Hey look, there's Gilly," one of them yelled, "hammering abs."

"Yep, nothing's changed here," I answered back and added, "So you survived another Channel Airline crossing?"

"Looks that way. "We're still alive."

I noticed the professional logos embossed on their luggage and said, "Impressive. How goes it?"

"Oh, just depends."

"Depends on what?" I asked.

"Depends on how well we're playing and the girls out there."

"And, how are the girls?"

"Same, the same everywhere. Some good and some to stay away from." They looked at each other and laughed at the seemingly inside joke.

"Better than here?" I asked.

"No. Everyplace has they're 5s and 10s. By the way, I met this girl on Channel coming over here. She said she knew you or something like that."

"Yeah?"

"She seemed like she'd be a lot of fun," he said.

"I met her a couple of weeks ago. Patty Tuck introduced us," I explained.

"Patty Tuck's still around?"

"Yeah."

What's she up to?"

"You know Patty. She lives in another world. Ya never know. I see Billy Tuck almost every day."

"Hi, Ross," my brothers said as they looked across the kitchen. "You guys having fun this summer?"

Ross answered, "Yeah, but with your brother, you never know."

"Yeah, we know."

"So, how long are you staying?" Ross asked.

"Just the weekend…All-Star break. Hey, we heard Bones got burned this morning."

"Yeah, mom took him over to the doctor in Cherry Cove."

"How bad?"

"He's walking, but we don't know yet."

"Well, going to get this stuff to the cabin. Talk to ya later."

Mother walked in and said with hugs, "Oh, look at my boys. They're all grown up."

"Mom, it's been only a few months." They laughed. Dad stepped in and said, "The boys need a little work. Let's start early tomorrow morning. Get your stuff in the cabin, and then relax until diner. It's fish night."

"Great. Let's change in to something more island."

Off to the cabin they went with some of the counselors following. Now, with that over, I knew Jody was in the Isthmus… probably staying on the Geronimo with the Tuckers. I continued on with the hammering and Ross said, "So, Jody's in."

"So, what's it to you?" I snapped and added, "She's a nice, clean-cut girl. Unlike the girls you've been known to hang around."

"What?"

"Yeah, I could take this girl to meet my mother. I bet Kimberly would love to meet your mother… but, oh, I forgot, she hasn't written back." With that, I began to laugh and I added on to my joke, "Maybe she's pregnant or something, and she'll want to meet your mom."

"Now you've gone too far!" Ross said, as he pointed his finger at me.

I knew I had, but I was determined to put a stop to any further badgering about Jody.

Shorthanded, Ross, Jeff and I worked into the night with the dishes, and it was almost nine when we finished. I rushed to the cabin to put on my best jeans and T-shirt. "Don't leave the light on, guys. I might not make it in tonight," I said with a chuckle and sprinted down to the snack bar. Distracted by the night's possibilities, darkness took me by surprise, causing me to stumble and hit my head against a rock. Not bad but enough to show a little trickle of blood, and signs of swelling began to show up on my forehead. But, I regained my composure, checked out the lump and continued on to the snack bar, looking for Jody.

There was Ty, standing in front and, as usual, looking sharp as ever. "Hi, Ty. What's going on tonight?"

"Not much. By the way, I played pepper with your brothers today."

"Have you seen them around tonight?" I asked.

"One of them was here earlier with some girl."

"Who was she?"

"I've never see her here before."

"So, who else is walking around?"

"The usual Isthmus weekenders. The Knowles, the snack shop girls. Oh, I just saw Jeanie Colmary and her parents. Yep, pretty much all the same crowd. Who are you looking for?" Ty asked.

"This girl Patty set me up with a couple of weeks ago." Just then, out of the dark, Ty's Patty showed up. She was as vibrant as ever. After her charming, "Hi," she pulled at his arm again and they both said, "See you later."

I continued my search for Jody and ventured onto the snack bar patio. Couples were already swaying to the slow melodies from the jukebox. I noticed the Boy Scout counselors and the female version, the Sea Scouts, had invaded the Isthmus. I scanned the dance floor and tables and saw Randall engaged in deep conservation with one of the Knowles. He looked at me for a minute. However, he had far too many things on his plate to bother with me. That's good. Me too. But, where was she? I walked into the snack bar hoping to find her waiting there, but no luck. After seeing me searching around, Linda said, "Are you looking for your brother? He was in here about an hour ago."

"No, not really."

"He was with Patty's friend"

"Small girl in cutoff jeans?

"Maybe," Linda replied.

Feeling concerned, I barged out of the snack bar and into the dark. Man, it was getting later every minute. I checked the pier… back to the snack bar… the beach… nothing…nobody. Where could they be? With my head pounding, I went back up to the snack bar.

Linda came over and asked what happened to Billy Bones. I quickly explained the hot oil story and then stepped back outside. There stood Tuck with his backpack and said, "I'm going to stay at the camp tonight. Okay?"

"Sure, but have you seen Jody?"

"Yeah, she's here."

"I know that, but where is she?"

"I don't know, but she left the yacht club at Fisherman's a long time ago."

"Okay, Tuck. I'll be up to the cabin in a while. See you then." I stood in total bewilderment while he left.

I slowly walked back out toward the ocean to where the lights of the snack bar meet the sand. Suddenly, out of the dark stepped my brother… his arm tightly around Jody. There are times when looking into someone's face tells it all. No need for conversation. When they both looked up at me, I knew what they were thinking. That moment became a perilous drama, with me trying to deceive my pride, trying to safeguard it from the truth. What was at stake here? It was just too murky to understand. I was ambushed. I never saw it coming. I didn't say, "hi." There was no reason. My first impulse was to get away, sort this thing out.

I did so by quickly slipping back to the dark beach, searching out comfort. I found a table and sat alone to consider what had just transpired. Was it a question of loyalty or lack of it? Was this just the product of folly… pretending something was there that wasn't or just a simple matter of misplaced hope? Why not Randall? That would have made more sense. You expect that from an enemy, but my brother? What was I going to say? I felt like this guy who went 0 for 4 yet the team won in the bottom of the ninth, and now I had to appear happy just because it's the right thing to do. So what is the explanation? How do I handle this, with some kind of a witty comment? It was all just too awkward. I needed to quell this cold numb feeling that rotted in my gut. And, would saying something make any difference anyway? I'll say nothing. Nothing says it best. Besides, nothing witty was coming up to save me. No question who the winners and losers were here.

I slipped into the dark cabin late that night, begging not to be heard. On my bunk, looking into the darkness, I began to ask more questions. How do I find a way out? Jeff had warned me. I remembered his speech. "Remember the golden rule. If you like them more than they like you, drop them like a hot potato. Gil, you never do that. That's why you have these problems."

In a panic, I began to scramble up some hope. Maybe later I'll find a way out of this. But, why can't I just have one more time at bat? One more chance to make it right? The idea abscessed into a compulsive thought. It'll all work out. An illusion? Yes. But there was hope that the reality will somehow catch up to the dream. For now, all that was left was to think about tomorrow. I'll face the usual questions from my friends. How will I answer? When the dark night was turned over by the first ray of daylight, I heard my brother slip in, as silently as I did. Once in his covers he fell asleep.

I awoke to find my cabin completely empty. Even my brothers made no attempt to wake me. That was a good thing. Or did they all know by now? Fortunately, nothing ever was said about it. I think nobody wanted to tilt my boat. Saturday passed into Sunday and my brothers left. I was left standing alone on the highest mountain, watching the sailboats, one by one, retreat out of the bay and on into the channel.

A few days passed, and then I received the letter. I knew who it was from. This time, I never attempted to smell its fragrance. This whole relationship became too tart, and there would be no going back. All I needed was an explanation. I opened it, and, to my surprise, she offered more than that. Jody went on about being too impressed and overwhelmed by the attention she got from my brother. She apologized and asked if I would give her another chance. She even got messy with her emotions and then ended by pleading for me to write her back.

Again, fate played right into my hands. You see, I realized then this thing had become more about pride than romance. I should have known. It was so familiar. I knew it was over between us the moment they walked out of the dark that night. But, what was missing was my choice in the matter. If it was to be, I'd just like it to be my idea. And, now it was. I was secured by that thought. This would be a lesson. I would learn something about relationships. Maybe I won't go that far. But, all of a sudden I was revived and delighted at the prospect of not having to post my first rejection to some daunting memory. And, retrieving my pride from the grasp of my brother's charm made this even more satisfying.

CHAPTER 26

# Summer Pruning

Right on time again, the Blanche W. pulled in at 11 a.m. Ross, Billy Tuck and I, along with two more friends, Shane and Chris, waited patiently with a spirit of suspense. Mother had given in to the pleadings from a few of her former Pious X High School students. They could come over, on a trial basis, to spend a week and help in the kitchen and handicraft room.

It was midsummer and a brilliantly hot sunny day. The kind of day, we decided, that demanded we wear our sunglasses for protection from its violent rays. However, I must admit, we had ulterior motives... looking cool. The passengers were four of my mother's favorite former female students. That morning, she let me know of her reservations. In a camp with so many boys and some 25 male counselors, with all of that testosterone pumping, placing these young girls in the same lot made for a rather high-risk proposition.

So, as the Blanche unloaded her passengers and these young girls stepped out onto the dock one by one, I knew we were in for trouble. "Wow, Mom sure miscalculated this one," I thought as I introduced myself. Actually, I knew there was really no need for introductions. Over the years, I'd become accustomed to mom's students knowing all about her boys. After meeting everyone, we picked up their luggage and began the walk back to camp. As we paraded the girls by, our staff and campers immediately took notice and let out muffled, yet noticeable catcalls. This was to be expected. Feeling welcome, the girls smiled and waved. Mother was waiting in the kitchen and showed off her hospitality by offering the girls lunch. Later, she gave them a detailed explanation of their duties and her expectations, reminding them that our campers' safety came first. With that out of the way, they got settled into their cabin and were instructed to be back in the kitchen by 3 p.m.

In the meantime, Tuck, Ross and I slipped into bathing suits and strolled down to our beach, hoping to get another look at the new help. Sure enough, in just that short time, the girls had slipped into their brightly colored bikinis and lay out on their towels. Showing off, we dove in and swam out to the float, only to be followed by the girls. After some time making small talk and pointing out the hot spots in the Isthmus, the girls remembered my mother's request to be back at the kitchen by 3 p.m. They jumped into the water and swam back to shore, hurriedly dried off, then ran out of sight.

Ross, Tuck and I stayed for a while and then we also swam back. There was Clyde, knelt down on the sand. He'd captured some ladybugs in a bottle and was in the process of drowning them by filling the bottle at the water's edge. After putting the lid on he watched them struggle and slowly pass away. Bizarre, to say the least. Disturbed by this deviant behavior, I threw some sand, hitting his backside. "What in the world are you doing, Clyde?" I asked, without expecting an answer. Like usual, he had no idea. Just impulse, I guess. Trying to explain himself was beyond him. So, I threw another handful. I got his attention this time. "I am going to tell Virginia!"

"Go ahead dumbo," I said and tossed more sand at him. His response was to run into the water and take off his trunks in an attempt to wash the sand out. This was too tempting. I ran down to the water and grabbed his floating trunks.

The tantrum began again. "I'm going to tell Virginia, and I'm going to tell her about....you raiding the scouts, you and Ross sneaking food out of the kitchen at night and also about the flaty!"

"Okay, Clyde. Go tell her and see what happens next," I threatened.

Next thing we knew, he marched out of the water naked and began to continue down the beach. That was way over the line, so I called out, "Okay Clyde, here are your trunks. Put them back on!" But, no way, he thought he had me now. He climbed the bluff overlooking the beach and searched around for something to conceal his privates. After finding a box in the trash, he stepped in. Wearing only the box, Clyde walked through the center of the Isthmus, in front of the snack bar yelling, "Gilly pants me!" Keeping on with his mantra, he strutted up the walkway. Our campers gathered around, jeered loudly and, along with our new arrivals, began to laugh uncontrollably. Mother stepped out on the deck to see what the commotion was about. Seeing Clyde in his new attire, or lack thereof, she asked, "What are you doing, Clyde?" "Gilly pants me, Virginia... he pants me!" Now, the fact that almost the entire Isthmus took notice of this ridiculous display obviously made my situation with mother a little tenuous and, at the very least, deserving of an explanation.

So, I went on with mother about how we tried to give him back the trunks he'd taken off himself. However, mother pointed out, "Clyde's emotionally challenged." To which I replied, "Don't you mean he's a wacko?" She reminded me about her favor to his father but conceded that we had about come to the end with Clyde. There was just too much disturbance for the camp, and she agreed the things he did were alarming.

After eating dinner and working in the kitchen with our new help, Ross, Jeff and I felt there might be some unexpected possibilities here. We walked up to the cabin and sat around for about an hour or so just talking and brainstorming about our strategy for their conquest. About to doze off, I was startled by a knock on the door. It was Clyde. I said, "Don't open the door, Clyde. Just yell to me what you're here for."

"Virginia wants to talk to you in the morning."

"What about Clyde? What did you tell her?"

"I told her… you raided the scouts…you're reading Playboy and…."

"Shut up, Clyde. Get out of here!" Then, after thinking about it a little I said, "Hey Clyde, wait a minute." I needed to redirect his demented mind. "Clyde, tonight, Ross, Jeff, Tuck and I are going to have a party with these new girls. Want to come along?"

"Sure!"

"Okay then, stay awake and about 10 tonight, I will knock on the back dormitory door. You open it, and we'll be on our way."

"Okay," he said, sounding excited at the prospect. "Now remember, don't tell anyone. You hear?"

"Okay. See you later."

"Better get back to the dormitory before the lead counselor sees you're out."

"Okay," Clyde said, and off into the night he went. "What are you talking about, Gil? Clyde? No way."

"Man, I've had enough of this Clyde thing guys. Ross, get your flashlight. We need to raid the kitchen." In stealth mode we snuck into the dark. Ross let me stand on his shoulders and crawl through the kitchen window. I opened the door from the deck, and we were in. With the flashlight now on, I opened the refrigerator. "Ah, there it is," grabbing a large container full of syrup for the

286 · CATALINA SUMMER

morning's pancakes. I found a medium-sized pan and filled it with the syrup then mixed in some flour. While I stirred, Ross caught on to what we were doing. "Wait a minute, Gil." I didn't and said, "All we need now are some feathers. Ross, go get a pillow."

"Oh no, Gilly. Now you're really going to get me in trouble with your mom."

"Relax, Ross. Clyde can't say anything cause he'd have to admit he snuck out. Right? What's he going to say? That he was sneaking out with us to meet the girls?" We both laughed at that and slipped back out of the kitchen, making certain to lock the door as we left. Sure enough, at 10 p.m., after we softly knocked on the back dormitory door, Clyde stepped out and, for whatever reason, was dressed only in his skivvies. Half asleep, he was easily coaxed to the road between the cabin and the dormitory. After we emptied our concoction over his head and tossed on the feathers, he stood in disbelief. I said, "All right Clyde... now listen. If you ever tell on us again, something worse is going to happen." Because of his predicament, Clyde couldn't call out his normal, "Virginia!" So, he merely ran back to the open dormitory door, as we escaped back into our cabin, laughing all the way.

Minutes later, the door to our cabin was kicked open, breaking through the bats we'd leveraged against it. Then Tauso said, "Get up, all of you guys!" Visibly angry and sleepy, he screamed out, "Who did that to that boy? Do you have any idea how it makes him feel?" His empathy speech went on for a good 20 minutes. Then, thinking he hadn't made his point, he yelled, "Gilly, if it weren't for your dad, I'd put a boot up your ass!" Then, paying little attention to the abused cabin door, he slammed it shut and trampled off into the dark. We returned to our bunks and started to fall asleep when Ross announced, "See guys? That's what happens when we go along with Gilly. That's the first time I agree with the head master. Why do I even listen to you? We're all going to be sent home tomorrow!"

"Actually, only you, Ross. Don't forget my mother can't send me home… cause this is home." I laughed. Eventually, we slowly gave in to the night air to find our sleep.

Morning came early again, at the expense of the already abused door. Bamm! It opened. The head counselor yelled, "Ross, Gilly and Jeff, you're wanted by Mrs. Lefebvre in the kitchen!"

"What about Tuck?" He just shook his head.

"Okay, tell her we'll be there in a few minutes."

"Not in a few minutes, son. Right now!" And, off he went.

"See, I told you so!" Ross said while pulling on his T-shirt. "You went too far with Clyde last night."

"Hey, I know nothing. It was all Gil's stupid idea," Jeff added.

"Okay guys, geez, no need for us to bite at each other. You know I'll fall on the knife for you," I explained.

"Yah sure, that's really going to help," they both chimed in together.

So, off we went to the kitchen, expecting the worse. As we came up the ramp, my mother was waiting. Her friendly, "good morning boys," was missing and she counted each one of us by name as we came onto the deck. "Gilly, Jeff and Ross, we need to have a little talk." Next, she motioned toward the bread room. Once in, she shut the door and the explanation for the conference began. "Last night we had some problems and knowing you boys weren't a part of them makes this easier on me."

What? Thankfully, each one of us held tight on this good news, not giving anything away with our expressions but probably showing a little surprise. Mother went on. "Two of the new girls, and I take full responsibility for them, were caught in the back bay last night with four of our counselors partying. They also had alcohol in their possession, so the sheriff had no choice but to cite them all. Those kids took advantage and created a bad situation.

So today, I'm calling all their parents and sending them home on the Blanche. One of them was Chris, so Johnny Cuevas is going to have to work overtime for a couple of days on the lifeguard stand. Gilly, we're going to need you to help him out until we can get another replacement. Two of the girls will stay. They had nothing to do with this situation. However, the one counselor I'm not very happy to let go is Shane. I know he's been a good friend to all of you. Nevertheless, he was caught with the others and will be held responsible for his indiscretion. Remember, boys, our primary responsibility is the safety of our campers. They were left unattended last night while the counselors were out partying. We can never make that mistake again, and all of our staff must understand that."

"But really, Mom, Shane?"

"I know, Gilly, he's been around with us for years, but maybe this, in some way, will help him understand that there are consequences in life. I just thank God we've never had a problem on the beachfront by a distracted lifeguard or any emergency while our counselors were out partying into the night. In short, we're lucky nothing happened while they were gone. But, we can't afford to be just lucky with our campers. So, I know it's hard. But that's life. Some decisions are hard. You guys are going to have to take a double shift in the kitchen and cover the counselors' spots on the playing field. And, Gilly, you're going to manage our all-star team against Avalon on Thursday while you dad's away recruiting enough counselors to make it through the summer. I've already talked to the people who are leaving today. So no need going over this with them. And, Gilly, Shane's taking this thing hard. Do your best to make it as easy as possible for him."

One thing about my mother, she was easy to get along with but, once she felt her trust had been violated, there was no going back. All of the troubles I got into, if she directly asked me about them, I would tell her the truth. There was no way I was going to damage that trust. She used to tell me when those issues occurred, "Sometimes, Gilly, I wished you wouldn't be so truthful." I think that's why, occasionally, she wouldn't even ask me about the things that went on. But, remember, I said I would answer truthfully to the question she asked. Hey, I may be honest with her but not stupid. No sense in me bringing up situations she knew little about, was there? Now dad… well, that was another story.

Pruning… yeah. Sometimes we need this in our lives, to correct and cut back when indulging too often in too many things. It can become overbearing. More importantly, it is times like this when we develop and grow. As for Shane, he was filled with regret for letting down our family. Not just the Lefebvre family but the bigger family that we'd created together, over all those years.

For me, I hated the idea that we would probably never see much of each other again. That was just too much to comprehend. His leaving was the end of a chapter. Later, I would experience a similar apex in my life when the Oakland Athletics released me and closed the book on my baseball career. It was at that point like this that old dreams were discarded to make room for new ones to blossom. It's as necessary and natural as the changing of the seasons. Even more, it's an integral component to life itself.

It is said, "There's a rainbow behind each storm." There was this time... Clyde. Mother had had enough of his antics and sent him home on the Blanche that day as well.

CHAPTER 27

# Climbing Mt. Lebushtuck

Have you ever sat back and gazed at a splendid picture of some amazing, remote setting, located in a reclusive corner of the world, probably supplied by National Geographic or a travel agency brochure? Did you feel the place was untouched or untarnished by human hand and just begging you to come on over for a visit? Me too.

There I was one morning on our camp porch, eating dried eggs and sucking down pancakes, soaked in syrup to disguise their taste. I looked over, and there it was. A grand majestic mountain loomed over the Pacific calling out to me. I became inspired. Why hadn't I thought of climbing it before? That mountain probably had a name, but that didn't matter. What mattered was I didn't know it. I couldn't stop staring at it as Ross sat down next to me and said, "So Gil, what is your shallow mind dwelling on today?" No, I'm sure he didn't really say it that way. I think he actually said it more like, "So what stupid idea are you coming up with now?"

Undeterred I said, "Ross, I have a good idea."

"Right," Ross said, as predictable as ever, as he began to gulp down a forkful of wet pancakes.

"See that mountain over there?" I asked. Refusing to give me his attention, Ross struggled on with his breakfast and then finally asked, with a mouthful of pancakes, "What mountain?" Okay, so Catalina's rugged coast consists more of hills pretending to be mountains than actual mountains. But, the point was, they were there and you just wanted to jump in and explore, search out and find a path known only to goats. Be the first human to step on the top, see what they see. Isn't that what brought us to America? To be the first to explore? One step for mankind...

There I was with Ross, massaging that exciting prospect. I know I fabricated the scenario, but that's what it's all about. Isn't it? I pressed on. "Look at that mountain out there, Ross," now pointing into the air. "It's been out there for years... no centuries, and I'll bet nobody has ever climbed it before!"

"Who cares?" Ross asked, breaking his silence and grunting with a mouthful of food. I knew, as usual, he hoped to quash my energy, so I continued on, as if he wasn't part of the conversation. "Just think about it. I bet it has no name."

"Really? I bet it does. You just don't know it."

"No. You're wrong, Ross. It doesn't!"

"Yes it does, Gilly. You just don't know it!"

That caused me to think this thing out a minute. I stopped eating and asked an impartial bystander, Billy Bones, who had just come up the porch and was recovering nicely from his burns. "Hey Bones, do you know the name of that mountain over there?" Still asleep but walking, Bones said, "No," and continued on into the kitchen without missing a step. I turned back to continue my offense on Ross. "See! He doesn't know. Even if it has a name, it doesn't count if no one knows it."

"So what if it doesn't?" Ross said, now just tired of this dialogue that was going nowhere.

"So what?" I asked

"Yeah, so what?" he added, as he got up to turn in his dishes.

"So what? Well, whoever climbs that mountain to the top, gets to name it. That's what!" Now giving purpose to my adventure, "And, right after lunch, I'm going to climb it! I'll be the first, and I'll name it! So go on down to the beach, sit there looking at girls in bikinis and dream your life away. I'll be climbing that mountain and making history."

Just then, Billy Tuck came struggling up the porch, and I poured out my idea on him. "So Tuck, you coming along?"

"Yep. Why not?" he replied. I turned to Ross and said, "See, Tuck knows, and he's not even a USC boy. Must be Irish."

"What? Me Irish?" Tuck laughed.

Seeing my overflowing excitement, Ross waved us off and began to walk away. I tried one more time, "See Ross. Tuck has vision. And you? Television, armchair television."

Ross continued to walk away mumbling, "Right, Gilly. You have vision all right. Now, go to the moon and stay there!"

"We will! And, we'll be the first!" I called out after him.

Now, not only did Tuck and I have an inspired plan for the day but an adventure, a journey, a conquest! Turning to Tuck I said, "We're going to the moon!" Tuck gave his usual reply with a broad smile, "Okay, Big G. We're going to the moon. Now, where is the moon?"

"There, Tuck," I said, now pointing out in the distance.

His chuckle hit full stride and became a laugh. "Whatever, Gil."

So, in the cabin right after lunch, Tuck and I prepared for our heralded mountain adventure while Ross prepared for the beach. Even though we all slipped trunks on, Tuck and I were not going to the beach this fine summer day. No, we were going to climb our way into the history books. In a condescending voice, Ross said, "See you later, dummies. I hope you make it to the top and fall off.

Just don't come back. The world will be a better place. You'll be doing mankind a favor…one step at a time."

"Well, we'll see whose names will be added to that mountain, Ross. One thing's for sure, it won't be yours!" I yelled as he walked out with towel in hand, on his way to the beach. Just then, in stepped Peter Bushman, one of our new counselors and asked with a cautious tone, "Hey Gilly, is it okay if I go with you and Tuck up that mountain today?" Wow. Now we had a real expedition. Another visionary… "Sure Bush! We're leaving in just a few seconds. Get your things. We'll meet you at the bottom of the path in about five minutes." Off he went as Tuck and I anxiously looked around for supplies. We grabbed a towel, not knowing what good it would do at the top of a mountain, and, dressed only in trunks and flip flops, we rushed out of the cabin finding Bushman waiting and reading a Sporting News on the camp's path. A noble task, I thought and said, "Leave that here, Bush. We'll pick it up after we conquer that mountain." This must be how Chuck Yeager felt just before he broke the sound barrier. Our minds now played tricks on us. We were really becoming believers in this quest. The excitement kept building…building and building as we advanced to the trail that would lead us up.

It was the Sound of Music replay as we went single-file up the trail. If there would have been an orchestra and a helicopter with camera attached, they could have recorded us singing our way up that hillside. The world was ours for the challenge, and all was well. We felt a oneness with divine providence guiding us upward. After getting past Little Fisherman's, the mountain began to climb us. It made us work hard, and the path narrowed to just rocks. They hovered above us now. It was time to make the important decision of which route to take to the summit. So, we sat down to ponder over our strategy. Soon Tuck said, "Hey Big G., we've got company." Sure enough, right on the next hill, I caught a glimpse of movement. It must be a goat. More movement. No! No way! Looking across to the lower mountain just above Big Fisherman's cove, there was evidently another expedition.

It was Ross and Bones, and then a third person immerged. It was Ret. They were scrambling and climbing to the top of our mountain! They'd tricked us! Man, they deceived us into thinking they were going to the beach and there they were, hoping to get to the top first and claim the right to name the mountain.

"No way! No way," we all proclaimed as they traversed just above us, propelling rocks down to slow our climb. "It's on! To the top," I yelled.

Instantaneously we were caught up in an out-of-control frenzy that added an enthusiasm akin to a World Series to our quest. Our emotions jumped off the Richter scale. My pulse rate and blood pressure could be heard drumming up steam in my head. My dream had been squandered by those guys. My fault, it was that intensity and irrational purpose I used to cajoled everyone to the importance of this venture. I needed to breathe more life into the occasion. "We must beat these guy up that hill. And, the only way we can beat these guys is to climb around to the cliffs overlooking the mainland and scale the rocks straight up." A little dangerous, but we'd done more. This was Korea all over again. I likened this to Douglas MacArthur's cutting off the North by taking a risk at Inchon. Off we went, to the outer crest of the mountain. If we could make it successfully, we would outflank them. So we began our ascent, climbing straight up. That was our only chance. We single-filed it up the mountain's edge, knowing each step would be a formidable one. The risk factor was evident. We stopped for a moment, just to catch our breath, and then continued upward. At one point we needed to climb over a protruding rock. I stopped and said, "Guys, we need to stay together here. Give each other a hand. Tuck, I'll get to the ledge, then you take my hand and I'll pull you up." Up he popped and Bush was next. There was no time to procrastinate. All depended on just doing – no looking down, no resting. We didn't quibble about the precarious situation we found ourselves in. There was no looking back at that moment. I was reminded of the climb coming back from Little Harbor, when we placed our campers in harm's way. Here we were again, locked into the side of treacherous cliffs, dangling for our lives high above the rocks that waited below. But, there was a distinct difference. There, we survived death as a conclusion. Here we didn't fear death…we feared an enemy. It was that attitude that kept us plodding on.

Finally, success. All of our team safely reached the ridge. Now, for the pay off, we rushed around the ledge to a level spot. We did it! Ross's expedition was below us now, and gravity was on our side. We held the high ground, and, as we sat on the ledge getting caught up in all our hype, we made matters worse for our challengers. We gave them back some of their own medicine by rolling rocks down onto them. It was totally effective. They had to take cover as each rock bounced around, forcing them to cling to the hillside to avoid the incoming firepower. Pinned down, it was their turn to eat crow. Suddenly, we remembered our mission. Tuck said, "Let's go!" And, we began to race up the last 50 yards straight to the top of the mountain. The only thing stopping us now was the top, and that was when we could go no farther. Once there, looking down, we could hear Ross yelling and scrambling about. When they finally arrived tarnished, scraped and out of breath, I said, "So you were going to the beach…huh? Well, it didn't work, did it? You think you fooled us…didn't matter." But it did. We'd won the day. And now we could name it. Just feeling relieved to be sitting safely on top, Ross, Bones and Ret made no attempt to provide a reply.

Me, Bush and Tuck huddled to discuss the name. It was

simple. The first part of each of our last names, "Le" for Lefebvre, "Bush" for Bushman and "Tuck" for, yeah, Tucker. We made our proclamation. "As of this day and at this precise time, this mountain will be forever named Mt. Lebushtuck." And, that did it. Oh, it might have a different label on a topographical map somewhere. But, they're wrong, and we didn't care. We climbed it. We named it. From this day on, it was over, decided, done.

Mt. Lebushtuck was more than just a place we named. It was about a time in our lives when we left our mark, a point of reference, a time capsule left behind, because we knew we soon had to move on. Yet, maybe someday, from that day to the next, we would be inspired by what we did then and possibly come back here to see who we used to be. Maybe, just maybe, it could explain who we would later become and give us a reason to carry on.

Looking back, we were on Mt. Everest, all of us, up there. All equals in the world, each in his own special way. Rich or poor, it didn't matter. We were oblivious to a world that had yet to claim us. Yet we knew, when we created the challenges, they were ours to win or lose.

For a few moments, we all just sat there in silence that day, at the top of the world, looking far off out to sea, wondering where it would take us. Not knowing that years from now, life would lead us back to this place, a place where our souls would finally find us, here on the other side of heaven.

CHAPTER 28

# Flying Without Wings/A Quantum Leap

The advertisement proudly boasts of an, "enjoyable, comfortable flight to beautiful Catalina Island in the hands of our experienced vintage airline pilots." To wit, let me make my case against that. After numerous flights on those amphibian planes, I've had the opportunity to chat at considerable length with those "vintage" pilots and, even though my aviation literacy is a bit lacking, let me illustrate some of my concerns.

Once aboard and in flight, the pilots unleashed stories describing their adventures in the Battle of Britain's air war or how they survived air raids above and below Korea's 38th parallel. These stick-and-rudder ace pilots alleged their notable acts were accomplished without all the modern technology pilots have today. Oh no, not them. They flew by the seat of their pants. They were trained only with one gauge in the cockpit…the gas gauge. They learned multi-tasking while in the air, making loops and firing their cannons at enemy planes with just a hope and a prayer that their wings would stay on long enough to accomplish the mission. That's great stuff for Hollywood. But, hey, all I wanted was to fly 19 minutes safely across the channel wearing a bathing suit, flip-flops and T-shirt. And, just maybe believe that a few planes carrying a few nice girls had made it to the island before me. However, if it takes a WWII citation hero to get me there? I'll take the Great White Steamer any day.

Yet, the pilots had explained, unconvincingly, to me that airplanes are the safest way to travel. This only makes sense, I counter, if I'm traveling by air. They brag about all the backup safety systems. Why worry when the plane can fly with only one engine? Heck, the plane could fly itself by remote control. Some have gone so far as to suggest this plane can practically fly without wings.

Can you really fly without wings? Maybe so, at least Channel Airline thought they could, and they had quantum physics to back them up. Let's think about that. What is quantum physics? Does it mean anything or stand for something? Does it relate to things that really happen or is it just a set of nebulous numbers, leading to a well-educated guess? Or merely another way of saying, "I don't know" but still wanting to remain relevant? The true believers of this quantum physics stuff like to provide a whole lot of statistics. Once they've got you confused, they attempt to sell you the car. Proponents of quantum physics say it's more than that. It's about probabilities, much like weather reporting. You have a 30 percent chance of rain, meaning there's a 70 percent chance of good weather. So, what do you make of that explanation? Not much, I say, especially if it's raining when they give you the numbers. Then isn't it really 100 percent chance of rain?

No, you don't get it, they counter. Okay, I suggest, for the sake of an argument, I put away my umbrella and I'm soaked. The rain is dripping off my nose. Do I still have a 70 percent chance of it not raining? Or does it mean in between the drops you have a 70 percent chance of not getting wet, because it's not raining there? Some people give my probabilities related to my chance of crashing in an airplane as remote. So, since I crashed my first time up in Channel Air, or should I say the first time I came down and survived, isn't it like taking a flu shot? You get a little dose, and that gives a whatever less chance of getting the flu... kind of an immunity argument. It follows, I guess, that crashing and surviving is advantageous. Now my chances of crashing again are, statistically speaking, pretty much null and void. Also, didn't I fortuitously gain some percentage probabilities? That's beneficial but even better, I argue, if I don't want to die while flying, I just don't fly! Isn't that foolproof? Statistically speaking, like 100 percent? However, quantum physicists say no. Maybe your chances are more remote, but the possibilities and probabilities...you'll probably fly again. "But, I won't!" I protest. No way, they reply, you can't say that. You can't ever get rid of the probabilities. That's statistically impossible. So flying without wings, statistically speaking, is possible. Just think about it. You can never reduce a fraction to nothing. It just doesn't work that way. It's bad math...they say. The point being, you can see how far we've gotten from the commonsense idea trying to justify flying. So, let's return to the pressing decision I needed to make about air travel. Using this distorted logic led me to believe I'd still take the Steamer every chance I got.

Yet, there are times when flying is worth the risk... which it never is, for there's far too much of a downside to call it a risk, it's really a verbal slight-of-hand proposition. More like playing Russian roulette, but it happens nevertheless, and I do fly. I did with Channel Air for many years. Here's how one flight went.

First thing you became aware of in the early days of travel on the amphibians was the unusual nature of this undertaking. Think of it as an adventure and a thrill ride all rolled up together. It wasn't by chance that, in Avalon, you bought your ticket from a booth located inside the Waikiki Club. After purchasing this lotto/airline ticket, you were presented with the opportunity to be welcomed by your pilot, sitting at the bar. You could share a gin and tonic while waiting for your scheduled flight, which was exactly five minutes following his last drink. He was a friendly sort of fellow, and, if he liked you, he might let you buy another round. There was no reason to panic for the excess; since you were with the pilot, you couldn't be late for the flight. And, by then you would be too stooped up to really care if you made it back or not. I think that was part of the plan. Much like the dentist when he gives you a little novocaine…not a lot, just enough to take the anxiety out of it. Of course the pilot's reply was something to the effect of, "It's five o'clock somewhere," even though you're supposed to be airborne at 12:15.

I had to fly home from Avalon on camp business one of those "five o'clock somewhere" days. The pilot apologized for arriving late. He'd simply lost track of time and was ticked that he had to leave half his drink on the bar. Since I was his only passenger he said, "Come on up and sit in the co-pilot's seat." From there I could smell the booze on his breath. So, here I am, the only person on a nine-passenger plane, returning to Long Beach Airport and he declares, "Hey, let's have some fun!" We proceeded to taxi out into the bay. And then, what he called "fun" began. We flew directly over the Sea Scout's sailboat, getting just enough lift to scare the hell out of me and the girls on deck below. While barely escaping the tip of the boat's mast, he let out a great roar. The crazy pilot then proceeded to fly the plane about 100 feet off the water all the way back to Long Beach. "Why so low?" I asked. He shouted back over the noise of the engine, "If we have a malfunction, the ocean is just below!" Okay, if that didn't make his day, his approach to the airport did. He flew in so low that the plane almost landed on the San Diego Freeway and then proceeded to hit dirt in front of the concrete runway. The plane lurched up in the air and came down so hard it sounded as if the wings fell off. But he just laughed and said, "Hey kid, did we have fun or what?" After fumbling with my seatbelt, I jumped out and ran to the airport bathroom to relieve myself.

It was worse than the Long Beach Pike. What made the Pike so some much fun back then was sometimes the rollercoaster (like Channel Air) did go off the track and fling itself into the harbor.

One of the more comical flights I ever took on Channel was with our family friend Bernard Parks, later to be Police Chief of Los Angeles. My parents loved to fly into the Isthmus during spring break, so they asked Bernard if he wanted come along. So he did. This was Bernard's first trip on the amphibians. Leaving Long Beach Airport aboard a Channel airplane was really a rough takeoff. With its pontoons mounted on the wings' ends, you kind of bumped and wiggled your way down the runway, then somehow physics came into play and the plane lifted off. Don't ask me how. We soared over the City of Long Beach and then out to sea. As usual, we made what appeared to be an emergency landing, just missing the sandy beach below and the backside of Cat Harbor. Then, with a swish and a flop onto the water, that was it. Bernard wondered why we were so silent, as if in prayer, all the way over. No comment, no need to alarm.

But, later on the return trip, as the plane revved up its propellers to pick up speed, getting more lift with each bounce, things began to get more interesting. When we came in for our landing, everything seemed okay until we touched down at the Long Beach Airport. Then the unusual vibrations turned into loud screeching noises. And, from our windows, we observed the pontoon on one side scraping the concrete, sparks flying and parts falling along the way. We continued to screech on down the runway and eventually came to a sudden stop. By this time, we could see the already approaching fire engines with lights flashing and sirens blaring. The pilot didn't budge or say anything. Once the rescue crew arrived, we began to move about. Everyone was all right but left with a residue of heart-throbbing panic. Now, Bernard wasn't accustomed to this type of flying or landing, if you could call it that. As a result, he said, so everyone could hear, "Don't you think there's a cheaper way of landing these planes?" With that, everybody broke into loud nervous laughter. And, of course we were later comforted by the airline's explanation for this mishap. "Pilot error not mechanical failure." Those days, I guessed, it was easier to replace a pilot than an airplane.

So, once again I made my pledge. I would never fly again on any airline, especially that airline. I chuckle when I think about it now. It reminds me of when I went to confession every Friday. The priest would inevitably say, after giving me a penance, "My son, go with God's blessing but don't continue in your ways." I'd assure him, "Yes father," making a promise I knew I wouldn't keep even before I had finished my first, "Hail Mary." The reality is, there are hundreds of stories just like mine about this last great American adventure ride from Long Beach to Catalina Island. I've even blamed Channel Airlines for my fear of flying along with my lack of progress during my baseball career… where daily flying is a way of life. Nah, maybe it was my temper inherited from dad. That was also a possible prognosis as to why he loved me so entirely – I was so much like him. But fear of flying always gave me an out. "Does not fly" was even written in my deployment documents while in the Army. I thought by the time I got orders to sail over to Vietnam, the war would be over. Whether real or not, I've become a jinx to air travel and to anyone who has had the misfortune of flying with me. And, I placed that flaw in my character directly on Channel Air.

You had your choice, two and a half hours of seasickness and vomit or 19 minutes of unmitigated fear. Take your poison. Ultimately, air travel to Catalina was squelched, not so much by the lack of business but the lack of people who wanted to risk their life on an E ticket thrill ride. In the end, air travel to Catalina suffered as the result of several accidents and financial considerations. However, those flights, like so many other aspects of the Catalina experience, gave many of us a wealth of memories, packed with laughs but, unfortunately for others, tragedy also. Still, what is certain, those stories will be passed on through generations.

CHAPTER 29

# The Swim

On Tuesday and Thursday afternoons, you could usually find me swimming the Isthmus bay, while Ross kept tempo rowing next to me, like one of those slaves from the movie Ben-Hur. We both were held captive by my mother's latest project. Mom, like my dad, was an extreme athlete and both were asked to work the swimming venue during the 1932 Olympics in Los Angeles. World-renowned swimming stars like Buster Crabbe, Johnny Weissmuller and Esther Williams frequently worked out alongside my mother. Her reputation as a stylistic women's trainer came about because of her many years of ocean swimming off the coast of Long Beach. She became a magnet for those who hoped to swim the Catalina channel. On her second try in 1952, Florence Chadwick became the first women to make the 21-mile swim from the islands' west end to San Pedro's shore in 13 hours, 47minutes. This put the Catalina channel swim in vogue and surpassed the popular English Channel swim as the long distance swimmer's place to make history. So many accomplished swimmers in the late '50s put the channel swim in the back of their mind, and my mother was just one person who could possibly help make their dream come true.

Johnny Cuevas was her new prospect. He started as a cliff diver in Mexico and then set his sights on the channel swim. Jonny had come to my mother's attention while she searched for qualified camp lifeguards. He offered his services in exchange for food and board, along with her time training. Mother let me know that Johnny wasn't really that skilled of a swimmer and needed a lot of technical changes in his stroke. But, possibly, he had the heart and desire to overcome that. However, his age also worked against his plan. For a swimmer, Johnny was just beyond his peak. Yet, mom would give him a chance; besides we always needed a good lifeguard, and his character was impeccable.

So there I was, swimming alongside and pacing while my mother called out to Johnny, "Pick your elbow up higher on your stroke. Keep your head in the water. You're breaking and rotating too much. You're using too much energy. This isn't a sprint. You're going to be in there for half a day." On and on she went. Sometimes when mother had other things to do, my older sister Yvonne would take her place. She'd keep Johnny on the regimen and always seemed to inspire him. I think the fact that she was a very attractive observer might have helped make the workout all the more pleasant. But for me, after about 40 minutes of the pacing stuff, I wanted out. After realizing I'd lost interest, mother would give in and say, "Okay, Gilly, you're done for the day. Go ahead and take off." Sometimes, Ross didn't get the message and rowed on alone for some time. I'd have to wait to pull myself in the boat or give up and just swim back to shore on my own.

Eventually, Johnny, going through his daily ritual of swimming the bay, caught the interest of many of the locals and tourists. They would ask, "When is he going to try it?"

"Where is he going to begin the swim?"

"What does he eat to get the energy?"

"What type of body grease does he use to keep warm?"

And, "how about those sharks?"

Already a success, at least around the Isthmus, Johnny's story grew.

"The currents and swells across the channel can be formidable obstacles for a channel swim, but it's the cold water that can really get to you. So early September is the best window of opportunity," Mom stated. Therefore, her training program had Johnny peaking for that date.

One day, mom called me in and said, "We need to train with a little more distance. I've talked to Johnny, and we're going to have a practice run from the Isthmus to Avalon. That's a 13.4-nautical mile swim, and, if he does well, then I'll know we're ready for the channel. Gilly, I need you to spend more time helping with the pacing. I've asked Pat Quinn to do most of the long stuff, and he also volunteered to pace Johnny into Avalon." Mind you, Pat was the Navy Seal guy on leave and worked as our camp lifeguard and diver.

The swim began to crystallize as a tangible objective. First a swim to Avalon and, three weeks later, it would be the channel. The anticipation and excitement in the Isthmus gained momentum, putting Johnny at center stage. Training with my mother also gained momentum, putting additional pressure on us all to play more prominent roles in the quest. Undertakings like this succeed as a result of team effort. Escorting the swimmer with pacer boats helps keep them out of danger and provides access to food, hot broth and gel. We were all reminded to be careful not to touch him, that would disqualify the swim. Mother explained this was to be a very important trial run, not only to see how Johnny reacted to the swim but also how smooth the support group worked.

So, very early that late August morning, we all assembled at our stations. Yvonne, who had by now befriended Johnny, would be riding in the main support boat while Ty took the oars. Like most of the islanders, he was also a proficient swimmer. He would be point man for this attempt. Also, part of my mother's plan was this interesting old guy, Karl. He had experience rowing support for both of Florence Chadwick's swims. We were lucky he was available and looked forward to his recommendations. Karl was a vagabond who lived a hermit's existence on the island. He lived in an old shack at the rock quarry that lies just between Long Point and the Isthmus. He was also notorious for entertaining the scouts at campfires by walking on hot cools – interesting fellow, to say the least. Karl alleged he'd parted from civilization in order to live a more spiritual life.

Mother added Pat Quinn to her roster as primary pacer, who would be escorted by Ben Hawkins in an adjacent boat and his friend Lee Goulding as secondary pacer. They could take turns hopping in and out of the support boats to interchange the pacing duties. Mother was in a powerboat and, along with the camp nurse, prepared to meet any unforeseen difficulties. It wasn't as scientific of an operation as today's swims, but it was efficient nevertheless. Johnny would be swimming about a half mile off of the shoreline. The tides would be less of a problem than the ocean currents during the channel swim. However, we needed to make Long Point before 10 a.m. because the navigational charts showed dramatic changes in the direction of the tide, threatening to make the last part of the swim extremely difficult. We needed to press on with that in mind. Mom said Johnny should complete the swim at about the nine-hour mark. If we left at 5 a.m., we should clear Long Point at 9 a.m. and our ETA in Avalon would be around 1 p.m. So, we all nestled around in the early morning dark, making preparations. Just before sunrise we noticed a small fleet gathering about the bay, offering their support and becoming a permanent flotilla, following us all the way to Avalon.

Mother gave last-minute instructions and was ready to start

her clock. Johnny posed for a few pictures and, after waving to the crowd, entered the water. It was on to Avalon with Pat Quinn at his side. Butterflies worked their way around all our stomachs. We still weren't sure if Johnny could make this trip, but it all started out well and everyone was in a festive mood.

Minutes ticked by and we were well into our first hour, as Johnny stayed steady in tempo. He'd passed Bird Rock, turned right and headed, stroke-by-stroke, straight for Long Point, which was clearly visible as the sun began to burn off the early morning fog. Somehow, when the sun comes out, smoldering the morning chill, especially at sea, a sense of renewal comes with the warmth, inspiring all kinds of keen, optimistic thoughts.

We sat in the boat with my mother and watched her monitor Johnny's condition. I spent most of my time not so much watching Johnny swim but enjoying the seagulls flying and chirping, keeping close at the prospect that we might throw them a bit of chum. Then, a seal bobbed about, trying to make out why we where disturbing his domain. As time went on, more boats fell into our parade, wanting to see the swimmer and just be part of the occasion. Johnny was on pace, and my sister encouraged him while Ty rowed in stride with Johnny's cadence. At last, there it was, Long Point, just ahead, maybe a mile. It was the halfway point, and, it looked like Johnny would get there before the magical time when the tide changed. That was good news and everyone cheered from the support groups that continued to tarry about. It was at that moment, when it looked like the swim was going right on schedule, that optimism began to slip in and the routine became expected. Then a yell came from one of the boats outside of the flotilla. "SHARK!" Again from another boat, "SHARK!" Right off to the left, a fin sliced through the water. Lee Goulding was in our boat and quickly grabbed his fins, pulled them on, picked up his mask and, with his other hand, took hold of his arbalete. He jumped in the water, making sure to keep his eyes on the fin, and ran protection for Johnny. The shark appeared, took a look around, then quickly swam away. Tranquility settled back in and all was right.

Reaching the halfway point was a milestone for the swim, and it was time for Pat to get out of the water and for Lee to take on the pacing duties. Mom called out, "Pat, how are you feeling? Time to get out and rest up. We'll need you later." Surprisingly Pat said., "No, I'm feeling fine." Mother said, "Okay, but when you start to tire, get Lee in the water." About 45 minutes later, Johnny stopped and talked to Pat. Pat yelled to my mother, "Johnny's getting stomach cramps." We moved our boat closer.

"How do you feel Johnny?" mom asked.

He replied, "All of sudden my stomach's cramping up."

"We're almost there, Johnny. Let's try it for a little while longer and see if it goes away." Hoping my mother was right, Johnny started up again.

"How about you, Pat?" mom asked.

"I'm okay, Mrs. Lefebvre. I can stay with him." Mother instructed Lee to get in the boat with Ty and Yvonne, in case Johnny had to be pulled out quickly. Yvonne now talked to Johnny, attempting to build up his spirits. But, before turning the corner at Long Point, it was obvious Johnny's stomach pain was too excruciating to continue. "Johnny, we've got to get you out of the water!" Mom shouted. Johnny refused, not willing to accept the situation. Yvonne and Ty became concerned. The tide was changing and it seemed as if Johnny was swimming upstream. Using the shoreline as a guide, no matter how hard Johnny swam, he stopped moving forward. And, it soon became obvious he would not make it past Long Point. Realizing the extent of his condition, mother ordered him out of the water. Ty and Lee helped him into their boat. We pulled aside and Johnny was transferred onto ours as the nurse began to tend to his issues. Meanwhile, Pat was still in the water and swimming about 100 yards in front of the boat, oblivious to what had just happened. Ty raced up to him and Pat looked up while he told him, "It's over. Johnny is out of the water."

"Hey, just around the corner is the casino. I can make it! I'm feeling fine." he said.

Ty relayed Pat's determination to mother, and she said, "Okay, tell him go for it."

And, now Pat the pacer became the primary swimmer as Lee jumped into the water to pace him. The tempo began to accelerate. This ex-Navy Seal guy started working like a well-oiled machine. They passed Toyon Bay, and now the casino was right in front of them. By now, the news reached Avalon about the swim, and literally hundreds of bathers had pulled themselves off of the beach to stand in front of the casino, holding onto and standing on the rail, clapping and yelling encouragement as Pat swam on. After rounding the corner, the swimmers saw the shoreline, some 200 yards ahead. Now the crowd moved to the beach, where local news people gathered, hoping to capture the story.

Struggling with fatigue, Pat, along with Lee, landed on the sand. The crowd again broke out in applause, and ships in the harbor began to honk their horns. Mariachis that wandered around the downtown streets, playing to the tourists, jumped into the spontaneous celebration. Reporters asked, "Which one of you is Johnny Cuevas?" A dead hush came over the crowd as mother, now onshore, answered, "Neither of them. Johnny got severe stomach cramps, and we had to pull him from the water, just west of Long Point. But Pat," she added, placing her hand on his shoulder, "who started out as the pacer, completed the entire swim untouched!" The crowd began to cheer again. It didn't matter the name. Someone just became the first ever to swim from the

Isthmus to Avalon! The party carried on all day. Pat and Lee were treated to meals, drinks and all sorts of fun well into the night. The story of Pat Quinn's swim and the nuance that surrounded it caused him to be a legendary hero, at least in the Isthmus.

However, that's not where this story ended for me, because there was still Johnny Cuevas. A kind and gentle guy who migrated from a small ranch somewhere deep in Mexico, he struggled for years, taking on one job after another, all for the dream of swimming the channel. It would all be worth it, he'd tell my sister, for the chance to fulfill that dream. But now, those dreams had been torn to shreds. There was nothing to hang onto...nothing to retrieve. It wasn't just lost. There would never be another chance. Johnny's age wouldn't allow it. He just ran out of time. And, relief from his pride? There was no window to crawl out and no fortress to hide his failing.

Years later, looking back, mother said, "Johnny built his mountain so high, he couldn't make the climb, and it was just too far of a fall." Johnny did come back to work with us for a short while. Then, sobbing, he gave my mother his two week's notice. He thanked her for all of the attention she'd given. And, to avoid any conversation and save a little bit of dignity, he disappeared. Johnny left in the back of the truck during one of Taylor's milk runs to Avalon one morning. We never saw him again. My sister sent him a letter addressed to some remote location at a Mexican cattle ranch that was never answered.

Later in my life, I would face similar situations, playing out over and over again. On cut days, that's when players got released from their pro baseball teams, this old crusty manager, before reading the list, would step up on a bench and raise his hand, showing he only had four digits. Evidently, attempting to put levity into the situation, he'd say, "I know what it's like to be cut." Then, he'd proceed to demolish lifelong dreams simply by reading out names. I think those guys who got cut would have given up more than a finger to not be on that list. It wasn't just a finger that was cut. It was hearts and hopes, something to look forward to, something to look back at.

But, life must go on. For what else is there? All we can do is to just start over again. Yeah, it's difficult to find a new niche, something to pin new dreams on and begin the process of reinventing ourselves. But, it's there, the chance to begin again. I just didn't see it back then.

Chapter 30

# The Big Game

As young as I was, I still considered Avalon's Wrigley Field my old friend for two reasons. First, in the late '50s, outside of Triple-A teams and the Los Angeles Hollywood Stars, who played the game more like tag-team wrestling matches, professional baseball had yet to invade the west coast. Major League Baseball and its heroes were purely an east coast phenomena. The closest a kid could get to one of those legends was to buy a pack of Topps baseball cards and chewing gum, which, by the way, preceded television in my section of town. After introduction to the game by my father, at the age of two, possibly earlier, pictures of Mickey Mantle, Joe DiMaggio, Whitey Ford and more were plastered about on almost every wall of our home. Not even the privacy of the bathroom was excluded from the torrential display of Yankees propaganda. Even there, magazines were well placed so that, while dwelling on the natural things of life, one could become cultured in the nuisances of the game.

Yeah, Topps brought it all home to us in our remote corner of the North American continent, Inglewood, California. Not only did Topps give us the stats, history and achievements of each ballplayer but also, on the flipside of the card, his photo. This had a profound effect and introduced some of us on the west coast to the demographical and cultural changes going on across the country. A case in point, I once ordered a baseball card of Larry Doby and, after weeks of waiting, it finally arrived. I rushed to open it and, once unwrapped, I jammed the cardboard-flavored gum into my mouth. Next, I grabbed for his picture, only to discover that Larry was black. "He's black?" I asked my dad. "Hey, dad, they must have given me the wrong card."

"No Gil, it's the right one, he's black all right."

"What a remarkable discovery," I thought. I even shared it with my sixth grade class the next day.

Then came the rumors. Wrigley was bringing his Cubs back to Avalon for spring training. Now that was a seismic event out here on the west coast, and the excitement spread from around the corner to across the bay. Major league baseball had made its way to Hollywood, by way of Catalina. Maybe we were ready for a major league franchise to move out west. Rumors were formed, history was made and the ripple effect began. Later in 1958, Walter O'Malley followed suit and brought the Dodgers to Los Angeles. Heck, it was even right here in Avalon that a local sportscaster jump-started his career. Yep, Ronald Reagan covered the Cub's training camp, and we all know what that led to.

The spring event lasted for only a few years. However, the Cubs left an artifact behind, a miniature replica of Chicago's Wrigley Field. Decades later, the fathers of Avalon commerce saw no commercial purpose in restoring this relic of baseball's past and bulldozed it down along with the famous St. Catherine's Hotel, making way for a pavilion and a thriving beach crowd. I'm biased, of course. Although I do fear city planners might someday share the same sentiment about the casino or the Blanche W.

Nevertheless, Avalon's Wrigley Field became an old friend.

I played my first game, got my first hit and struck out there so many times, they should have put me in the hall of fame for that alone. Also, I stole so many bases, second base became my second residence. And, of course, home plate was where I first learned how to respond to umpire calls. Things like, "Whatever blind man," "your ass" and "you're out of the game," became common phrases. It was also there I developed the ability of talking trash with the opposing catchers. It's a distinct technique, you know. Think about it. The feat of hitting a baseball while carrying on a conversation with the catcher requires the ability to multi-task. I also learned to become oblivious to the abuse handed out by the opposing team and from irritating and obsessed partisan fans. Later, it would be a great lesson when I majored in political science. I discovered there was little difference between the partisan on the ball field and participants in the democratic process.

It had been drummed into my head that baseball was the great American sport, in which rugged individualism was tempered to advance the best interest of the team. I didn't really know how all that worked out in baseball. I left those esoteric aspects of the game to some columnist disguised as an analyst, who rarely stayed around the game to see the end.

It was then, after the game when everyone left, that I stayed behind, always the last to leave so I could talk to them in silence. Oh, they were there all right. I know it. They taught me about life's hopes and dreams…success and failure… popcorn and hot dogs. It was lots of fun, not to mention invaluable for my short but illustrious attempts at Major League Baseball. But for now, at the age of 18, I was about to mount a formidable task, not as a player but a manager. Our All Stars against the very best that Avalon could come up with.

For the past five years the Catalina Baseball Camp record

against Avalon had gone unblemished. Beating Avalon was never an easy task, though. We had kids from all over California, up to the age of 15, playing in this game. Avalon had all their best talent from Avalon High, and that made for a very competitive game. Coming to see the game? Maybe 30 fans who came off the beach or stepped out of their stores. However, don't let the numbers fool you. This was bigger than a USC-UCLA cross-town rivalry football game...bigger than Notre Dame, Gold Dome and all, coming to town – at least for us. The news was passed around like a blazing fire, fueled by a torrent wind, sweeping through the stores, the barbershop, onto tour bus drivers, to hot food venders on the pleasure pier and into the pizza parlors on almost every street corner. Each player on Avalon's roster was a relative to someone else and, inning by inning, their plays would be recounted for posterity at the first hole of Avalon's golf course or in one of the local bars.

The best would be out in front, managing their boys...Lolo and Frankie Saldana. The integrity of Avalon was all in their hands. A Freudian equation kept spawning in their mind. Could this little remote corner of the world compete against all those mainlanders that banned together for the assault?

"Do those fellows from the Isthmus west end," one newspaper story read, "have all of the panache, glamour and prodding to carry the day?"

So there I was, at the helm, managing our team for the first time. Our head counselor was unable to help. He had to attend to a camper that accidentally speared himself while diving early that morning. "It's up to you, Gil." He gave me dad's lineup card and added, "This will be a defining moment in your life."

Would it be a defining moment in my life? No way. It was just a game, wasn't it? The game had little, if any importance to the baseball world, except the one located in Avalon's one-square mile. Still, as much as I tried to convince myself, I knew whatever the result of today's game, it would be played out in Lolo's barbershop for years to come. I needed to search back to my ancestry, gather all the knowledge I'd gained in those short years of my life and become the carrier of the torch, the link to the legacy of the Lefebvre Catalina Baseball Camp.

While sitting in the back of the Blanche W., on our way to Avalon, hoping to stay out of Ross's ramblings with my team, I wrote down some notes. The objective of baseball is rather ironic. Just think about it. Home plate is where you start from and yet that's your final destination. Baseball is like the games of life and chess. But, you have a chance to slide across the board. It's a place where double plays are as sacred and artistic as the Sistine Chapel, where high fives are always Kodak moments. My creative juices were flowing and I chuckled to myself, fearing my team would somehow pick up evidence of my pathological clowning with the game. I continued musing. Baseball is a place where hot dogs and peanuts can carry a higher price than steak, where the difference between three strikes and four balls can be the center of a philosophical discussion, where it's hard to find a pitcher who can throw a fastball but easy to find one who throws 26 unnamed pitches. It's where hitting a rock with a stick had advanced into a quantum physics debate. Or, where the Miracle on 34th Street is the result of a missed ground ball on first base, at least in Boston. Baseball is a place where what you say about the game rarely made sense. Like, "kiss the ball goodbye"…possibly a little rough on the teeth. Or, how about the "batter eating out of the pitcher's hand"…I wonder what he was serving up? Or try this, "He can't hit his weight." "It's no picnic." Should it be? And then there's overstating the obvious, "Baseball is played between the lines." Geez, does anyone play games outside the lines? Then there are sayings that strike up moral dilemmas. "Can't steal first base." Of course not, but who would want to, except an irate manager not getting the call. Oops, there's another one. "Not getting the call." Call from whom, an informed fan? Who would? I ask because there are some calls I really wouldn't like to get. Finally, they say baseball is a game where, "the difference between winning and losing is just 90 feet away." Nonetheless, spectators of all ages sit in the stands for three hours acting as if they're on a cruise liner going nowhere. And, after attending 162 games, it may not be an antidote for civilization, but it sure qualifies you as an avid baseball fan.

Once the Blanche docked at Avalon's pleasure pier, I rushed back to the real world, putting away my humble pen and dabbling paper to begin preparations. Now, it would be all about the game at Wrigley Field. As we marched there together, I began to talk to our players about the history of the field. It was important to get them excited about the place and give them a perspective of the significance of what they were about to do. At the end of the block, the first evidence the park was near were the large palm trees. They stood majestically tall in the background of the residential bungalows that flowered along the avenue. When we finally arrived, it felt as if we were entering a magnificent amusement park while walking under an arched gate that opened up to center field. As we stepped onto the sunburned grass, I motioned for everyone to sit down to take in the view.

"This, my friends, is Wrigley Field!" They sat uncharacteristically silent as they took it all in. I went on, "Some of the very best players in our game have played here. You'll remember this for the rest of your lives and be able to tell your grandson about this one day. I know I will. This is where my brothers, Johnny Collins and I played our first game. Right Johnny?" Johnny nodded his head in agreement and smiled. All the campers knew he'd just signed with the Cleveland Indians, and I'd brought him, along with Ross, to help out. "Okay, now let's get to the game." I pulled out the clipboard and started reading my dad's opening roster. Even though dad was attending other issues that day, his handprint was on everything. He'd meticulously set out instructions on how I was to play this game out and with whom. After reading the roster, I brought the players back to the moment. "Guys, put your bags in the dugout and get warmed up." They got to their feet, walked across right field and, for the first time, became aware of the prying eyes of their opponents, loosening up along the third baseline.

Baseball, like most sports, can be an intimidating event. Until you get into playing the game, all kinds of negative things can enter your mind. But, after the first pitch, you begin to go back to remote-control mode, just repeating the things we'd practiced over and over again. We relied and counted on this factor. Even at the young ages of 14 and 15, most of our players had been in All-Star games and tournaments of their own, back on the mainland. So, they weren't short on confidence. As they benched their gear and started putting on their cleats, I stepped out of the creaky old wooden dugout, which swaggered with character. I walked over to greet the legends of Catalina baseball, Lolo and Frankie. We went over the usual formalities. I glanced discretely at their players, just to get a feel of who they were sporting. On the way back to the dugout, I looked over to the stands and noticed a few familiar faces. Yep, there's Ret and Tay with their following of Avalon girls, dressed in the usual Catalina swim attire. That is, not enough cloth to be accused of being decent and just enough not to be accused of indecent exposure. But, it wasn't those few fans that I was concerned with. Standing next to third base, I went on with my visual tour and zeroed in on whom I'd been looking for: A 6-foot whatever guy, courting a goatee and a marine emblem inscribed on his arm, which became noticeable every time he finished his follow-through. "This is your starting pitcher?" I called out to Lolo.

"Yeah, Gilly, That's him."

"Did he get a citation in the Korean war?" I asked, and Lolo laughed as I added, "By the way, did he pay his way over here?"

"No Gilly. He's one of Avalon's best recently graduated pitchers. He was a good one for us." I smiled knowing Avalon was always suspect for putting mainland ringers into their lineup. Never been proven, but that prospect was always there. "Didn't matter much," I thought. We'll get to him. Lolo motioned they would take infield practice first, so I went back and sat down with my kids. "Okay, remember. This is nothing more than a game of hit, run, throw and catch. Make the game simple. Make the plays and the game will be ours." The players sat on the bench watching Avalon's infield and, in cocky tones, made comments about each opponent. Then, it was our chance to look good. We rushed out of the dugout and went through a sharp infield display, which made any of our seven or eight fans proud. We let them know how baseball was played. Jake Flynn was our 15-year-old pitching optimist. He believed in himself more than I did, but that was good. We would need some of that today.

Then, the umpires stepped out onto the field. The time had come. The pregame warm-up was over and they called the mangers to home plate. We went over the field rules and it was play ball… start your engines…post time. Avalon's home team broke onto the field. A few of their guys looked a bit confused about who was going to play what position but finally decided, with the help of Frankie's ranting. And, like a pinball, they bounced around and fell into place.

In strolled the 6-foot plus guy to the mound to take his warm-up pitches. "Not a bad fastball," I said to Ross and Johnny as we huddled together, "but wild, and his curveball has a slow bend to it." I stepped over to my on-deck batter. "Remember, look for your pitch... the fastball. Then, take care of business."

On we played, running through the innings, keeping score, all the while hoping not to desecrate this place. We knew someone was watching up there. They always do. For, in some small way, this day was becoming part of history. It was being written down with every swing, with every pitch, with every play. This was the way it was supposed to be.

My starting pitcher, the prima donna from Westlake, had good reason to feel he was the best on the field. Because, at that age, usually pitchers are the most versatile athletes on the team. We worked our way through the early innings. Our defense proved they could execute and, to my surprise, Lolo and Frankie's' group were up to the task, keeping the score even, 0 to 0. By the fifth inning things began to take shape. My pitcher, Jake, went up to the plate and, with one runner on, hit a towering drive that cleared the center field scoreboard. I leaned over to tell Ross, "It probably bounced all the way down Catalina Avenue and is sitting on the beach." Now I was feeling a little more comfortable, with a two-run lead. But, in the bottom of the fifth, Jake got into trouble, walking the first two batters. I went to the mound and said, "Jake, you're looking a little tired. All okay?"

"I'm okay, Skip. Don't worry. I'll get it done. Really, I'm all right."

"Okay, but any more trouble and..."

"I know. I know, but I'm okay. I've been here before."

But, the next hitter took a ball then laced a single up the middle. One runner scored, and they had runners on first and second. "Ross, we've got to pull him...now."

"No, Gil, let him have another man."

"By then it'll be too late! I don't want to work the game from behind." I called timeout and went to the mound. "Jake, it's time to go. You've done fine, but you look tired, and you're not hitting the spots."

"No, Skip. I feel fine!"

"I know how you think you feel, Jake, but you're coming out."

"No way, Skip! I just put us ahead with the dinger last inning. It's my game to win or lose!"

"Sorry, Jake. You're out of the game. Now give me the ball!"

Infuriated and turning red, Jake started a short tantrum, turning around looking at the scoreboard and turning back several times. Then, reluctantly, he placed the ball into my outstretched hand and stomped away. I brought in our second pitcher. While standing on the mound watching the reliever warm up, I noticed the bench and spectators looking out at center field. I turned to see Jake run along the right field line, climb the steps to the scoreboard, snatch off the two runs and walk back down across the first baseline. Then, he stepped into the dugout, all the time holding the placard from the scoreboard with the number "2" on it. By now everyone was bursting with laughter. All I could do was shake my head. When I finally got into the dugout, I opened my arms, as if to make a swan dive and said, "Jake, what was that all about?"

"Those were my runs. They can't take them away from me. Not here in Wrigley Field."

"Okay, okay…Let's play ball."

The game took off. They got two more runs, and then we got a triple play. Ross seemed worried so I said, "Hey, no problem. In games like this, triple plays are part of our set strategy." He rolled his eyes. "Just wait, Ross, keep your guys alert at first base. We'll win this thing by moving runners. So, don't miss my signals. We'll win this thing!"

While their pitcher warmed up between innings, I walked to the third base box. The umpire stopped me and said, "Lefebvre, you've got to shut down your catcher."

"What do you mean?"

"Lefebvre, this guy's been watching too many baseball movies. He keeps taunting the hitters about their girlfriends. He's getting way too personal out there. We're going to get into some sort of hassle if you don't talk to him." I took a deep breath and said, "I'll take care of it."

So, after a three-up three-down inning, I stopped my catcher on his way back to the dugout. "Mel, what are you talking about to the hitters?"

"Well, Skip, just giving them something to think about, something to break their concentration."

"Keep doing that and the ump's going to toss you out of the game. No more, okay?"

"Okay, Skip." But, after two more pitches the umpire stood up, pointed to my catcher and yelled, "You're out of the game!" Mel threw his mitt into the dugout, as I told our backup to get his gear on. I gave Mel an expression like, "What the heck?" He looked back at me and said, "Sorry, Skip. Just a bad habit. Don't worry, I'll get over it." All I could do was shake my head, turn to the backup and say. "No talking trash to the hitters, you hear? Or, I'll pull you myself!"

After the inning was over, I walked past the umpire and asked, "How's he doing?" The umpire chuckled and replied, "Your backup catcher keeps telling the hitters what great swings they have. Asking them things like, 'Is it always such a beautiful day to play baseball here? Are your parents in the stands watching you today? Where is your high school here?' I guess you could say, no problem with this guy." I shook my head again and walked over to third.

Here was the situation. We were down by a run. The score was 2 to 3 at the top of the eighth inning. I had runners on second and third… one out. I called time and motioned the third base runner over to me. "Mickey, you're our tying run. It's just 90 feet away. Look down there!" He did. I continued. "If I call a squeeze play and the hitter bunts the ball in play, do you think you can make it?"

"Yeah, Skip. I can make it."

"Okay, Mickey. Are you sure?"

"Yeah, Skip. I think I can."

"No. Are you really sure you can? Because, Mickey, this is one of those defining moments in your life. You've got to do it. But remember," I added while pulling him close and making eye contact, "don't go home until the batter puts the ball in play. Got it?"

"Got it."

Having prepped him and knowing surprise was the key element to this grand strategy, I gave the hitter the bunt sign. Over in the first base box, Ross put his hands up. Just to let me know, "It won't work." But I knew it would. It always did, especially when Ross thought it wouldn't. So, it was all set. And, if time had slow motion, I could have seen the pitcher start into his windup. Once movement toward home plate was made and the ball was in the air, going 80 miles an hour but seeming only like 10 in my slow-motion mind, the hitter turns undetected to bunt. The infield is playing back. Everything is as it's supposed to be. The ball slowly closed in on the hitter. But then, it happened. The bunter foul-tipped the ball in the air, just above the catcher. The catcher stepped out, moved around a little, waited and caught the ball as my runner slid across home plate. Then, he casually threw the ball back to third for the double play.

As we gathered in the dugout, I yelled, "Runners, you've got to wait until the hitter puts the ball in play before you attempt a squeeze play. This is not a suicide play. It's a squeeze play!" I walked to the other end of the dugout. Ross leaned over and said,

"Dumb move, Gilly."

"What are you talking about?"

"We had time. One out in the eighth…two men on…dumb move, Gilly."

"Okay, Ross. But if it had worked, would it have been a dumb move?"

"But, Gil, that's where you never get it. It didn't work!"

Knowing, like so many of these encounters with Ross, this one had really nowhere to go, I walked away. But in the back of my mind, I knew, just maybe, he was right for the first time. I even considered putting Johnny Collins in, just to slow down their offense, but no. I couldn't win that way.

The game ended. We lost for the first time in all our years of playing against Avalon. They deserved it. Still, it was a tough crow to swallow.

Staying out of reach of Ross's scorn was an easy task on our way back. Mother had hired a new lifeguard, who happened to be a girl. Not just any girl but one that made the business of lifeguarding in her tight red Speedo. That proved far more appealing for our campers, especially for Ross, who sat with her on the way up and continued now on the way back. This was good. It kept him out of verbal striking distance and maybe allowed enough time for me to come up with a counterpunch to his unwarranted accusations.

Sitting in the back again, I looked out at the casino. As we passed, time allowed me to cool off. I reviewed the game and how I had managed it. One thing struck me. "Why am I doing this? It was just a game," I thought. As my eyes perked up to the message that my brain was sending, I looked around the boat and found him. I stood and walked to the middle of the aisle. There he was, attempting to sleep through the trip back. I asked one of the campers if I could sit next to him. He said, "Sure," and made room. I put my arm around his neck as a friendly gesture then broke the silence when I said, "Hey Mickey. Do you have a girlfriend?"

"Yeah."

"Do you have a picture of her?" Without answering, he pulled out his wallet and proudly showed it to me. I took it and looked at it for a minute, such a beauty in a cheerleading outfit. Pointing to the picture, I said, "You know, Mickey, now that's really a defining moment." It brought out a great big smile. He got it. We began to laugh together. It was a Hallmark moment, and I'm certain Norman Rockwell would have loved to have captured it.

Not knowing what she carried, the Blanche W., like so many times before, sputtered her way around Long Point and on back to the Isthmus.

CHAPTER 31

# Settling Scores

T hey say there's something to it. That, "the enemy of my enemy is my friend." I wasn't so sure about that, but, what I did know, Randall, me, the Boy Scouts and the baseball camp hadn't appeared to see eye to eye on anything. It wasn't that remarkable when you considered we shared the same island, hunted down the same girls, camped at the same beaches and dove in the same coves. Through the years, a terminal cross-town rivalry mentality developed. That was all about to come to an end. And, it happened this way.

The Boys Scouts' summer program closed about 14 days earlier then the baseball camp. While our camp was busy organizing end-of-season tournaments in the back bay, their staff became a noticeable presence all around the Isthmus. As I rushed down to pick up our incoming mail, I ran into Janet Knowles. She'd come in from the Tamara yacht. Janet was highly skilled at picking up the local gossip and always quite aware of what was up for the weekend. This time she was anxious to spread the news. "Did you hear what happened last night with Randall?"

"No. What did my good friend do now?"

"No. This time it wasn't Randall's fault, Gil. He was just

sitting around the snack bar patio, trying to make it with some girl who came in off the Sundance, and in walked the Blue Cads."

"Who?" I asked.

"Don't you remember that college fraternity crew from down toward the San Diego area?"

"Those guys that caused all of the problems last summer? I asked. "Yep. Those are the ones. They tried to get into Randall's business, had words and took it out to the beach. Lots of pushing and shoving turned into quite a fight."

"Okay, so what happened?"

"Randall got the best of one of them. Just like he did with you." She smiled.

"Wait a minute, Janet. No way! Who told you that?"

"That's how the story was told to me."

"Yeah, by who? Randall?" I laughed.

"Okay, both of you macho guys can work the story out whichever way you want, but this is what happened last night. They finally went back to their boat but said they'd be back tonight."

"That's it?"

"That's it."

"So, the scouts and the cads have a thing going on? This I've got to see." I walked into the snack bar to check things out. Linda and Carol were making lunch preparations. "Nobody's here yet, Gilly." While walking back down the steps, Ross came running up. "Your dad wants you to pick up 12 loaves of bread from Press." Just about then, someone bumped me from behind. I turned around to find some guy in a sleeveless tank top with "Cads are Bad" written on it in bold red letters that matched his sunburned skin. Except for the burn, he looked like a cross between Kookie Burns and Fonzie from Happy Days. "Hey, what's up?" I asked.

"You talking to me?" he asked back.

"Yes. I'm talking to you and maybe you should say, 'excuse me.'"

"For what?"

"I guess you didn't notice, but you bumped me," I explained. As always, Ross was paying special interest to my eyes. He knew the drill. They were getting larger by the minute. I suspect because Mr. Wannabe Fonzie had interrupted my happy day.

"No, you were in my way," he argued. "Where's your apology?" And, with that he began to point his finger at my chest.

"That's not a good thing for you to do," I warned, "if you want to keep your finger on your hand, that is." Seemed all this apology stuff was walking its way to a threat. "So, you're one of those Cad Blue guys, or whatever they call you?" He opened his mouth to speak but I interrupted. "Yeah, you are. It's a good thing you got it written on your shirt. Probably so you'll remember when you forget."

"Looking for trouble?" he asked.

"Well you've come to the right place. Elvis?" I said and begin to laugh at him. "Hey cad guy. They tell me Randall took care of one of your boys last night."

"Is that so?"

"Yeah. That's what I heard."

Obviously bothered he said, "Well, it's not over. Sooner or later, we'll finish it with those Cub Scouts. You must be one of those pussy baseball guys."

"Really? 'Pussy baseball guys?'"

"You know that well, dirt bag."

"Dipshit, you just invited us to a meeting tonight on the beach," I said.

"Bring it on," he said, now beginning to coil like a rattlesnake, causing my eyes to get big enough to pop out of my head. Sensing trouble, Linda walked out for a look. Seeing her there, one of his

330 · CATALINA SUMMER

sidekicks walked up and said, "No, Rich. Later." They both turned and began to walk away. My macho wasn't ready to leave me yet. "Yeah, Richie. See you tonight. Bring your comb and brush your teeth. Make sure to look good for tonight, Richie boy. Cause it's going to be your last." His friend grabbed him and off they went down the pier to the boat dock. Linda said, "I never liked those guys. I don't want them in here tonight." And, she walked back into the snack bar.

"Another dumb thing you got us into, Gilly."

"What do you mean 'us?'"

"Did I hear you just invited yourself to a party tonight?" He laughed and shook his head as he muttered, "You're nuts, Gilly. Has anyone ever told you that?"

"Yeah. You do every day." We walked around to the back of the snack shop to get the bread from Press Taylor.

Tay was unloading the truck from Avalon. "Hey, lost the game in Avalon," he said.

"Yeah, we did."

"No, you did, Gil."

"Oh, oh been talking to Lolo?"

"Right. He said, "'Gilly blew it.'"

"Okay, I guess there might be a little truth to that. Hey Tay, some nice looking girls you were with at the game. Why didn't you introduce them?"

"You baseball guys couldn't handle it."

"Really? Ross, could you?" I looked over to Ross and chuckled. He turned a little red and asked, "Why am I in this conversation?"

I went on. "Those cad guys are in the Isthmus."

"Yeah, I heard about Randall and the scouts last night."

"Yeah, I just bumped into one and he invited me and our baseball guys to a meeting tonight."

"Gil, they have a lot of jerks out on their boat. I saw them last night, so you'd better come with a few of your friends."

Ross jumped in, "He doesn't have any."

"I got you, Ross. Although I am not sure you'll be much help," I said.

"It's your fight. I didn't badmouth that guy. You did. I don't need to have you pick fights for me."

I changed the subject. "Tay, I need 12 loaves of bread."

"Got them right here. Just need you to sign off."

With that he, gave me a clipboard and handed me a pen. I scribbled my name then turned to walk away. Trying to put a little levity in the situation, Tay called out, "Have fun tonight, guys."

Wouldn't you know it, practically before we got to the top walkway of camp, our counselors had already gotten the news. Some of them were there when Randall had his bout last night. Well, this really put me in a pickle. Couldn't back out – didn't want this to turn into mere boasting and prideful gestures. My big mouth just wouldn't let me alone. What the heck, play on. Probably by the end of the day it might all pass anyway.

Not so. Everywhere, I mean everywhere I went, the story was out. It's always funny how the channels of communication work. The young guys knew what was going on. But, we were so neatly tight-lipped, the older generation didn't know what was up. We had this big thing about to happen, and they never had a clue. It just happens that way.

The day carried on as normal. Ross, Tuck and I continued to debate the trouble I had gotten us into. "You know what? Those guys keep coming back and causing more problems. Hey, if we don't deal with it tonight then when? Sometime, when we're out alone with some girl… then what? We won't be able to even go into the snack bar. It's now or never. They'll just keep on playing that bully game."

"Geez, Gil, you're making too much of this. They probably won't even show up."

"Oh, they will Ross. They have no respect. What do you think Tuck?"

"I think you're right, Big G. We've had trouble with the scouts, but at least it's understood the weekend and the snack shop are neutral zones. Anyway, these guys don't want to go after girls; they just want a fight."

"Let's go down after dinner," I said. "Maybe they'll not show or really cause trouble and get thrown out of the Isthmus."

Tuck added, "I've seen those guys get all liquored up above Little Fish, and they get totally out of control."

"Geez, Gil, another fine mess," Ross grumbled.

"Well, Ross, you don't have to come down with us."

"You know I will, Gil, it's just…well, I never know why I always do. How many times now? So, no sense talking about this stuff. Let's just get to it."

After a quick change in the cabin, Ross and I walked down the path to the snack shop. It was another warm late summer night. The moon made quite a show of itself as it flashed across the water. As usual we stopped to talk to Ty, chatted about really nothing and let him go on his way. I saw Bombard's kids playing just off the patio steps. All seemed normal. No hint of what lay ahead. I looked around the patio, just to see who was in the Isthmus. It was still too early for the Saturday night crowd. While we waited for Tuck, Ross and I went in and ordered our usual…extra large chocolate malts. We nervously talked and laughed it up with Linda and Carol for a while about everything and nothing, trying to forgot about the cad boys. Eventually Billy Tuck showed up and said. "Hey, the cad guys are down by the baseball camp beach area. They're throwing bottles out at the float, seeing who can hit it."

"Okay, let's go." We stepped outside. Ross suggested, "Maybe we should tell Bombard. He'll call the sheriff."

"No," I said. "This is our problem and it will keep coming back to us if we don't take care of it." An unexpected surprise filed in behind us as we started down toward the beach. Out of the dark came about seven or eight of our counselors, who were obviously ready to take this thing on. "Good timing, guys," I said. And, on we went, like Wyatt Earp and his gathering clan, marching on to the O.K. Corral. But for us, it was down to our beach. Stopping on top of the bluff above the scene, we looked right down on top of them. Sure enough, there they were, throwing beer bottles and rocks at our float. One of our counselors turned his flashlight on them. They whirled around, and it became obvious they were lit up, especially from the amount of spent alcohol bottles flung about. I wasn't sure how many swaying bodies were down there, but we knew what they were here for and that what they'd say would make no sense. Our lead counselor talked first. "This is no place for you guys. You'll want to just move on."

One of the cads pointed up to me. "That guy there pushed one of our guys today at the snack shop. We've come to teach him some manners."

"Look guys, this isn't worth the trouble. Besides, we'll just call the sheriff, and he'll kick you off this island for good."

"Oh really?" You gutless punks would do that?"

Now my pride got the best of me and my eyes started getting bigger. I'd never backed out of a fight before. Although I'd never really won a fight either, but that just goes along with it. I could see we were definitely outnumbered. Still, I couldn't stop my rehearsed speech. "Here's the way this goes. It's okay for you guys to get all liquored up," I said, stealing a line from Tuck, "and howl at the moon anywhere you want. But throw bottles and rocks on our beach, well that's another thing!" Pretty good start, I thought and went on. "So who's your chief? Who do we need to see about this problem?" When a short stocky guy stepped out, I pretended to laugh. "Yeah you're the joker who can't walk straight. Not only can't you walk right, you can't even throw your bottles far enough to the float, let alone hit it."

"You baseball pussies want to come down here and see what we can do?" That was it. The candle was lit. The rumble was on. Something felt familiar about all this. It kind of reminded me of some of the brawls we'd gotten ourselves into when one of our batters got intentionally thrown at. When that happened, the bench unloaded, and we met on the field. Clearly, this might be a little different. There were no umpires around to break this up.

But, just before we could get down from the cliff, flashlights came out of the dark from the pier side of the beach. Both sides stopped to look, standing back and thinking someone must have notified the sheriff after all. Who were these guys? Now, one by one they trained their flashlights on the cads. Behind the lights a deep commanding voice spoke loud enough for all to hear. "Lefebvre's right. Take your show somewhere else. Stay out of the Isthmus. We're not going to call the law. No. We're going to finish this thing right here. And, believe me, most of you will be flown out by the Coast Guard medical team. Now, that's just the way it is. Man, look at some of you guys, you're way too old to have that kind of problem. It's your choice. You're outnumbered 10 to one here. So, go on your way and never come back, or let's get at it."

Time seemed to freeze after his last word. The tension could not have been higher. All was said that needed to be. Then, suddenly something gave way. The brinkmanship of the evening went our way. Seeing all that was against them, they dropped their bottles and rocks and began to back off, disappearing into the shadows. Where? That wasn't important because the Isthmus would swallow them up and take them home.

Who was that guy with the booming voice? Without another word they turned to go. I grabbed Ross's flashlight, ran a few yards ahead and shined the light where the voice was last heard. A head snapped around. It was Randall. I was left with nothing to say. No smart quips. No jokes to brighten the moment. No claims of victory. Reaching into my bag of tricks, I found nothing. It was hard to say, but I did. A mere one word summed it all up, "Thanks."

"Okay, Lefebvre. We're in this together." And, without another word, he slipped back into the night.

The next day, we learned the cad boat was searched by the sheriff. Finding nothing but empty beer bottles, they were allowed to leave. Although, the sheriff warned them, if they ever stepped foot on the island again, they'd better bring a lawyer.

The scouts left the next day. I never knew how they found out we were going to be there that night. I'd heard about Randall's problem the night before, but it's still a mystery. Billy and I went down to meet the Blanche the next day and caught a glimpse of the scouts' charter pulling away from the pier. There was Randall Cunningham III, standing on the bow as if searching for me. He knew it was all over now. He would find himself a real war to fight out there somewhere. Our eyes finally met, as I stood there on the end of the pier. Tears welled up in mine. Who knows why? I never did. As his boat pulled away his hand flashed to his head, giving me a tight salute. Then sharply he brought the hand to his side, turned and disappeared into the boat. We stayed there for a while, Tuck and me, just looking out until the boat fell out of sight, not knowing what to make of it, but never forgetting.

What came out of this so-called big fight? Was it the whole "the enemy of my enemy is my friend" thing? Or did our Isthmus family grow larger? Did it really matter? Possibly in the end, love, hate and anger create the best in us. Maybe it was coming together in times of strife, causing a bond of brothers. Probably one or all of those ideas put together. I'm not sure, but I know it allowed me the opportunity to see others in a different light. It also enabled me to view myself far more favorably than I deserved. It's really hard to beat down pride…that cost so much. But, by doing so, there are rewards. I can now laugh as I relish and recall stories and conflicts about Randall.

We both had a lot at stake. As we grew up together as enemies in our little world, we had our self-image to protect. That was important, while we were so young and all was still so new. We had yet to be tested. We didn't even know ourselves, much less each other. And proving what we were to each other confirmed what we believed of ourselves.

So, in a game of four square, there on the island, we lived out life. Taking, giving and competing, yes, but not for what you think. It wasn't always between us. No, we competed with ourselves, sustaining each other along the way, hoping never to expose our flaws. Most of all, our struggle was with what we disliked as we looked into the mirror. What reflected back was sometimes quite different than reality. We needed each other to find that out. So, not knowing it, we served each other well.

CHAPTER 32

# On The Waterfront

The weather was giving us an early preview of fall as Ross, Tuck and I sat with some of the other counselors in the TV room late one night. The campers were all tucked in while we watched a rerun of one of my favorites, On the Waterfront with Marlon Brando. He portrayed an ex-boxer turned dockworker who eventually took on the mob and literally fought it out with them on the wharf. In the end, battered but not beaten, he attempted to walk across the shipyard to lead his fellow workers away from the corrupt union. Bleeding and dizzy from the recent beating, he staggered to the line. Wow, what an ending. Now that's a guy who left his mark.

It got me to thinking, "Wonder what we could do to leave our mark…to make the Isthmus a better place than when we came?"

"Hey Ross. We need a finale!" I declared.

"A what?"

"A finale! You know, like they do at the end of fireworks. Something grand, something to go OOOOH about and remember 60 years from now." He looked back at me, as he always did, in that strange, bewildered way, as if addressing some sort of accounting problem, then, turned to his business mode of clarifying the situation. "Calm down, Gil. What the heck are you talking about?"

"A finale. Yeah, Ross, something to finish off the summer, you know what I mean. Like you finished off Kimberly."

Ross quickly laughed. "I never told you that. And, you can be sure I'm never going to tell you anything. That eats you up doesn't it? Not knowing."

"No, it doesn't. But what's that got to do with the finale? Anyway, try to keep on topic, Ross. Let's see….a finale…. Hey, I've got it. The smugglers! What if we capture them? That would be something big. Like make the evening news or even the Los Angeles Times kind of big! They'll remember us for sure! The smugglers from the Old Chinese Trawler in the back bay. Yep. Let's go case the place out. I'll bet they're smuggling something besides lobsters. There's got to be drugs and guns and who knows what else in there. Those guys look really seedy. I've told the story around, but no one seems to care. Well, its time they do care! 'I just want to be somebody,'" I said in a mumbled low voice, parroting Brando from the movie.

"Don't even try, Gilly. It's not going to happen," Ross said.

"I guess Tuck and I will just have to catch those bandits by ourselves, if you don't have the guts."

"You and Billy Tuck? Now that's a joke. By the way, are you the one who trained him to call you 'Big G.'?"

"Heck no. It's just that Tuck respects quality and, apparently, that's what you're lacking."

"Respect? Respect for what?"

"Hey, are you going in with us or not? This conversation's over. The finale or what? Last chance, Ross. They'll forget you tomorrow. No ink and print for you."

"Okay, okay." Ross gave in, buying in to my rather distorted logic, but added, "Remember, nothing stupid."

"No, of course not. We got away with our last trip in there didn't we?" I reminded him.

So the next day, Tuck, Ross, Ret and I huddled together and put out the plan. "After finishing off games at the diamond, we'll start our surveillance. In the afternoon we'll climb the mountain just above the trawler and keep a lookout for suspicious things going on down there. When we see some action, we'll run back, tell the sheriff and that's that. Easy."

We began our reconnaissance and, sure enough, there they were, scurrying around in an outboard motorboat. Laying low to the ground to keep out of sight, we watched as they putted up to the trawler. Three rather large robust barnacle-looking guys stepped out, looked nervously around and disappeared into the bowels of the barge. Time passed. Nothing. Then about 45 minutes later, carrying three large bags, they finally came out. After loading the bags in the skiff, off they went to an old fishing boat moored at the edge of the oncoming fog bank. As they climbed aboard, the mist swallowed up the bay and the boat disappeared with it. "Jeepers creepers!" I said to the guys. "We need to get down there. You know, there's definitely something in there besides lobsters."

We really didn't have to worry about newspaper fame because, after a few days, just about everybody in the Isthmus knew about it. We talked it up over malts in the snack shop, on the beach to our campers and on the pier waiting for the Blanche. And, by now the locals thought we were loco besides being the biggest buffoons in the neighborhood. My dad even took me aside and asked, "So, Gil, you and the boys working on your backup career in law enforcement as what, Inspector Clouseau?"

"Okay, Dad. I know everybody thinks this is a joke, but we'll show them."

By now our big finale had been on level three yellow alert. I notified the guys we were now in the critical orange high-risk, level-four stage. "Everybody's laughing. They think we've built this Chinese trawler issue out of proportion."

"But you have, Gil," Ross argued.

I turned for my usual support from Tuck. "Big G., you're right," he said.

"Thanks, Tuck. I knew there was someone around here with a little common sense."

"Geez Gil, Tuck would walk the plank over any nutty thing you came up with."

"Yah, and you walked your way right into Kimberly all by yourself. Really?"

Ross jumped back. "What? Not that girl thing again."

"See, Ross. Do you even remember her name? Oh, I forgot. It was just too dark in there. Any port in the storm, hey, Ross?"

"You don't make any sense, Gil," Ross snapped.

"Okay, all I need to know is, are you in or out, Ross?"

"Why not? Doesn't make any difference now, 'cause they all think we've lost our oars on this one." Now giving up on his attempt at insurrection and efforts to sabotage our plan, he mumbled, "Yeah I'm in."

We moved forward and then, suddenly, the table was set. While surveying the old trawler from the top of the hill, we saw an old dilapidated half-breed of a boat sail in. It slipped into Cat Harbor and anchored in the cover of the late afternoon fog. Again, those awkward-looking, Neanderthal-type men lurked about, obviously preparing for something big. "This is our time. It's all going down." I knew about such things. I'd seen it in movies dozens of times. "Now, guys, it's show time!"

Into action we went. Ret took off toward the Isthmus to alert the sheriff. Tuck began his lookout role. Ross and I advanced down the hill, dressed in bathing suits, sweat shirts and flip-flops, with our trusty baseball bats in hand. We planned to discard the flip-flops once we got closer. No need to slow us down. Determination to catch these guys red-handed and hold them until the cavalry arrived might have clouded our judgment. No worry. If it all fell apart, our escape route was to run as fast as we could to just about anywhere, each in different directions. This way, they'd have to break up to follow our tracks. Again, foolproof. Saw it in a movie and it worked.

We closed in on the Chinese trawler but, just before mounting her deck, disaster struck. I stumbled through a broken step. Following me so closely that I could feel him breathing down my neck, Ross fell over the top of me and crashed into the side of a steel beam, one of the few left standing. Blood began spurting from his nose, and my foot stayed painfully squeezed between the boards. Ross said, "Oh my God. I think I just broke my nose." I tried pulling my foot out from the broken floorboards. Tuck, positioned up on the side of the hill, whispered in a yell, "They're coming! They're in the skiff. They're coming!"

"How many?"

"Three of them, and they don't look very friendly!"

"Tuck, give me a hand." He rushed down to help out. It was then I realized, "I think my ankle's broken." With the plan of running in all directions now in serious jeopardy, we backed ourselves into the hull of the boat. Down some stairs and way back to the very back, where it was pitch black, once again we found ourselves tiptoeing trough lobster-infested waters. Once more, they were flipping and snapping their claws, playing havoc with our feet. Now, disturbed from their slumber, they gave out an eerie twitching sound. It seemed like the whole hull was in motion. With nowhere to go, we settled down into the cover of darkness. Stilled by our silence, the room began to rest. Our eyes searched for light as we heard two-legged creatures beginning to come down the busted steps. The torment of our pending demise drove our hearts to pound wildly. We could only hope the sound of our hearts thumping wasn't as loud as we heard it from inside our heads. "Don't move," Ross whispered. We didn't and, in silence, listened. As a door opened from the back of the trawler, we could make out a shadow of a man, preparing to make his first step inside. The light was bright enough to give us a clear view. Holy cow! The man looked like he'd gone beyond death and was trying to find his way back. His bearded face exposed only one eye, a nose and maybe a mouth. As he entered the bowels of the ship, he raised a flashlight and began to spray it around the room. I found myself searching for God again and slipped into a short prayer, not even in complete sentences and void of adjectives and verbs. Wait a minute...is "please" a verb?

But, before my prayer got on its way, the light made its way to us. We looked like three possible suspects standing stoic during a police lineup. Then God came in, finally, and gave us a hand, even though I don't think we deserved it. We'd gotten ourselves into this situation without informing Him, so theoretically, we should have been on our own. Thank goodness for grace.

Then, it happened. One of the guys yelled from outside, "They're coming! Let's get the hell out of here!" And, away they went. The man scrambled, then we heard a big thump. Tuck whispered, "Probably fell down the step that got you and Ross." Wow. This was too much. Then, starting as a low swishing sound and soon becoming a deafening roar, a helicopter arrived. Yea! Ret got the job done and the cavalry was on its way. We ran, well I mostly limped, out of the water and up the stairs, carefully avoiding another fall. As we reached the top deck there was just enough light out to make a glorious sight.

Coming out of the fog, looking a lot like Thor was Big Al and his boat. Along with Birt Grove at the helm of his, they gave chase and soon surrounded the varmints, plodding along in their weighted-down skiff. Overhead the chopper sprayed its lights on the deck of the trawler. Standing there with bats in hand, it hit me that those bats of ours probably looked a lot like guns from the sky. A voice came out of the air, "Throw down your weapons. Lay down flat on the ground and spread 'em. Or, we will commence firing!" It didn't take much prompting and soon we found ourselves hugging the floor for safety. Ross turned to me and said, "Damn it Gilly, you broke my nose!"

Still clinging to the deck, we could see two headlights coming toward us from the yacht club road. After a few minutes, the local law enforcement arrived on the scene, climbed aboard and put spotlights on us. "Who are you guys?" they asked.

Ross spoke up, "We're from the baseball camp." One of the sheriffs picked up one of the discarded bats, took a few swings and laughed. "What do we have here? A Mickey Mantle 32-inch?"

"That's mine," I said.

The officer said, "Good bat. I'm a fan of his too. And what do we have here? A Stan Musial 31-inch, and both of them Louisville Sluggers? Damn, we could have used them in Korea." I started to get up but the sheriff said, "No, no stay down there. We're not done with you yet. So tell me, baseball guys, what's going on here?" Ross looked up, causing the sheriff to comment, "Oops. Bumped your nose, huh?" Then he yelled over to another officer, "Hey, sergeant, better get the first aid kit. Come up here and take a look at this kid. Now, what's the deal?" Still on the ground, I went through the story.

By now Big Al had shored his boat, stepped ashore and come onto the trawler. Everyone seemed to know him and smiled when he asked, "Are you okay, Gilly? Is that you, Ross? And that's Cliff Tucker's son, Billy. Yeah I can vouch for these kids. I know them all. In fact, Gilly here is Benny's boy."

"Really? The one that signed?" the sheriff asked.

"No, not yet."

"Well, then, I guess we'll just have to give them a ride back to camp and have some coffee with Mr. Lefebvre. Go ahead and call in the Fish and Game officials. Oh, and you'd better get the Coast Guard to check out that boat."

"Smugglers...check out the smugglers," I added.

"Okay, to check out the smugglers. All right, you guys can get up now. Sergeant, how does the kid look?"

"I think he broke his nose."

As I started to get up and put some pressure on my left foot, I fell back down, "I think I sprained my ankle." It had already started to swell, so the officer supported me down the stairs and into the sheriff's truck. Others put Ross in the back and Billy Tuck, who came out of the ordeal unscathed, slid in alongside Ross, obviously pleased to be part of the escapade. Later, he would say, "Big G. that had to be one of the best, if not the best we ever did." He might have been right. We had the police, game warden, Coast Guard, helicopter and all sorts of Isthmus notoriety out there that night.

As the police truck reached the camp, all the staff and campers lined up to greet us. I stepped out with the aid of my dad and mom, who'd waited patiently for our return. Me, unable to stand on my ankle, Ross with an apparent broken nose and Tuck smiling profusely all while the camp cheered us on, as if we'd done something really big. However, I'm pretty sure it was more in the line of a prank to go along with our folly. When the clapping and back patting subsided, adding insult to injury, the sheriff blurted out in a booming voice, "Boys, next time, leave the law enforcement to us!" This, I thought, was a comical commentary to my past years here at the Isthmus.

I was told the smugglers' boat was searched. No illegal substance or contraband was found. And the men aboard the vessel were not charged. However, they were cited for poaching, paid a large fine and went on their way. Clearly, for the next few days, life for us was an embarrassment. I had to be on crutches for a while. Ross could hardly see, due to the swelling from his nose, and Tuck, the only real survivor, loved every moment of it. We retold the story over and over, each time coming up with a new version that really didn't happen.

In the end, I guess we had our big finale. Maybe not as planned, but life doesn't always turn out the way you plan it... actually, most of the time it doesn't. Later, as Tuck walked and I limped about the Isthmus, people we'd never met before would stop and ask, "Hey, boys, know where we can buy some lobster at a good price?" And with that, they'd burst into laughter, then walk on.

"Hey, Tuck, who are those guys?" I asked.

Tuck would answer, "Must be Ross's friends."

# Catalina Summer

### sketches of the past

## Part Three

CHAPTER 33

# Winding Down

Sometimes, when there was nothing to do, I'd wonder up to Mt. Lebushtuck, one of my favorite places. From up there, on clear afternoons in early September, you could see all the way to the mainland. Often, so clear, you felt like you could reach out and grab it. From this vantage point, I was mesmerized by the ocean drama playing beneath. Being alone in this pristine setting was much more than witnessing a magnificent panoramic view. It was a phenomenon that pried on the heart, hypnotized my soul and begged me to reflect.

So it was on this somber note that I began to see the summers of my life, those Catalina summers, coming to an end, like October maple leaves that flutter to the ground, painting, as artists do, such brilliant spectrums and forays of color that carry the mind away. As a final gesture to the changing seasons, they create sketches all across the countryside, sketches of the past. The details and images are not always as clear as you thought they were, but isn't that what sketches are for?

Sitting up there, I knew there was no way of getting around it. This youthful attachment to the island was all winding down, and I would be moving on. Feeling a little like a castaway who returned to the modern world after living in isolation, I too would return to the mainland and make decisions about which direction to take.

How much had I grown in all these years? I came as a boy snatched off the streets by my mother's intuition at the age of 13, trying to be 18. Now, less than a decade later, I was leaving as a man, trying to savor the time when I was 13.

I also thought about my loves, though still never really understanding much about girls. Not necessary. Why? Because, as the night is to the day or the cold is to heat, or winter is to summer, only gives clues to how each is opposite yet dependent on the other. All that mattered was their ways were quite different from us guys. And, that was good enough for me. I didn't need to understand more. I then laughed at myself, thinking what I'd discovered this past summer, now cultured in the fine art of how to unhook a bra yet still wondering why I had to. There must be an easier way to get beyond that point. I'd also experienced rejection and found my way back. Oh, not all the way back, but a least I salvaged my pride. And, I discovered perfect love could be found by just holding hands. That was enough to keep me going.

About my baseball career, I never hit the 300-foot road. My brothers did repeatedly, and they moved on. But, for me, I had to accept myself, not accept defeat. I found out, since I could run faster than they could, there would be no need to hit the ball over the 300-foot road. That was a good thing. I just needed to learn to live with it. But, I'd never let Ross know he was right about that.

I could continue on with this baseball kick, it'd taken me this far, or maybe try to play as far out as I could in football. But, nah, college was never an option. I didn't think I would ever pass algebra. I really didn't see a need to find the X factors then and still don't. The Army was in the offering. Become a Green Beret or some kind of a hero, but the clouds were gathering around Vietnam, and that path could be terminal. But, for whatever reason, for the first time up on that hill, my well-oiled future became blurred and a sense of anxiety set in to complicate the matter.

About my friends, they were people with noble character who, from time to time, I could lean on, and I did. There were many of them that came and went throughout my camp experience. But, only a few found a way to stay connected.

My future? My dad assured me, it really didn't matter where it leads you. What mattered was that you enjoy it. It was kind of like wearing the right kind of clothes in winter, then summer. A career was more like provisions. It's something that comforts you along the way. And, yes, for me, I've always been on my way, not necessarily knowing where, nevertheless on my way. Maybe Ross was right again. After all, in the end, isn't it really all about the journey?

As to my search for God, I found Him and continued looking for His direction. Father James tried to help shortcut my journey. He gave me a jumpstart. However, it seems just too personal a thing to have one intrude in these matters. My read of the situation is that God made each of us special. He gives us the freedom to act and make our own choices. God has a place for me in His creation, and that alone is the very foundation that makes our relationship so unique. And, as always, when I've run out of answers, I meet Him on His turf, in prayer.

Then, there's the question of just living. I've always thought, to really live, I needed to overcome my fear... the kind of fear that comes with the insecurity of youth, uncertain that your ego and bravado can match your talent. I couldn't rely on luck or a quirk of nature, nor on God's providence alone. Yes, we have a destiny, I think. But, it's still up for grabs and, if not grasped, life becomes a crapshoot of just chances and probabilities. And, there's no merit to that... is there?

So, there was one thing left for me to do, before leaving this place. I needed to overcome that fear. Not by some reckless act. No. Not that way. It would come from a challenge. When you've said, "I can do this" and then you do it. I needed to take the risk, to step out there, by myself. Knowing all the while, later this would free me from faulting others for my failings. And, I had to do it soon, and soon would be only days away.

I thought about my parents. It is said that the role of the father was the disciplinarian and mother the comforter. There's something to that, but also a lot of nothing to that. Yes, my father always pressed me on, hoping to find a man there someday. What a task he had. I'm not sure we ever achieved that, even today. But he tried. He gave me a craft, a wonderful craft. He gave me a mold to cast myself into…his. Oh, he had flaws, but who doesn't? But, he had virtues that spiraled above the rest. To me that was enough. He wanted a way for me. I took another. Even in his objection, he encouraged me on. He gave me the wink I needed. I saw the twinkle in his eye when he set me free. And, he always discreetly put a $20 bill in my hand to help me stay there.

As for mother, she was hardly a liberated woman. Yet mom was never pretentious or demeaning about the role she played. She didn't need to be. She found her strength in just being who she was. And, we found comfort in the strength of her moral fiber. We'd never let a foul word loose around her. She never needed to ask for that. Her goodness required it.

Father pushed for our independence, to see us stand on our own, and we did. Mother did the same, in her own way. Sometimes, she'd offer a soft shoulder, when we didn't quite make it. But, after a short while, cleverly she pushed us on. From birth to independence, my mother and father were the rock I built my world around, the rudder that kept me on course. They were the sun on a cloudy day and the lighthouse that welcomed me home when lost at sea.

Sitting high up there on that island mountain that day, I didn't know how much I was leaving behind. Many years later, a colleague of mine asked, "Do you go back to the Isthmus often?" I replied, "No, not really." But I paused, to reconsider my response, then answered, "Yes, I go back every day."

CHAPTER 34

# Time To Go

W ho were these people, with names that time has eroded from the back of our minds? They'd come from everywhere and nowhere, like floundering meteorites splashing down from the heavens, playing major roles in the etching of our character. None of us would really know it then. We were too young and going about our way. No need to explain why or where we were going. It was enough just to say we were on our way. No reason to apologize for our past, for the past… well, it didn't exist yet. No qualms about the future because, back then, we defined things only in the present tense. For, that's all we had to go on. Catalina summers allowed all sorts of possibilities for the creation of lasting images, with few uncertainties to complicate, intrude or blemish those personal memories.

That morning's sunrise signaled the last time many of us would be together here at the Isthmus. A lot of them would never come back. Oh, some would dream about it. But, once awake, Isthmus thoughts would quickly dissipate into daily routines. So, for most of my friends, this last day was like a graduation, shaking hands, giving tokens and gestures to remind them how special they were. For those who'd enlisted alongside of me for the past decade, well, it just made it that much more difficult to say goodbye. The island would always be here and the stories would be told, but they would be gone.

Last night's farewell dinner included awards, presentation of bats, balls and, of course, camp T-shirts. Everyone got something. My dad always found ways to honor each camper. They left feeling special, and they were.

Some goodbyes had to wait because nothing became so busy as the last day of the season. Everything had to go back on the boat, locked up or put away. Most counselors would leave with the departing campers, leaving just a few to help with the final teardown, then drive the truck into Avalon and sail home on the Great White Steamer.

Our last meals for the summer were surprisingly special. My father called it, "More night." If you asked about the recipe, he would answer, "Some more of this and some more of that." There would be little reason to ration perishables. It would be another year before the camp would start up again. So, it was fill the plates with all you could. Anything in cans needed to be stored. All beds stayed in place but mattresses, torn from the beds, were placed in the open to air out then restacked in the rooms to wait all winter for our return. Next came the final wash down of cabin and dormitory floors, helped out by last night's water fight between campers and counselors. My father allowed this each session. I think he found it fun for the kids, even though sometimes a little reckless. But, for the most part, it gave a climatic ending, an exclamation back cover to this chapter of their summer camp experience.

Late on the last night, our cabin threw a goodbye party for Ross. Reminiscing Ross's latrine duties, we gathered up an old toilet and filled it with coke and ice. Before opening it, Ross sat atop the seat while we awarded him toilet bowl brushes and a case of Clorox cleaning powder. Posing for pictures while the radio pounded out some familiar songs, Ross was in heaven. He really took it to heart. I think he knew the important meaning of this last night. This would be the beginning of the end to a significant chapter of his life, and he wasn't about to let go that easily. Eventually, instead of champagne flowing, the Clorox bottles were cracked open and thrown about the cabin. What a mess, as Ross stayed seated smiling all the while, knowing it was all for him. It was his night.

The next day we scurried about, removing any evidence of the mayhem and for a very good reason. Before camp could be officially closed, our head counselor, along with my dad and mother, inspected every inch of the place.

After lunch, it was time to go. We loaded the campers' overstuffed luggage, jam-packed with precious souvenirs, some from Avalon, maybe some seashells, along with well-worn letters from home, all proof of adventures on the island. Some had only been in camp for two weeks, but it seemed like an eternity because of new friendships that, in many cases, turned into lifelong relationships.

Once the luggage was loaded, the inspections began, as we drove jam-packed trucks down to the pier. The campers took their final walk past the snack bar, where they'd sipped on thick malts and devoured juicy hamburgers while hanging out on the patio. And, then it was on to the pier, where we lined them from one end to the next, in conveyer belt fashion, to hand off the baggage to its final destination, carefully stacked at the end of the dock. Waiting for the chartered boat to arrive, final goodbyes were said all around. What do you say? Well, for some it was easy. Several were targets of jest while others were accomplished athletes who saw potential pro futures back on the mainland. And, you told them so, "I'll see you in the newspapers." Others would become producers and directors, even a few of them would return to farms or ranches. Some went on to city life, the way they did before they'd come to the island.

But when it came to the counselors that you'd spent so many years with, climbing this or swimming that or just surviving youth, well, that was something special, and words were hard to come by. You couldn't just say goodbye. That wasn't enough, but it wouldn't matter. They were caught up with the same feelings you had, not knowing what to say either. Water welling up in the corner of their eyes would be the most telling indication of what they did here and where they were going. It all mattered. We just didn't have enough practice on how to say it.

Everyone turned as the loud roar of the incoming charter passed Bird Rock and eventually nestled up at dockside. The campers began to file in one by one and, with a wave and a smile or some kind of witty gesture, they disappeared into the boat. The last to board were the counselors and, one by one, the few of us who were left behind said our goodbyes. We might never see them again and, even though names might have been forgotten, we would talk about them for generations. The kid we called Chicago? Yeah he really was from a gambling mob family. Great guy. To this day, he'll always be Chicago and the rest will remain anonymous. I said goodbye to the Hawkins brothers, who'd hitched a ride back to San Pedro. It was back to school for them.

Then there was Ross. His eyes seemed to be hidden out of sight by the dark bruises. They contrasted well against his Italian skin. Well, there's nothing I could say that could eloquently sum up the uncommon bond we'd created. I began to say something, but he jumped in. "You tried to kill me these past five years. I know my chances of staying alive have just increased with me getting far away from you." It was a good laugh, maybe because there was some truth to it. We both knew it would all change. He was going on to college and would soon find a career that would consume his life. We'd keep in contact, but not like in the past. We'd shared so much, but he had to move on. There were things expected of him. Not wanting to close off our relationship, I merely said, "See you later, buddy."

"Not if I see you first. I'll run!" He replied in rapid succession.

We smiled, neither one of us would let on how much we really meant to the other. And then he was gone. The boat began to pull out. I saw him come to the top deck to look out and wave, and I yelled, "You had a good ride on the Kimberly Express!" He smiled broadly and then pointed at me. The boat turned, and it was off. I sat there, at the end of the pier, for about a half hour as the boat passed out of sight. When I turned to go, there was nobody left. Where do I go? Mother and father had retreated to their cabin's front porch, taking a well-needed rest. The few counselors that were left took off to whatever part of the Isthmus where they could find company.

And, for the first time in over three months, I had nowhere to go. No mountain to climb, no quest to conquer, no game to play, no schedule to follow. I was lost. I started down the pier and saw Billy Tuck walking toward me. Life seemed to pour back in. I waited for him at the end of the pier. We chatted a while, then I said, "Well, it's almost over, Tuck. What do you want to do?" Looking out at the bay, we could see the moorings were almost empty and the beaches mostly deserted. After all, it was September. "What about you Tuck?"

"My dad said we'd sail home late tomorrow afternoon." We both looked down the beach and spotted the flaty still tied up next to our float. Tuck looked over at me, knowing what was on my mind. "Hey, Big G., how 'bout a sailing lesson?" I laughed, remembering that the last time we did that, we fell out, and the flaty sailed on just as well without us. "Sure, why not. When do you have to get back to the Geronimo?"

"Sometime later in the afternoon. The yacht club's throwing this big year-end party."

"Okay, let's go then!" We dove in, swam out to the float, crawled aboard and off we went. The bay was entirely ours. The sea breeze was kicking up enough wind to hold a full sail, and the cool air tempered the scolding sun. We sailed the afternoon away, laughing at all of the stuff we'd survived together. "Hey Tuck, just think what kind of summers we would have had if we'd listened to Ross's complaints." As Tuck laughed he said, "But, Big G., you almost killed him three or four times."

"That I did...that I did, Tuck," I said, using my best Irish brogue imitation. "At times I thought it might have been a good thing if I had. No...I guess not. I'd have to explain his demise to his mother, and that would be messy." Again, we laughed at the idea.

On into the day we sailed, back and forth until the sun shut us down. After tying the flaty back on the float and swimming ashore, Tuck trotted up the trail to Little Fisherman's. Again, I found myself at a loss with what to do and where to go, and the day was about to end. I walked into the practically empty snack shop. One or two of our remaining counselors were there, hoping to make it a night. Carol greeted me and said, "It's all quiet now, Gil." I asked, "What are you up to?" Carol answered, "Back home to college." Linda added, "My dad wants this place closed down, then it's back to Avalon." We all said, "See you later," as I stepped out of the snack shop. I wandered down the beach for a while and eventually ended up at my parents' cabin. Dad told me that an Oakland scout called him this morning and wanted me to play in a semi-pro game in two weeks. "Gilly, how's your ankle?"

"It will be fine by then."

"He's really interested in signing you. So be there. I'll get you directions. It's in the San Fernando Valley somewhere."

"Okay, Dad."

Mom spoke up. "It sure is quiet now. I really enjoy these last few days here. I can wind down before going back to teaching." I left and wandered my way through the darkness up to the empty camp. There was just a small light left on in the kitchen. It was getting late, and I didn't want to sleep in the cabin alone. Too scary, so I grabbed a blanket, went to the last room in the dormitory, turned on the television and watched until I got tired, then slipped into one of the backroom bunks. The night was still warm enough to lay on top of the blanket, so I turned off the light, holding onto a flash light just in case. A little later I heard a noise coming from the end of the hallway. It was quiet, then I heard it again. I got up and tiptoed to the door, looked down the hall… nothing. Then, something moved. I raised my hand and turned on the flashlight. Standing there, in the center of the hall was a barefoot girl in Levi's. As my light traveled up her body toward her face, I recognized her. It was Patty. "Patty, what are you doing here?" Now recognizing the voice behind the light, she said, "Gil, is that you?"

"Yeah, what's up?" I asked.

"Well…I went out with a guy, and… it didn't work out. I know my parents will be partying throughout the evening at Little Fish, so could I hang out here for tonight?"

"Sure. I've got some blankets in the backroom. I'll go get…"

She interrupted with a smile, then surprised me by talking hold of my hand and walking us back to where I'd laid out the blanket. "You don't mind do you? It's so warm in here," she said, while sitting down and reaching to the bottom of her sweatshirt. And, with one swift pull, Patty lifted it over her head, leaving her upper body exposed except for a lacy white bra. She laid down and motioned for me to lie next to her. Patty was always too formidable, too intimidating and forward of a girl for me. She'd advanced well ahead of her class through puberty. And, because of this, I guessed she'd had to deal with the demands of older guys. I thought this was probably why she came on with such brashness and ease.

Me, I was always playing catch up. To her, I was like a younger brother or a friend. Even though I was a couple of months older, I think she felt safe with me. We talked a little, as I nestled next to her, more just to keep us warm as the evening air began to chill. We drew even closer. She turned over while talking of nothing and prompted me to unhook her bra and rub her back. I did. It was better than holding hands. She talked about Jody and how I should have given her another chance. But, that didn't distract me from the feeling I got just rubbing her back. The conversation began to get lost in sleep, as she slumbered into shallow breathing. I wondered how long I could take this as I continued. She rolled over onto her back, in casual response to the play of my hands, searching more for comfort, putting her breasts on display but somehow still neatly packaged by the seductive lace bra. I rested my hand across her uncovered skin. She seemed to smile at this gesture, as she breathed out a sigh then slowly turned on her side, away from me, but adjusting her body tightly with mine. Slowly, I too closed my eyes and let my hand come to rest on her bare shoulder.

The next morning came quickly, and, as the light broke through the window, I opened my eyes to find Patty gone. Not even a mention to me. I never really knew what that night meant to her. Probably nothing, just passing the time with a friend. She most likely never even remembered it. I'm glad I never pressed her on it. That would have made it all… less perfect, too complicated. It would have ruined one remarkable night. Interesting thing about that spontaneous sensual interlude, it prompted me to raise the bar. That was as great as it gets. Nothing could be as perfect and as pure as that night. The image it created would never leave me. Best to just leave that one alone, not even try.

I ran down into the kitchen, where the aroma of ham and eggs drew me in. As my mom served them up she said, "You know, Gilly, every year at this time, even more so this year, I feel sad. I know things will never be the same. You guys are all growing up so fast. I'm going to miss you. You'll be the next and last to go, and I'll sit here next year not knowing why I'm really here. Your dad seems to take this better than I do. So please, remember to visit me whenever you get a chance, it will mean a lot."

"I will, Mom." We hugged to hide away a tear. I was about finished with my breakfast when dad walked in. "Okay, Gilly, we need to button everything up today. There's really not much left. Then you and the rest of the counselors will drive into Avalon, give Preston Taylor the rest of the perishables and take the White Steamer home."

"Right, Dad. But first I'm going down to the beach, take a short trip on the flaty, say goodbye to Billy Tuck and then be back to finish up." With his permission, off I went. There was one thing I had left to do. So, I waved to mom and dad, sitting there on the porch, knowing I may never come back.

CHAPTER 35

# The Dive

N ow, there are some very special events in your life, like
kissing your first girl, getting into that first fight or even
riding your first bike. These are events that go above and
beyond memorable. This day would be one of those. But, in order to
understand its importance you had to go back to when it took root.
Back to when Tuck and I fell overboard, and the flaty sailed on to
maroon itself on Bird Rock. Later, when we went back to salvage
it, the inescapable idea dug deep into my soul. After navigating
through slippery bird dung while climbing around Bird Rock, we
eventually arrived to the mainland-view side. It was late afternoon
and the light breeze, as usual for that time of day, kicked up white
caps that punctuated the horizon. It was such a spectacular sight
to see small craft sailing from here to wherever and sails of all
colors randomly taking on the elements. Tuck and I sat there,
captivated by the beautiful montage of Catalina adventures from
a completely different vantage point than we'd ever seen before.
This side of Bird Rock had a uniquely remote and distant feel to
it. After a while, we broke from our trance and went exploring
its cliffs. The seagulls that nested there kept hovering overhead,
attempting to distract us away from their recently laid eggs. We

came to a cliff overhang and gingerly slipped out to its edge. And, that's where and how this feeling began to fester and grow.

Everyone has his or her own way of connecting with the island. Some fish, others dive beneath the sea to enter another world. Some like to skirmish about her surface, camp her out, climb her mountains, ski the bays or sit for hours painting her breathtaking views. We'd experienced all of that, but Tuck and I had one special thing we loved more than any other, one thing we felt tested our skills against those of nature. We loved to find a place high above the water and dive…just dive out. What a thrill, thrusting out into the air, freefalling, and, if done right, plunging through the surface, engaging the ocean below. It became more than just recreation or an adrenalin rush. It became a challenge. Each peak, higher than the last, became a more formidable test of our skill. Something just begged us on. Tuck liked to jump feet first. Me, I loved to fly like the seagulls, propelling myself into the air, stretching my arms out, arching my back and, at the peak of the dive, exposing myself to the blue water below. Like that feeling you get reaching the first mound on a rollercoaster after climbing slowly to the top. It was that anticipation that made the challenge even more worthy. Then there was the fall, falling at a speed that portends danger ahead. At that point the thrill of it becomes the talent. When you dive from the cliff and you're in control of it all, it becomes art…meaningful and personal. The will takes over and, for this brief moment in time, you become the master of your destiny, confirming what you believe of yourself.

What made it so appealing was the grand setting of it all. It would be like challenging the world and winning. Now, I don't know if that made any sense, but that's what I was thinking. Tuck said, "I don't think it's as high as it looks. It's just that you have a small landing place and you have to dive out far enough to clear the rocks." All of this nonsensical chatter worked its way into a planning session while we sailed back to shore, "This is our secret, hey, Tuck?"

"Yep, but Big G., I think we could make it."

"Let's just sit on the idea, and when things really get boring around here, who knows. We just may go out there and beat that baby." It was then the seductive impulse became the seedling for the challenge. Was it all about the height? If we made that dive, then where would it end? Maybe, that would be the end. But none of that negative stuff was discussed openly. That would only give us reason not to do it, and we were too confident to consider that. Nature had to prove herself to us first. Only then, could we be lured away from her pull. But a part of me hoped this misplaced idea, like some of the others, would simply pass away, getting lost among all the other schemes left to do.

However, as days turned into weeks, eating up the summer like a cow grazing in the field and then moving onto the next pasture, this thing, this bold undertaking became an obsession. I needed more room, more space to supply my ego. Oh, if I could only survive this summer and go back without it, it would all end there. But it wouldn't. All I needed was a reason to give into this impulse, but all of Tuck's optimism kept me going forward. Where was Ross now when I needed him most? He would've called this thing crazy, and, maybe this time, I would have given in to his misguided logic. I even started to blame him for not being there when I needed him most. Yet, what the heck, Tuck and I always won out, didn't we? Also, there were those countless nights, waking from the chilling dream of leaping out over the rocks, knowing for the first time I wouldn't make it. But that was in the night, full of darkness and restless sleep. When the day broke, those fears were discarded with the trash. No, this had become my rite of passage. And, like many other things going around at that time, I never knew it. I just felt it. I'd chosen my own war. Now,

I must fight it. So, for days, this thing became a popular topic of Tuck and my conversations. Clearly we knew we'd saved the best for last. And the only thing that troubled me now was, the last day was at hand.

On my way out to the pier to meet Tuck, a friend, Dave Wells, stopped me. Dave had been working with Ty and Birt and, like me, was sometimes compulsive. He loved to drive fast. "Hey Gil, you got time?"

"Sure, Dave, what for?"

"I need to drive to Parson's Landing. Like to come along?"

"Yeah, okay to take Tuck with us?"

"Of course. Meet you at the top of the road."

"Okay!" I said while running off to get Tuck. Soon we both walked up the path to the road that wanders around the cliffs, from the Isthmus to Parson's Landing at the west end.

Once Tuck and I climbed in the truck cab, we were quickly reminded of Dave's reputation for excess speed on these dangerous gravel and dirt roads. He cornered high above the coves creating dust clouds, sure to blind anyone following too close. Even with the thrill of the ride, the view up there was as advertised, beautiful as ever. If you didn't know better, you could easily believe you were at any one of those far away exotic summer locations, Cancun, Hawaii… anywhere. Catalina Island has it all. Each cove surrenders to your sight with its own personality. What made the ride especially fun that day was the distraction from the upcoming dive. So, for a few hours, we buzzed down to Parson's and returned safely back to the Isthmus. Now, it was on to the dive and where that would take us.

Tuck and I slipped into the flaty just past noon, when the sun was high and brilliant on the water, tempting us to drag our feet as we sailed on. The wind was at our back and the sails were full. Tuck mumbled something about downward sailing technique as he made minor adjustments, keeping his eye on the sail. "What the heck are you doing Tuck?" I asked.

"Trying to get us into a dead run," he replied.

"Sounds good to me, but why the hurry? We've got all day."

"No, my dad wants me back to help him load up the Geronimo."

So, there we were, in the small flaty, alone in the bay, heading directly into the white stoic rock. As we came closer, it grew in size and, as before, appeared far more formidable than from shore. For about a half hour or so we worked the perimeter of the rock, where bird droppings overcame the fresh sea air. We moved to the backside and located the cliff where I'd make the dive. Tuck pulled down the sail, putting the boat in a stall. I took out my mask, spit on the glass and made the necessary adjustments. Then, I jumped into the water and swam around, checking for what was below the surface. When I returned I said, "Looks good. It's deep all right. Once I make it over those shore rocks, which shouldn't be too hard, it's all blue water around here. Must drop off 60 or 70 feet. No problem, but getting to the edge of that cliff…well, that's going to be another story. I've just got to walk out there. Plant myself and dive. No waiting around, just clear the rocks."

By now, my heart began to beat faster and my hands began to tingle as I looked up. "Okay Tuck, let's go drop me off, then you come back around here and pick me up after the dive." Tuck pulled out a paddle and rowed the boat up in between two boulders and said, "Gil." (The "Big G." was notably absent.)

"What?" I asked.

"What about your bad ankle?"

With all this going on in my mind, I hadn't worked that one out yet. "What can the dive do, break it off?"

Tuck laughed. "Ross was right. You are crazy!"

"No, Tuck. I can do this." As I stepped out, he backed the flaty off, leaving me clinging to a rock. I found my way around, climbed out of sight and began my ascent. Almost at the top, I stepped on a rock that suddenly gave way. Instinctively I attempted to protect the injured foot and put all my weight on the other. It gave way, turning my ankle with a crack. I had to sit down and rest away the pain.

So there I was, with possibly a fractured foot and definitely a sprained ankle. Why stop now? What's the difference? The dive might be easier. Beats climbing back down the cliffs. I think it was that line of thinking that got me up, but I needed some more convincing to make the dive. I was just about to arrive at the summit when I stopped to enjoy the sight of all of the seagulls flinging about. I looked down to see them gliding with the wind and chirping at me. No way. Could they actually be cheering me on? Finally, I reached the edge and, for the first time, Tuck came into view. He saw me and waved up. I sat down, feeling little pain in my foot and ankle now; they'd left my thoughts completely. I had something else contending for my attention. I sat there examining, taking in and strategizing the dive. I had no problem with this part. It was just the doing. I'd done this before. Still, heights always scared me. Funny thing, when there was water at the bottom and I knew was in control, it didn't bother me as much. Maybe that's why I never liked flying. I was never in control.

All that was gone now. I just needed one last prompting. I reached into my mind, which could hardly be heard above the loud pounding of my heart. I needed to discipline myself now. I heard dad's voice echoing in my mind. "It's easy to hit a 90-mile-an-hour fastball in a batting cage, but with a 3-and-2 count in the bottom of the ninth and with two outs in front of 40,000 roaring fans... now that's a different thing. How you handle that will define your character, and I can't help you there. It's all up to you." Knowing I could never let him down, I got to my feet. I told myself, "All I have to do is take five steps, plant and thrust out." I began by taking a slow hobbling step forward. I knew then, there was no going back. It didn't matter if it was a 100-foot drop or 10 feet. It just didn't matter. It was all going to stop right here. No more questioning. Then, as if choreographed, after my last step, I planted both feet. All I remembered was the echo coming from down below, "Big G., you can do it," as if Tuck were chiming in with the birds that now definitely cheered me on. They must have known what it was all about.

Clearly in the end, it was all of them who pulled me over the cliff that day. Tuck, my dad and all the others that encouraged me along the way. I soared higher than ever before, opening into a magnificent swan dive so high I seemed to float out there forever. Before peaking, I kept form with my body arching high above the waiting sea, stretching out my hands as far as my arms could take them, to show the world it wasn't just survival I had in mind. No, I needed to make my statement of who I was and who I thought I was. Maybe they'd be one in the same. After all, it didn't matter what the rest thought.

That day I knew, once I reached that peak, I'd begin to fall back into the reality of the thing. But it wouldn't matter from here on. For I'd taken something from the day that could never be taken back.

# Catalina Summer
## sketches of the past

### Part Four

CHAPTER 36

# Wake-Up Call

It was 3 a.m., and I found myself pounding away on my computer keyboard, again. A new message pop-up notice came on my screen. Usually I wait, but my wife had sent it. What the heck? So I clicked in to find out my principal Marta Machin had called late yesterday and wanted me to come back to campus as soon as possible. "No way," I thought. I had five more days left on my vacation, and I really didn't want to go back before that. While eating breakfast my wife asked, "Did you get my e-mail about Marta?"

"Tricky idea, emailing that message."

"Well, it's the only way any of us around here can get your attention lately. No one wants to interrupt the fun you're having up there writing."

"Yeah, you're probably right. But, in my defense, when the idea is there, I've got to put it down. I'll call her at nine… too early now. Oh, and by the way, to resolve your concerns about me spending too much time on the book, I think I've got this one licked. It's just about finished off. Got only a couple of chapters left. Then, that's where you'll come in, to edit. Sounds like fun, hey?"

"Yeah, just like your others. Real fun. I hope this one won't have as much drama."

"No it won't. You're getting used to my style." Her crinkled nose made me think she needed a little pep talk. "Besides, you're really getting good at it. Could be a new career for you when we retire."

"Lord I hope not," she said while smiling, and she kissed me on the cheek.

I returned to the computer to put the last touches on my morning's work. When I got to the top of the stairs I yelled down, "Tell anyone who calls I'm still asleep. I'll call back later. Okay? Hey, are you listening?"

"Yeah, I got it. You're asleep."

Not very confident she'd lie for me, I went back into my office to finish up with a thought. When I attempted to do that, minutes could easily turn into hours. I heard Marcia call up, "You've got to pick up the phone. It's your Marta, and she sounds frantic."

Darn. "Okay, I'll take it up here. Good morning, Marta. What can I do for you?"

"Good morning Giiilll," she greeted, in her Cuban English. "I'm sorry for calling you on your vacation."

"Me too," I thought.

She went on. "But I need your help."

"What's up, Marta?"

"When B-Track came back in session…we allowed some 43rd Street kids in."

"No way! Didn't Randy and the other campus police tell you not to mix 18th and 43rd streets? Geez, Marta, that's like putting an ignition switch into a bar of C-4!"

"Well, it's too late now," she said with obvious concern.

"So, Marta, what do you want me to do?"

"I hoped you could come to school today." There was a long

silent pause. "I'll pay you Z time, you know the higher salary scale."

Again I asked, "What would you want me to do?"

"Giiilll, you can get the news out around campus to keep the trouble down, just until we work things out between these two gangs. You're so good with those kids."

"But, Marta, you can't work things out between those guys. It's not going to happen. Just let campus police take care of it. I'm sure they've got a handle on it. You just need to listen to them." Again, there was a long awkward pause.

"But, Giiilll, I don't want this thing to become a gang-related issue."

"Listen, Marta, it already is. No matter how you move on this, it's going to become public. But, if you let Randy and the LAPD pull out the 43rd members and hold them, at least you won't have an incident that will make the LA Times. A large portion of the school is 18th Street. It's their territory. That's the reality of the situation."

"But Giiilll, I still need your help today."

"Okay, okay. I'll come in, but it won't be until after lunch, and it's going to be only for the day. I've got another five days until I go back on track. Anyway, Marta, we've got over 4,000 kids registered at Belmont. I'm most familiar with the C-Track kids.

"I know, but please come in as soon as you can," she pleaded.

"Okay, but in the meantime, listen to Randy. He's good with this stuff. That's why he's head of our campus security."

"Thanks so much, Giiilll." Obviously relieved, she hung up.

"Marcia, I've got to go in, just for today."

"For what?"

"I've got to hold Marta's hand. So, when I come back, start figuring how we can get lost for the next few days, until this thing blows over at Belmont." After an early lunch, I grabbed my briefcase and hopped on the 5 Freeway going north from San Juan Capistrano. It takes about 95 minutes in good traffic and half a day in bad. There was a lot of time to think about my past experience. How did I become this facilitator/ teacher or whatever they called me to Latino gangs? Maybe it was working with gangs at Redondo Beach Parks and Recreation Department or my years of teaching at the Los Pinos Detention Facility in the Capistrano Mountains. Whatever the reason, I had to admit, it seemed as if I knew what they were thinking before they thought it.

I got off at the Main Street exit, went west a few blocks and then entered Belmont High's secured parking lot just in time, because it was about to be locked up as standard precaution after lunch. I drove my Ford Escort with its two cracked windows into my spot. It looked like it had been through hell and back, but there was no way I was going to risk taking my other car downtown in this area, especially as a teacher. Things happened pretty quickly down here. I got out of my car and ran into one of my favorite colleagues, Dave Lawrence. "What are you doing here? Can't stay away? Not enough action at home?" Dave asked.

"No, our principal called, and I couldn't get out of it. So, Dave, what's going on here?"

"I guess you didn't drive around front when you came in."

"No."

"Then you missed all the excitement. Marta let the 43rd guys enroll on B-Track. Randy and the boys told her that wasn't a good idea. But, Marta, as always, knew best and predictably, at the beginning of lunch, 43rd Street got jumped by 18th and all hell broke loose. Security jumped in, but there were just too many things going on at once. Forty-third ran into the administration office and Michaels, the assistant principal, got caught up in it all and kind of got hurt."

"Not like the night school principal? They could hardly

recognize him after the beating he took."

"No, Michaels got only a few bruises. His pride was wounded more than anything else. But this thing just continued on, and you know LAUSD's response."

"I know. There are no gangs on LAUSD campuses."

"Of course Marta called the attorneys first and then asked Randy to call in backup, which, of course, he already had. Everything's starting to quiet down now since the ambulance has left. But, there are still some small fires to put out." As we climbed the steps, he continued to fill me in. Dave and I walked across the flats among students rushing to class while security, like Australian sheep dogs, kept them moving in the right direction. The late bell rang and the hallways vacated to silence. Dave went back into his room, and I stepped down the stairwell leading to the main floor. Belmont's built on the side of a mountain and has an unusual maze of staircases. If you're not familiar with them, you could easily get lost, and that wouldn't be a good idea at this high school. I wandered into the main office to see secretaries going about their business. Katrina, Marta's assistant, looked up to greet me. "Lefebvre, great to see you. Marta's been waiting for you."

"So where is she?"

"Not sure. She's out and about. Just a second, I'll check." And, like a commando in the field, she whipped out the walkie-talkie she had strapped to her side. "Marta where are you? Lefebvre's here. Over." Through some static, I could hear her familiar voice come back. "Send him down here to the health office, and tell him to hurry up." I turned and went down the hall but, before I got to the health office, Marta stepped out. "Lefebvre, I need your help, come with me." We went a few doors down, and she showed me into a room where the school nurse was putting the finishing touches on a Latino male student. The bleeding had been stopped, and it didn't look critical. Marta whispered, "We need to get him down to the health office without anyone seeing us."

Marta had taken over Belmont's principal position, with very little or no senior high experience. She'd been one of those politically handpicked appointments, made by some wannabe superintendents, and placed in a Latino–majority, inner-city school. And, in of all places, Belmont, mostly to buttress the idea LAUSD was attempting educational reforms. Therefore, any adverse publicity wasn't going to help out their obvious politically correct placement. Also, remember the zero tolerance thing? Well, it was a zero.

For the moment, our mission was to move the bloodied kid down the hallway and into the health office undetected, while Marta ran down to her office to call the district attorneys for advice, again. After leaving him there, I went back to Marta's office. As she talked on the phone, she opened the door and motioned me to sit down. Marta was always such an impeccably dressed lady who paraded around school in matching dress and pantsuits. They all were accentuated by colorful varieties of Latin blouses, and she always sported the finest brand name shoes. Her hair was flawlessly styled as were her manicured nails. She was a nice lady, but at Belmont punctuality and fashion weren't necessary perquisites for strong leadership. It was her lack of common sense and her propensity toward political protocol that found her out of place here. While Marta finished up her conversation, Randy, our LAPD campus police officer, stepped in. Marta motioned him to sit down next to me. "So Lefebvre, you missed all this, hey?" Randy said with a warm smile. I just rolled my eyes. Marta set down the phone and said, "So Randy, what's happening here?"

"Well, Marta, we warned you about letting 43rd on campus."

Marta replied, "But they looked harmless, and somebody's got to take a chance on them. All kids want to learn, if given an opportunity."

"Sure, Marta. Lefebvre, look at this learning tool," Randy said sarcastically as he took a long switchblade from his jacket. "This is what we took off of one of those 43rd kids, who just wanted a chance. But, ah gee whiz, I guess he's just going through some troubling times. Marta, if you're not going to listen to us, why have us around?"

"You police people don't understand. I'm running this school, not LAPD," Marta said with a quivering voice.

"You're wrong again, Marta. When we're talking security decisions, we make the final calls!" Randy said loudly and then turned to me. "Remember, Lefebvre, Marta allowed every gang member on campus to be extras in that gangster movie, True Colors. Add that to the list of bright ideas from this administration!"

"Now Randy…" Marta interrupted.

"Enough of this. I'm out of here. See you later, Lefebvre." And with that Randy stood to leave but turned around and slammed the blade down on Marta's desk. "Here, Marta, give this back to the opportunity-seeking 43rd Street kid. He'll probably need this to cut up his sandwich at tomorrow's lunch." After Randy walked out and slammed the door behind him, I sat there in awkward silence with a visibly angry principal. She plopped down in her large principal chair and began to cry. "Look what I have to deal with, Giiilll."

I waited for her to stop sobbing and look up at me. "Marta, if you're not going to take their advice, what do you expect?"

She took some tissue out and said, "I'm working on getting Randy and his guys reassigned to another school."

"Geez, Marta, that's not going to help the situation here at Belmont. They're not the problem. Anyway, I missed it all, Marta. No need for me today. I'm heading on home. And, I have important plans that can't be changed. So, you won't see me until next Monday." We both stood, and I turned to leave.

"Thanks for coming in, Giiilll."

"Why? I didn't do anything."

"Still, you know the kids so well here, and you make things easier for me."

I walked out of her office and passed by Katrina. "You and Marta work everything out?" she asked.

"Yah, riiight," I said, knowing she knew what I meant.

On my way to the parking lot, I stopped by Dave's classroom and opened the door to a quiet setting. His students were taking a test, so Dave motioned me in. He asked in a low voice, "So, what have you been doing these last few months?

"Let's see…I've been writing again."

"Another political theory book?"

"Nah, I'm not sure, maybe more like a journal about things when I was in Catalina."

"Really? You were in Catalina? For what?"

"My dad had a baseball camp there for some time, and I spent almost every summer on the island. That's what I've been writing about."

"Have you ever gone back?"

"No, not really," I said, but changed my mind. "You know, I think I've probably gone back every day."

"Wow, that sounds pretty deep."

"Yah, I've never gone back to the Isthmus physically though."

"Why not? Is it too expensive on a teacher's salary?" he asked jokingly.

"No, I've never had a reason. Practically everybody I know is gone. What's there to go back for?"

"Well you won't know until you do. And, just think about it, you wrote about the place, so maybe you ought to go back, just to see if you got it right."

We said goodbyes. I left, got into my car and drove away. I

put the drama of the day far back in my mind. No use talking to anybody about what happens inside those gates. Who'd believe me if I did? So, on that nice sunny day driving back down the I-5, I started to review my conversation with Dave. Why not? Why not go back to the island? Maybe I left something there, and I'll find it again. Or, find something I never knew was there and see it for the first time. Or, more likely, see how flawed my memory is. I just needed an excuse to be gone. I could book a last-minute Mexican cruise to nowhere. I could always go up north to see my daughter in Seattle or my other daughter in Monterey. But, back to Catalina? It's been so long. Yet, the closer to home I got, the more the idea began to find legs and run through my mind. Why not? By the time I drove up my driveway, I decided to run it by my wife and see what she thought. I walked into the house to find my wife sitting out back reading. I greeted her with a kiss, and she asked, "How's Belmont and Marta this fine day?"

"Everything's normal. Nothing unusual. Hey, I was talking to Dave Lawrence," now framing my proposal in the best light I could, "and, he said since I spent most of our vacation writing about nostalgic stuff that happened so long ago, it was sort of surprising I'd never been back to the Isthmus. I didn't have a good answer so..." Now putting it in her lap, I asked "Why not go back? It would be fun. Just for a few days?"

She surprised me by quickly answering, "Yeah, that's a great idea. Take a few days and maybe even call Ross. See if you can talk him out of the office."

"Talk Ross out of work? Tough trick, but since he likes you better than me, maybe if you came along?"

"No, not me. Someone's got to supervise our remaining kid and, besides, I'm already going to a women's retreat this weekend."

"But that's this weekend. We'll be back by then."

"So, what would I do while you and Ross tell those same old

stories over and over again?"

"Hey, after you see where they happened, you just might like the place. There's probably no need to worry about it though. The Ross thing won't happen. He'll be busy as usual."

Off I went up to my computer again, but before I started, I checked my e-mails and jotted down a message to Ross about the trip. After pushing send, I began to write on in the journal, book or whatever it was becoming. About 10 minutes later the phone rang. "Get it, Marcia," I yelled down the stairs. "Whoever it is, tell them I'm out, busy." A few minutes later, Marcia yelled up, "It's Ross."

"What? Okay, I got it. Hey, Ross, no meeting today? Is your company going broke, or did you get fired? And, if there's no meeting, what are you there for?" I laughed, letting him know I was joking. As usual he, didn't laugh back.

"No, damn it. Shut up for a minute. Hey, I like the Catalina idea. I can get away for a few days. Why don't you see if you can arrange for a stay at the Banning House? There won't be any problems getting on the Express this time of year. Look into it, Gil."

"Okay."

"Call me later, when you've got it booked. Bye."

"Bye. Hey Marcia! Did you hear the conversation?"

"Yes."

"Get to work and see if you can get this thing going."

CHAPTER 37

# The Return

At five o'clock in the morning, you can bet the house it will be foggy in the San Pedro Harbor, and it was. Ross arrived right on time, stepped out of his silver Lexus and motioned me over to help with his luggage. Looking out into the early morning fog, he said, "Nothing's changed around here. You'd think after 50 years we'd get a clear start."

"Hey, at least we're not taking the old water taxi. Remember?" I asked.

"How could I forget? It took me days to recover every time I took one," Ross said.

Marcia came over and handed out the Express tickets. I grabbed coffee for everyone, and we all sat down inside the terminal to wait for the boarding call. After a while, Ross got up and walked to a window overlooking the harbor. Noise from cars running over steel plates on the St. Thomas Bridge could be heard as horns, screeching tires and even a siren began to seep into the senses. The smell from the old fisheries up the channel added to its nuances and began to jar the memories. When I stood up alongside of him, he said, "What an awful smell."

I took a deep breath. "Yeah, some things don't change, not

around here anyway."

"Seems like a lifetime ago," Ross said.

"Yeah, it has been a while."

"Remember the girls? That's the last time we left from here. Man, Gil, it's hard to remember that far back."

"Well, Ross, I'll bet you have vivid memories of that night in the tent."

He looked at me with his usual grin and said, "You still haven't let up on that."

"What was her name, Carla? Oh no, it was Kimberly. Yeah that was it." He looked over at me and smiled. I asked, "Did you ever see her again?"

"Yeah, no… well, I called her once, but, hey, it was different when we were the only males around." We both laughed at that. Our conversation was interrupted when, over the intercom, we heard the announcement. "The 6 a.m. Catalina Express to Two Harbors is now boarding." We gathered our luggage and queued up with a few others. Stepping aboard, we handed our stuff off to one of the crew and then went looking for a good seat. Ross found three together on the top deck. "Even though it's chilly out here until the sun comes out, I'll risk sitting on the outside, rather than face the prospect of becoming queasy from the ride over," he said.

Marcia slid in alongside him and closed her eyes for a few more minutes of rest before taking off. Finally, all preparations ended and the boat began to pull out of the terminal, gradually adjusting its course into the main channel while passing under the St. Vincent Bridge. Wide awake now, Marcia took out her camera and began clicking photos of Ports Of Call Village and the fisheries as we glided by and saw boats unloading their catch of the day. Next, we passed the women's prison, and, for the first time, the sun began to breach the lingering fog. Little by little we could see the outline of the San Pedro breakwater. Ross and

I stared out there, smelling the tainted air. An odd odor, but we didn't mind so much. For it seemed to work as a catalyst that inadvertently took our senses back to another time.

And then, as if ambushed out of the latent mist that hung around, the roar of the lighthouse horn blasted across the bow. Our thoughts let loose, becoming elusive and animated, as the sun finally broke through. Ross said, "I thought this boat was fast." The Express captain must have been listening because immediately the boat propelled full throttle into the channel. Ross smiled as I said, "Told you so." The Express began to challenge the moderate swells, overcoming them one by one, kicking up spray that scented the air, bringing it all back. We both became consumed with thought. About what? About everything. In moments like these, no need for conversation. I was with my best friend, my only wife and on my way to paradise.

Marcia put her camera away and stepped up to hold onto the rail with Ross. "Are you guys starting to tell those same old stories again yet?"

Hearing the question, I jumped in. "No need to. We're going to be there in 35 minutes and then show you around as proof of life..." Before finishing my statement, the island came into full view. It was as if we were sailing a pirate ship, hunting down some exotic paradise, finally revealing itself and almost taking our breath away. Later, when Bird Rock popped up from the horizon, a tear began to form. But, of course, I kept that to myself and thought about the day I'd left my mark. I could see Billy Tuck in the flaty looking up at me. But, I wasn't about to explain. That was something only between us.

We pressed on into the harbor. Our excitement grew and, like all good tour guides, I pointed out the most prominent landmarks. "There's Big Fisherman and Little Fisherman coves. Oh, and there's the path Tuck used to walk to the Isthmus. And see over there? That was the road where we ran back that night after we raided the scouts. Remember Ross?" Marcia inhaled all my gestures, knowing how much this meant to me and actually looking interested. Just before we were about to dock, she asked, "Where's this Mt. Lebushtuck?"

Ross laughed. "He told you about that day?"

"Over and over again."

"Did he tell you he almost killed us with those rocks?"

"Hey, you're still here aren't you, Ross?" I asked.

As the Express docked, Ross went on. "Gosh, Marcia, we did this so many times. Bringing the campers over, riding the Blanche and diving for coins. Oh, and right up there on the pier, that's where your husband and Randall really got into it."

"But, what a great night that night, hey, Ross?"

Ross blushed, then said with a big smile, "Gilly, you'll never know how good it was."

"Inside joke?" Marcia asked, and we both nodded. After unloading, we walked up the plank and stood at the end of the pier. Sketches began to paint their way into my mind. I couldn't have kept them out if I'd wanted to. From there, we paused to take in the view of the beach. The volleyball court was still on the right and, on the left, it opened to the old Round House and the Wild Goose Lodge with the iconic snack bar and restaurant patio in the center. "There it is, Marcia. Take a picture." She did, and we started walking off the pier. Ross stopped for a moment and said, "Marcia, see the dinghy dock down there? We used to dive over it into a small opening. Remember, Gil?"

"Yeah, that was crazy, and there's where I got paid by tourists to make shallow dives." We kept walking. "There's the harbor master's office where Doug, Audrey and Carol kept busy making sure all ran well in the bay." Next to it were a few trucks, and one waited for us. "Lefebvre party, right?"

"Yeah, that's us."

We handed our luggage off, and he tossed it in the back of the truck. "First time here?" he asked.

"No." I said, and then changed my mind. "Well, yes. Actually, we've never stayed at the Banning House before. Last time I was here, it was the girls' camp and Lady Cruikshank never let us near it."

"Jump in. I'll give you a ride up there," he offered.

"No, thanks. I think we'd rather walk."

"You know, it is just up the road about a half-mile," he said.

"I think we can find it."

Off he went, leaving us a few yards out in front of the snack bar entrance. "There it is… as advertised, the Isthmus restaurant and snack shop. Not much had changed. "Hey, Ross, there are a little more bricks out here, but not much more. Let's go in and see what it looks like. Marcia, this was the place where the weekend crowds gathered. Out there was where Ty Ewing and the Bombard kids would play late into the warm evenings." We entered the snack shop. Linda, Carol and the others were gone, of course. A girl with a sweet smile asked, "May I help you?"

"No, not now, just looking around. Been here a long time ago, from the baseball camp."

The girl, not knowing if that was the name of our boat or a campsite, didn't take notice. She just continued on, "Well, we have fresh bakery items if you're going to be around in the morning."

"Sounds great."

"I hope you enjoy the Isthmus. Are you staying at the Banning House?"

We all nodded yes.

"I'm sure you'll enjoy your stay."

"How long have you been working here?" I asked.

"This is my second summer."

"Do you like it?"

"Sometimes."

Marcia asked, "Doesn't it get lonely?"

"No, not around summer. I think I'll stay a couple more months and probably move on."

I stopped her before she started in on a speech about the local tourist sights. We moved out of the snack shop and wandered into the infamous back bar where John Wayne, cowboy Jack White and Ward Bond would shoot at the ceiling with live ammo.

"Gil, was that really true?" Marcia asked.

"I don't know... probably half true. But, it's a great story isn't it? Although, this really is the actual bar where Cliff Tucker jumped on top and opened up every summer, with drinks all around." We made our way out to the patio. "Marcia, this is where us young studs made our play. Although, now that I think about it, we weren't really as good as we thought we were. At least, I wasn't, hey, Ross?"

He smiled. "Now, why do you keep bringing that up, Gilly?"

"No, it's Big G.... remember?" I asked.

"That damn Billy Tuck. You two drove me crazy."

Marcia said, "I know, Ross. I've been married to the guy for over 40 years."

Ross put his arm around her and said, "Marcia, I've always thought you must be a saint or angel to make that happen."

"Riiight," I said, with probably too much sarcasm. "Let's get up to the Banning House and change into something cooler. It's getting pretty hot."

They agreed, and we walked up the road on the left side of the snack bar. About half way up, I pointed and said, "See, over there? That was the camp." Little had changed. In fact, the tennis courts we used as batting cages and the yellow house still stood as relics. "We'll go and take a look later."

At the apex of the dirt road we saw a little red schoolhouse, donated by Cliff and Mirabelle Tucker, Tuck's parents. We stopped and read the plaque in front. Nice, but it hit me. Outside of the beautiful, natural landmarks, there was little documentation of the people that came before.

After passing the old Civil War barracks, still serving as the yacht club, we turned left and walked a few hundred yards up a winding road to the Banning House. Perched on top of a bluff, it gives guests the advantage of overlooking the front and back bays at the same time. You can relax out on the porch, taking in the Isthmus charm. But, for us, we needed to press on with our tour. Agreeing to venture back to Cat Harbor first, we rented some bikes. That would help us cover more ground in the little time we had. After gathering snacks from our bags, we were off.

I led us down toward the main dirt road, the one going from the Isthmus bay to the back harbor. And, there it was. The lecherous road that Ross and I would race down almost every day, either in the truck or running with the campers. I couldn't help but say, "Remember this road, Ross? Wow, how many times did I scare your pants off, right here?"

"Too many!"

We went on, heading into Cat Harbor and stopping just about 100 yards before we hit the shore. Again I pointed, this time to a patch of sand blended with dirt, neglected by time and weather. Marcia asked, "What is it?"

"What is it?" I repeated indignantly. "That's the baseball diamond, and, right here where we're standing is the 300-foot mark."

"Can't imagine that being a baseball field," Marcia said.

"I can," I said while looking out at the memory. It was incredible. I could see my dad kneeling down to talk with me as I sat on the bench. "Now, Gilly. They're going to try and take you off the plate with the fastball. If that intimidates you…well I guess you can try and make a good living playing the piano."

More images appeared as I looked out at the diamond. Kids, counselors, I could see them all and tried hard to remember names. After a while, I suggested we move on. There was much more to see. Humor quickly replaced nostalgia when I looked over into the blue water of Cat Harbor and said with a big smile, "Jimmy Brown's spear must be out there somewhere."

Ross added, "I bet that poor shark's been carrying that thing around for over 50 years." We all laughed at the thought. Marcia pulled out a bottle of Beringer's from her backpack and passed around paper cups. I uncorked and she poured. Marcia said, "Let's make a toast," while offering some to Ross.

"No thanks."

"Why?"

"Because he's so damn particular, that's why. He only drinks red. That's the Italian in him," I said with a chuckle. But, probably just to show me, he gave in. We sipped for a while and moved on, walking our bikes across the field. "Now that's another place where Tuck and Gilly almost killed me, again. Right on that jetty. There was an old Chinese trawler. I whacked my nose, and Gilly screwed up his ankle."

"Yeah, but, we got them, didn't we?" I added.

"Yeah, we did," Ross explained sarcastically. "Just poor old fishermen trying to make a living."

We sipped down a little more wine and mellowed on. After riding out to the farthest point of the harbor, we could see the backside of Catalina. Its rugged terrain burst up from the ocean and waves splashed wildly as they encountered the island shore. Ross spoke up, "Way down there off of that point is Little Harbor, and somewhere between here and there, Gilly almost killed half the campers."

"No way! You've got it wrong. I didn't. That was not my idea. That was the shithead counselor's idea."

"Okay, okay, but, hey, we did go along with it."

"And, we were lucky to make it back alive, Ross. I think God loved us more on that day. Up there somewhere, Billy Bones fell into the cactus patch and that big black cat and the woman showed up."

"Woman…what woman?" Marcia asked.

"We never knew, some hiker maybe? Whoever she was, I believe she helped us out that day."

The clouds began to attack the afternoon sunlight, so we retreated back to the Isthmus bay side, stopping only to show Marcia where the trees stood. And, from that vantage point, as we stopped in the middle of the baseball field, we could imagine how Channel Airlines gave daily shows, attempting to dodge those tall obstacles as the planes approached the back bay. Next, we went up the road closer to the eucalyptus trees. "That's where they hung the horse! Now that was a scary thing," Ross said.

"But, it put an end to our competition. Didn't it, Ross?"

One last refill of wine was poured and we traveled on, feeling pretty good as we came up on the haunted yellow house. "There's a lot of tales passed down about that place. Right, Ross?"

"Yep. I always hated to go out to the restroom at night after hearing Linda tell those scary stories."

"You didn't have to. Remember, Ross? We cut the hole in the cabin."

"You didn't tell Marcia about that too?"

"About what?" she asked.

"Nothing. Just another inside joke," I explained. Now, it was on to where it all happened, the main dormitory, however it's since been chopped up into little housing units for Isthmus employees. After dropping off our bikes, Ross walked around looking for the Mona Lisa window. It wasn't there. It had been lost in the modifications. The main steps were also gone, but the building was still there. Visions began to pop into my mind, recreating how it was, and I had to hide the tears finding their way into my eyes again. I'm not sure why. I'm not normally prone to this sort of behavior. I guess I needed them to flush out this wonderful past. We saw a guy coming out of one of the rooms. After chatting awhile, he described the co-ed housing for the local workers. After I told him it used to accommodate over 100 baseball campers, he said with a smile, "It's more like a brothel around here now."

"Sad commentary on the times," I thought. But, then I told Ross, "I don't know. Maybe we were just the same. After all, we did chase a few young women of our own. I just hope that we had a little more respect or at least weren't as open about it…hiding our flaws a bit better."

"So, where was this infamous cabin of yours?" Marcia asked. We walked around only to find prefabricated buildings in its place. "Ah, remember the party we threw for you?" I asked Ross. I think that's when he began to choke up. He remembered all right. "And, Ross, there's where the half-tents were." No need to say more. He knew what went on there. We continued working our way back to the snack shop. After making our selections, we sat out on the patio to enjoy. Ross finally got his red wine and we mingled in conversation over all that had gone on before. The breeze picked up, and the palm trees began to whistle their songs. We shared thoughts, like some kind of group therapy. But it wasn't that at all. It was finding our young hearts again, if only for this afternoon. Where to go from here? Who knew? We were simply content for the moment in this place, where we started. It was a part of Ross and my roots.

The day turned into late afternoon, and the sun showed signs of tiring. Marcia suggested we walk to the Banning House for warmer clothes, then come on back down to have dinner in the restaurant. "Great idea! In all my years here, I've never eaten in the restaurant." Ross agreed with the plan, but, when we got up to go, I suggested, "Hey, Marcia. Why don't you go grab some jackets for Ross and me, and we'll wander up to the mountain above Little Fisherman's together?"

Ross laughed. "What? Not Mt. Lebushtuck. I was lucky to survive the first time. No way I'm going to try again. I'll just go back with Marcia."

"Great view, Ross."

"No, Gilly. You go on ahead. Marcia and I will meander back to the Banning House and discuss how she's made it this long with you."

"Okay, be that way."

"Hope you make it back. Don't count on us to come looking for you," Ross called over his shoulder.

I followed the old path to Little Harbor, then on up to the point. Finally reaching the top, I looked out at the amazing sight. I wished I'd brought Marcia's camera. It always amused me to see all the photo buffs shuffling around American treasures with tripods and such, attempting to somehow recreate their image of the place, thereby vicariously taking some credit from the creator. However, no need for that, God was here that day. Up there on the same mountain I'd left over 50 years ago, thinking of my thoughts back then, I pondered how life doesn't always come out as planned.

A group of scouts scrambled up and sat down beside me. They shared their island camping ventures, and I passed on some of my own. Their interest caused me to babble on, lying and exaggerating about a variety of events. It helped refresh my memories.

As the conversation began to sputter and the boys went about their exploring, a nice-looking girl, probably in her late 20s stood by me and said, "I remember the baseball camp. Gosh there are all kinds of stories of those wonderful boys."

"You remember?" I asked.

"Yes I do."

Astonished at that, I asked, "You remember way back then?"

"Sure, my family's been around the island for years, and we'd talk about things. When I was younger, I got to know the island well. See out there?"

"You mean Bird Rock?"

"Yes, there's a legend early natives would bring their young men out there. And, as a rite of passage, they would dive off its back cliff. If they survived, that was a good thing."

I sat stunned at the story. She looked into my eyes, and asked, "Have you ever been out there?"

"Yes."

"I know…I know why young men go there." Abruptly, she jumped out of that thought and began talking about Karl, the hermit from the quarry, Big Al and Birt.

"So you've been all over the island then?" I asked.

"Mostly where people come and go, camp and such."

"Have you been down to Ben Weston?"

"Yes," she said with a sad smile.

"You know it used to be a ranch way back."

"I know, I had a boyfriend when I was in my early teens. We'd spend days down there. Loved it. Did you know there's a black panther running wild around the island?"

"Really? I saw one on the backside while hiking with campers way back when. It can't be still around. Guess it is must be part of her litter."

"Very dangerous back there on the cliffs," she said.

"Boy don't I know it."

"But you made it back. You're here," she said with a smile.

"Yea, I am at that."

"Well, it's been nice talking to you. I heard you with the scouts. It's seldom anyone comes around who remembers the history of the place." She got up, walked away and then turned to say, "Hope to see you here again someday."

I continued to gaze out at the bay and let my mind mingle with the wind and bounce on the whitecaps that came to play.

Just as the sun found its way behind the island, reminding me how dark it gets here at the Isthmus, I made it back to the restaurant. Dinner was surprisingly tasty, and, after another glass of wine, Ross and I reminded Marcia of the John Wayne stories. After that, we moved to the patio, where we met some older sailing couples who talked a good game about the past. We threw in a few names ourselves, but the baseball camp... well, maybe they might have heard about it. A small group of Boy Scouts bought some hamburgers and malts, then nestled around the patio with their gear piled alongside. I recognized them, and one came over to say, "Hi." He described how they'd stay at Cherry Cove overnight then some of them would go down to Parson's for a few more days. After goodbyes all around, they walked on.

"They seemed like nice boys. Where did you meet them?" Marcia asked.

"Up on Mt. Lebushtuck today. They listened to my stories. Oh, I forgot. Listen to this, Ross. One of the counselors, leader or whatever, told me about a black panther roaming around the island. Remember the thing we thought was a huge wild black cat, on the hike back from Little Harbor?"

"Yeah."

"She says it's still here!"

"You're kidding."

"No. She told me it was left by some boaters... Man, what an interesting girl."

"Lady or girl?" Marcia asked.

"Come to think of it, I really couldn't say. I was too caught up in the conversation, probably somewhere between her mid-20s and mid-30s. Will that do?" Ross laughed, and I added, "Don't do that Ross. Or, I'll start talking about your friend Kimberly."

"Kimberly?" Marcia teased.

Ross blushed. "Don't believe him."

"Okay, then let's move on," I said, making my point.

Later, Ross, Marcia and I wandered out to the pier to have dessert. It was an unusually warm night for this late in the season. The moon beamed across the water, and, for just a few moments, we deceived ourselves. Standing there, finding little to distract us we entered into a world we wished it to be.

Early next morning, after dropping our luggage at the end of the pier, it was off for some coffee, then a stroll along the beach. "Hey, Ross, this is about the place."

"What place?"

"The place where we put the rocks under Father James's sleeping bag." We both smiled, and I added, "A rather blasphemous deed."

"Let's chart it up to misguided youth," he justified. I looked up to the housing structures on the hill. "That's old Birt's house. He sure helped us out with the smugglers, didn't he, Ross?"

"Yes, he did."

My mind let me float back again, and I said to Marcia, "That's where Shirley, Birt's daughter, would ride Joey. What a horse. I loved riding but nobody rode like Shirley. Funny, sometimes it's the little things you remember, her running with that horse down that road." Then I turned and looked at the three cabins where Big Al and Phyllis stayed those many years. They never really spent much time there, for they were always out looking for something new on the island, a brand new experience that they'd share with us. My thoughts rushed back to the last cabin. There it was, mom and dad's retreat from the goings-on at the camp. Mom would sit on the porch, crochet and read just about anything. Dad would be sitting on the bed fingering through some sports magazine, trying always to figure it out. I walked up to an open door, looked inside and saw that it was vacant. What a poignant symbol. For, in the last two days I had seen the familiar places, but what was missing were the people. Time left them out. They weren't here. There was nothing to remember them by, like the old trawler in the back bay. Who'd remember? In time we'd all be forgotten.

Seeing the Express pass in front of Bird Rock, we drifted back to the pier. She docked and, before we walked down the plank leading to the boat, taking us away again, Marcia asked us to stop for a photo. Ross and I, with arms over each other's shoulders, posed for one more. With one final look at the front of the Isthmus, we turned down the plank to enter the Express. She slowly pulled away as we found our seats. Marcia called us up to the back of the boat where we stood in awe at the sight. One of the scouts stepped in and asked, "Would you like me to take a picture with you all together?"

"Sure," we agreed, and he took the shot.

I said, "Hey, these are some of the guys I talked to on Mt. Lebushtuck, when the girl told me about the black panther." I asked the scout, "By the way, is she on the boat with your group?" He looked puzzled. I shot back, "The girl that was with you guys yesterday on the mountain up there, now pointing to Mt. Lebushtuck."

"A girl? We didn't have a girl with us."

"But, I talked to her myself."

"Hey, you might have talked to a girl, but I can guarantee she wasn't with us."

"Did you see me talk to her?"

"No, not really. In fact, when we left the bluff, we saw you alone sitting there looking out to the ocean."

"Oh, well… thank you for taking the picture of us."

"You're welcome." He smiled, then went back inside. Marcia suggested we go in as well. "It's too windy out here."

"Okay, you two go ahead. I'll be there in a minute." They left and I stood there, still trying to make something out of this girl thing. Then, as we passed Bird Rock, the Express kicked into high gear. The engines began to roar, taking us home. No, not really. Just taking us away.

I took a glance at Mt. Lebushtuck. We certainly put our mark there. But then I saw a white figure near the top. I opened my backpack, grasped for my binoculars and put them to my eyes, quickly attempting to focus. I did and then searched to the top of the mountain. It appeared to be a lady in white waving…. to me! I dropped my hands, rushed into the boat's compartment and yelled, "Marcia come with me!" She heard the panic in my voice and rushed to the back of the boat. I raised the binoculars again, still seeing her wave. I gave them to Marcia and pointed to the spot. "Do you see her?"

"Where?"

"On the top of the mountain over there!"

She focused the binoculars and answered, "I can see Mt. Lebushtuck."

I grabbed the glasses back and looked. It was gone, she was gone. I said, now looking back at the cliff on Bird Rock, "That's where it happened."

She looked and asked, "You did it there?"

"Yes we did, all of us."

"It's getting chilly out here."

"Okay, go ahead inside." I turned the lens toward the disappearing landscape, then back to the mountaintop. It was still white all right.

I know what I saw that day, from the stern of the boat, but was it possible? I'll never know, yet I'd like to think it was.

CHAPTER 38

# Requiem To Youth

I sit here with my memory bank running low. Over time, it's been stuffed with paradoxes that are sometimes irreverent and often embarrassing to look back on. Nevertheless, I'm a total optimist. I tell that to my computer every day, and my wife and kids even say so. That confirms it... doesn't it? But, I had a world out there that depended on who I was, and now the world in which I live, work and associate depends on who I am. So when troubled and uncertain of what lies ahead, I've tried to find out more about myself and rediscover who that person is. I went back seeking to put all that in order. What I found in the recesses of my mind were misplaced episodes of my life that needed straightening out. Of course this can be a disastrous effort, telling stories as I saw them, possibly very different then how others did. But, though flawed, they were my stories. It was about those few people who I was blessed to pass along the way who likely never knew the impact they played in defining my life.

There's a good friend who I see occasionally sitting in his beach chair, taking notice of the rising tide. He takes the liberty of entering my life every so often, to survey my progress. Steve talks about how old we're getting and that, "our window of opportunity is closing fast." I respond, "Hey, we're in our golden years." As a retired police officer, he'll have none of that. Steve never finds color in his comments; he sees everything in black and white and responds, "What golden years? Gil, getting old sucks!" With that I laugh and say, "Love talking to you, Steve.

So, compared to Steve, I guess I am a Pollyanna. It seems I see things through different glasses. The foolish things I've done give amusement. The wise things thrill me. The achievements I haven't yet accomplished are good material to dream on. The what-ifs give me hope, even though they may never happen.

I've created a colorful mosaic that forms a pattern, a picture of those magical summer days in Catalina. I've left most of it up to memory, for that's all I have. They're my own stories to tell, and I needed to tell them. But, all of us, in our own way have a story to tell. This was mine, about that small space in time, shared by so many, yet so few.

Summers on the mainland during the '50s and early '60s were spent eating at the Witch Stand, drag racing along Hawthorne Boulevard or cruising Hollywood's Sunset Strip. You could also find some excitement at a sporting event, maybe even Dodgers Stadium. There were outside concerts and local drive-in movies. If you were really lucky you might kick back under the flight pattern at the LAX with your latest love while listening to the sounds of Elvis and Johnny Mathis. But, just 26 miles across the sea, we had our ways, though slower, some would say. But ours were just as exciting, the quality just as intense and the place just as quaint.

As to discontent with nostalgia, I take solemn issue to those who say, "The past should never be a hitching post for the future." Or, "There is no distance as far away as yesterday." Oscar Wilde once wrote, "No man is rich enough to buy back the past." Yet, I'm partial to what Albert Einstein said, "The distinction between the past and the future is only a grand illusion." And, I boast, I'm content to have had a past regal enough to redeem, a legacy to carry on, from times quite different than today, when images were real and wove the standards we live by.

We were imaginative, mischievous, roaring fun rascals, by some accounts, which blended well in the extravagant setting. Yet, our faith, the game and family tempered those dubious traits. Though we may have come up short, they served their purpose, nevertheless. From there we saw the horizon and sailed toward it. There was a cost, but we had to leave to see the worth of it. Some have survived… some not so fortunate, for the world has an insatiable appetite to consume. Some have made it back, just for the healing. Some never left, and some just dream they were there.

Life gets tarnished easily by time. It's the good story that provides the luster later. So, I'll always pass on the stories, making them even bigger than they were. Because, that's the way it was then, when dreams, hopes and the future were so big and some still called the island home. Oh, there'll be other times and places, but none will ever compare to Catalina summers…my sketches of the past.

CHAPTER 39

# Moving On

Aplace is just a place. It's the relationships that make it lasting, worthy and memorable. While writing this book I've had several friends, acquaintances and fellow travelers email me, updating me on the whereabouts and doings of some of the supporting cast.

There were the many unheralded campers, not only from the baseball camp but the Boy Scout and girls' camps as well. All of them, whose names are fleeting and just too many, were a large part of the Isthmus community story.

There were also those who labored to keep the Isthmus moving, who kept it running on time, consistent, within the scheme of things, because in a way, we all worked around that schedule. Then, there were the girls and families that worked the snack bar and restaurant, whose efforts, not only served the nutritional needs of the Isthmus crowd but also provided the very corridor of its social network. Some names go on and on from summer to summer, but families like the Colmarys and the Ewings stand out. Their wonderful grace, charm and love for the island have left their mark.

Can't forget the trendsetters. Those people who punctuated

the character of the Isthmus and created a culture that fit in with the time, the Hawkins the Tuckers and the Flints. Phyllis survived Big Al. She's now 92 and living in Oregon.

Karl the hermit passed away in a one-room cabin at the island rock quarry. His probate disclosed the enormous wealth of the man, all in property.

The boat guys and girls always had a special place, especially on the weekends. The Tamara brought us the Knowles girls. The Papoose, the Geronimo, and the Wild Goose were just a few of the boats that brought in some of the most notable Hollywood and mainland glamour. All of them played a part in accommodating the lively crowd of wandering, robust and sometimes out-of-hand sailors, who made Isthmus life just that much more interesting.

Then, there were the mainstays that kept the Isthmus together through the winters. Birt and Shirley Grove, the McElroys and Jack White, the rootin' tootin' real island cowboy who loved to duel it out with the Wayne-Bond bunch. And, yes, the Lady in White, though seldom seen, I suspect she's there nevertheless.

Nearly all moved on a while ago, with some finding warmth in Hawaii and some taking on business ventures elsewhere. But, most migrated to Southern California and sprinkled themselves just near enough so that, on a fine clear day, they can look out at the sea, find Catalina silhouetted against the horizon…and start to remember.

But, to those few visionaries of the island, individuals who have left their trail and continue to leave a large imprint on the Isthmus history, as bearer of a legacy to be passed on from generation to generation, their names need to be mentioned in the same breath as the likes of the other but few giants. They are the ones that fall into the same select group as the likes of the Westons, Parsons, Bannings and the Wrigleys. The Taylors and Bombards, with less pomp and parading, fit into the same mold.

The Taylors began with Preston. He set the table, and they came from all walks of life, begging to be a part of his wonderful feast. Linda, his daughter, remained a steady resident in Avalon and maintained vigilance to the oral history of the island.

Today, 98 percent of all Catalina visitors find their way across the channel, departing from San Pedro, Long Beach and Dana Point harbors, without a dose of Dramamine, by way of the Catalina Express. This was the vision of Doug Bombard, who lived most of his life at the Isthmus and now resides in Avalon with his wife, Audrey. He talks of fond feelings for the years at the Isthmus. These individuals, their accomplishments, their dedication to keeping the island commerce going, put them in the category as true island patriarchs.

My cousin Jeff tried to teach me something about girls. All I came up with was the image. But heck, I was just too young to understand it then. Jeff went on to play the PGA circuit for a while and is still good at it.

Clyde found a job in his uncle's wrecking yard. They hoped he'd somehow work things out there.

Shane made it to the big leagues. I miss that guy. Good friends are hard to find, but even harder to lose.

Tay and Ret's lives were just too short. Why it's that way…is beyond me.

Randall, I heard he got lost in that war…never made it home. But I think he may have wanted it that way.

Ty, what a gift of life. You can get a sense of his character, about how he felt about the Isthmus life in general and about the persona of the man, above all, so in love with his wife, from a letter he emailed while I was writing this book.

*The best week of my life was in November 1957, there were nine winter residents at the Isthmus. All of them, except me, left on vacation for a week or more. It was great. I had the whole Isthmus to myself for that week. I look back at that week as a highlight of my life.*

*I had three sailboats, a 20-foot Flying Dutchman sloop, which was a day sailor, a 23-foot Herreshoff sloop and a 30-foot Seychelles sloop. I bought both the 23-foot and the 30-foot in San Pedro. Patty and I sailed to the Coronado Islands and Santa Rosa Island and all islands in between. I eventually sold them. Patty and I rowed my 14-foot Catalina Wherry around the island in three days. My wife, Patty, and I were married 46 years and had a great life at the Isthmus.*

*Two months before she passed away she said to me, "Ty I want to go home to the Isthmus." I am sure she is there now.*

Carol Ostach would become my sister-in-law and help run the camp after it moved to Toyon Bay.

Linda Taylor passed on while I was writing this book. What a character, so unique. I wrote this email to her daughter, Ashley, the night before her death. Linda never received it. Let me share it with you here.

*I hear your health is doing you no good. My prayers are with you...that's a given. I just wanted you to know that my new book, Catalina Summer, is being edited as I write. Many of the stories in the book are the result of the conversations you and I had.*

*Linda, I just hope that I got your character right. Every time my mind takes a trip back to those Catalina Isthmus summers, I see you there, in the snack bar, walking about the Isthmus, just being you. God bless and many thanks for being there.*

*Take care,*

*Gil*

Lolo still labors daily in his barbershop. His brother Frankie passed on a few years back. When visiting Avalon, make sure you take the time to go by and say, "Hi." You'll enjoy the priceless memorabilia on the walls and agree that it truly is one of Avalon's unique historical sites.

Billy Bones grew as tall as the redwoods. Along with his brother Ben, he married and became a school superintendent. Can you believe that? Up north in Bayside, California. He tells me he likes to stay away from cactus and hot grease…never a good combination. Also, Ty reminded me, both he and Ben rowed all the way to Avalon on the swim. Unfortunately Ben was edited out of the published photo by some local news guy and never got the recognition he deserved. Here's to you, Ben.

Father James presided at my wedding, and he continued to provide sound spiritual advice, along with his blessings. Where he is now, God only knows.

And for Ross? He's still around. Big cheese out there, making high wages and, as always, bossing people around. Thank God, I taught him right. We keep in contact periodically, just seeing if we might have missed each other's funeral. I think there, we'd have something to say to the other. But for now, Ross might be contacting an attorney in the hopes of rebuffing any and all libelous or disparaging remarks against his character that are so well documented in this book. To wit, I've countered, truth is always a good defense to such an allegation.

About Cecil the seal, Ross and I finally dropped him back in the ocean off Bird Rock. He disliked Ross or should I say maybe his scent. For, on the way out there, he attacked Ross's jacket, biting it to shreds. At the time, I thought the possibility of throwing Ross into the sea and keeping the seal might have been a better idea.

Ode to Billy Tuck. After that day on Bird Rock, I only saw Tuck twice over the next 20 years. Billy Tuck survived battle in Vietnam, but he wouldn't win his war back home. It was in those trying days that I talked to him for just a moment. I was so involved in my life…I left his out. Life sometimes is like a cell call. You hear all is going good, but then you lose the call… a disconnect. Then, some years later, you hear quite a different story. The last time I saw Tuck was in his dad's office. It's been a long time ago, but not that long to forget our last conversation. Feeling awkward while leaving, I passed Billy, sitting alone at a desk doing some business. I wondered if he remembered, so I stopped and said, "Tuck, we had us some good times." Then as simple and as clear as Billy Tuck ever was, he said, now smiling with that big grin, "Yes we did, didn't we?" I never saw him again after that, but I will always hear those words. They still haunt me to this day. Life has a unique way of changing the conversation, and sometimes it's just too late.

As for Patty, who knows where the wind has taken her, what seas she had to sail. But, I know she planted a mark on me that she'll never know. I guess that's the way it was meant to be.

Me? I did get a Topps baseball card contract but, before it came out, I was released. Didn't even get the TV promised for the signing. I bounced around a few ballparks for a while then moved on. It took me years to return to the Isthmus. It never changed, the people… yes.

Oh yeah, I'm asked "what happened with the dive?" Did it go alright? Of course, that's obvious. I'm here, writing. I cleared the cliff okay, but the rest? I can't say how it all came out. The results are still mixed because I haven't finished it yet. Maybe someday, I'll be more certain of my answer to that question.

Finally, an obituary to my parents is simply this: My father never taught me how to lose but rather how to win. And, he'd add, "It doesn't always come just by numbers on a scoreboard. No, Gil, it's something more."

My mother? Well, what else can I say? She helped write the script. In my last cognizant conversation with my ailing mother, she smiled then said, "We had some good times back there, in the

Isthmus. Right, Gilly?"

"Yes, Mom, we did, didn't we………"

# *Epilogue*

*In The Other Side of Heaven*

*There is a place*
*Like no other place*
*But, it will never come again*

*There is a time like no other time*
*But, it only comes once*

*There are memories like no other memories*
*Which get lost in time and place*

*But, some survive*
*In spirit, in truth, though flawed*
*But, still one with God*

*Yet, not so long ago*
*There, in the other side of heaven*


*Gil Lefebvre*

# *Many Thanks to:*

My Sister Yvonne for the graphics, clearing up muddled memories and reminding me of forgotten details.

Carol Ostach for helping put faces to events lost in time.

To Ty Ewing who kept me semi-honest while telling the tales spun in the book. And for giving me permission to print his touching e-mails, which helped give this book a heart.

To Carolyn Brady Graps for hosting reunions that allow us to reminisce and keep shared memories alive.

To Jeannie Wolfe and John Flaiz for their support on both my Catalina books.

And of course, thank you to my wife who made the story presentable.

# Catalina Island

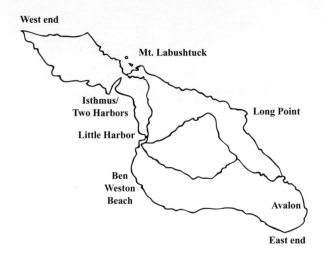

West end

Mt. Labushtuck

Isthmus/
Two Harbors

Long Point

Little Harbor

Ben
Weston
Beach

Avalon

East end

Gil Lefebvre
Political Scientist,
Educator and Author

Lefebvre, author of *Not Too Far To Have Never Been,* and *Unto Caesar Unto God,* presents another major literary work. Based on interviews with the people who lived the story, Catalina Summer will amuse, entertain, and put the cherry on your banana split. Gil writes and lives with his wife in Lake Arrowhead, California.